GIANT
BOOK OF
CROSSWORDS

D0313568

THIS IS A CARLTON BOOK

Puzzle content and layout design © Puzzler Media Ltd 2007
www.puzzler.com

This edition published in 2007 by Carlton Books Ltd
A Division of the Carlton Publishing Group
20 Mortimer Street, London, W1T 3JW

This book is sold subject to the condition that it shall not, by way of trade or
otherwise, be lent, resold, hired out or otherwise circulated without the publisher's
prior written consent in any form of cover or binding other than that in which it is
published and without a similar condition including this condition, being imposed
upon the subsequent purchaser. All rights reserved.

A CIP catalogue for this book is available from the British Library.

ISBN 978-1-84442-573-0

Printed in Great Britain

Puzzler

GIANT
BOOK OF
CROSSWORDS

**Nearly 400 fantastic word puzzles
from the UK's leading puzzle publisher**

CARLTON

ACROSS

1 Becomes less dense (5)
4 Mild stimulant (8)
11 ___ energy, power from wind or waves, eg (9)
12 Have the same end-sound (5)
13 Licence to enter a country (4)
14 Minor roads (6)
16 Ironic (smile) (3)
18 Child's plaything (3)
19 Swells out (6)
22 Audible respiration (4)
24 Too close-fitting (5)
26 Material on which to write letters (9)
27 Misleading (8)
28 Well-dressed (5)

DOWN

2 Quality of being truthful (7)
3 Small amphibian with a tail (4)
5 Ring or stadium (5)
6 Large wood (6)
7 ___ League, group of prestigious US universities (3)
8 All around (10)
9 Was drawn (to) (10)
10 Carry out orders (4)
15 Toupee (3)
16 Low hushed voice (7)
17 Diminished (6)
20 Fabric made from flax (5)
21 Takes food (4)
23 Canned meat product (4)
25 Hairstyling substance (3)

2 MINI QUICKS

1

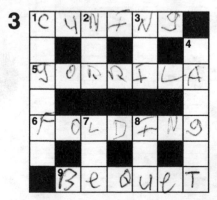

ACROSS
- **1** Serve (4,2)
- **4** Northern Asian medicine man (6)
- **6** Tending to leave greasy marks (6)
- **7** Gentle wind (6)

DOWN
- **1** Sundown (4)
- **2** Vocal hesitation (7)
- **3** In ignorance (7)
- **5** Wheel covering (4)

2

ACROSS
- **1** Hat or horse race (5)
- **6** Warehouse workers (7)
- **7** Biscuit eaten with cheese (7)
- **8** Liable to cry (5)

DOWN
- **2** Surrounded territory (7)
- **3** End a relationship (5,2)
- **4** Piquant substance (5)
- **5** High-interest moneylending (5)

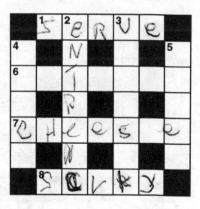

3

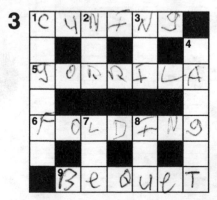

ACROSS
- **1** Crafty (6)
- **5** Long-armed apes (7)
- **6** Art of paper-folding (7)
- **9** Shout from the audience (6)

DOWN
- **1** Register as unemployed (4,2)
- **2** Chest bone (3)
- **3** Go a-courting (3)
- **4** Have high hopes (6)
- **7** Anger (3)
- **8** Noah's craft (3)

This puzzle has no clues in the conventional sense. Instead, every different number printed in the main grid represents a different letter (with the same number always representing the same letter, of course). For example, if 7 turns out to be a 'V', you can write in V wherever a square contains 7. We have completed a very small part of the puzzle to give you a start, but the rest is up to you.

24	8	20	17	7	16	17	■	11	1	26	19	20
16	■	23	■	19	■	1	22	20	■	10	■	14
23	7	23	19	20	20	25	■	20	22	16	9	20
23	■	13	■	17	■	6 Y	1 A	5 K	■	1	■	25
6	1	8	9	■	26	■	■	21	13	11	■	7
■	■	19	13	19	1	21	21	6	■	5	7	25
12	■	■	3	■	3	■	20	■	15	■	■	3
18	13	11	■	25	13	26	20	2	1	3	■	■
1	■	18	13	20	■	■	5	■	2	16	23	23
26	■	20	■	1	8	12	■	2	■	25	■	7
26	18	20	20	8	■	1	8	8	1	25	3	20
7	■	4	■	2	1	8	■	20	■	20	■	25
26	18	6	21	6	■	24	13	11	20	8	20	9

A̶ B C D E F G H I J K̶ L M N O P Q R S T U V W X̶ Y̶ Z

1 A	2	3	4	5 K	6 Y	7	8	9	10	11	12	13
14	15	16	17	18	19	20	21	22	23	24	25	26

4 CROSSWORD

ACROSS

1 Enlisted in the army (6,2)
6 Gradually (2,7)
7 Buffoon (3)
8 Minute organisms (5)
9 Satisfies (thirst) (8)
12 Devours (4)
13 Food thickener from seaweed (4)
16 Assess, review (4,5)
18 Decamped (9)
19 In like manner (4)
20 Gush (4)
23 Constant worriers (8)
26 Eastern country, capital Tokyo (5)
27 Typically English beverage (3)
28 Ungelded horses (9)
29 Bad behaviour (6-2)

DOWN

1 Mixed batch for sale (3,3)
2 For want (of) (2,7)
3 Charming (8)
4 Discover (7)
5 Applications (4)
10 Incapacitate (6,4)
11 Admiring term for your spouse (6,4)
14 Look with greedy or malicious pleasure (5)
15 Invited (5)
17 Toys on strings (5)
21 Requests signed by many people (9)
22 With few interior walls (4-4)
24 Highest adult female voice (7)
25 Transmit (4,2)
26 Playfully tease (4)

The answer to each of these clues begins with a different letter of the alphabet. The clues are not numbered, so you must work out where each answer fits in the grid.

A Declare (4)
B Person in charge (4)
C Dog (6)
D Pass away (3)
E Icelandic poetry (4)
F Gun, perhaps (7)
G Spectre (5)
H Dwelling of a solitary person (9)
I Prehistoric period with metal tools (4,3)
J In syncopated manner (7)
K Female blood relation (9)
L Humble (5)
M Game with winds (3-4)

N Convent resident (3)
O Moves faster through water than another (8)
P Forking out (6)
Q Group of four (7)
R Back a car (7)
S Digger (5)
T Buried gold etc (8)
U Last pulses in each bar of music (7)
V Competing (5)
W Closes one eye (5)
X Photocopy (5)
Y With a custard-like hue (7)
Z Vitality (4)

ACROSS

1 Music genre associated with Eminem (3,3)
5 Persistently annoy (6)
9 Academic institution (abbrev)(3)
11 Heathen (7)
12 Huge ape (7)
13 Istanbul resident (4)
15 Stomach (5)
16 Breathe heavily (4)
17 Cagily observed (4)
19 Australian wild dog (5)
20 Feeble person (4)
24 Volcanic tidal wave (7)
25 Sleeveless jumper (4,3)
26 Formerly known as (3)
27 Powerful (6)
28 Come back (6)

DOWN

2 Deduce, conclude (5)
3 Conceal (4)
4 Grinding to a fine powder (11)
5 Marker pen that overlays transparent fluorescent colour on text (11)
6 Unusual (4)
7 Spicy Mexican sauce or dip (5)
8 Balms (9)
10 Tube from a sink to a drain (5,4)
14 Billy the ___, Wild West outlaw (3)
16 Church seat (3)
18 Be jubilant, celebrate (5)
21 Entomb (5)
22 Angelic aura (4)
23 Make with wool (4)

Have double the fun with this puzzle: you've got to fill in the answers and the black squares! We've given you the bare bones to start and it will help you to know that the black squares in the finished grid form a symmetrical pattern, so that every black square has at least one other corresponding black square.

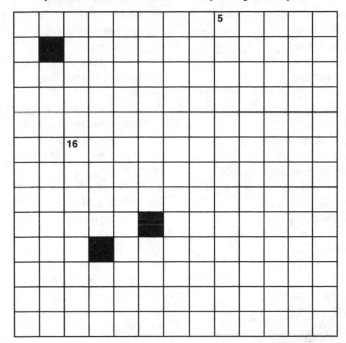

ACROSS

1 Unloaded
5 More knowledgeable
8 Be in debt
9 Add sugar to
10 Generously
11 Largest living deer
12 Unable to hear
15 Falsehood
16 English cooking apple
18 Loud noise
21 Possesses, owns
23 Desire
25 Dove's call
26 Avoid by lowering your head
28 Handle roughly
31 Ordinary dress, not uniform
32 Reward too highly
33 Make a mistake
34 Prescribed amounts
35 Under a false impression

DOWN

1 Calmed
2 Building made in advance
3 Very small amount
4 Finished
5 Feebly
6 Drained
7 With matching final sounds
13 Sizzle
14 Arab ruler
17 Grudging desire
19 Put under a spell
20 As well as
22 Wear marks on shoes
23 Duplicates
24 Drank in big mouthfuls
27 ___ in, entered on a database
29 Part of a sentence
30 Cure

8 CROSSWORD

ACROSS

9 Shrubs (6)
10 Police letter between alpha and charlie (5)
11 Permits (4)
12 Dumbfound (4)
13 Puts aside (5)
14 Eastern robe (6)
15 Notion (7)
17 Permanently (3,5)
19 Title of Russian emperors (4)
21 Drives (7)
23 Reimbursed (4)
24 In a ___, concisely (8)
25 Tarry awhile (6)
27 Little devil, wicked spirit (3)
29 Qualified practitioners in tooth care (8)
31 Discovers (8)
32 Delicate in texture, flimsy (4-4)
34 Dwindled (8)
35 Financiers (8)
36 Fingers idly (8)
39 Formal address to a gentleman (3)
40 Educate (6)
42 Rude, bad-mannered (8)
45 Identity (4)
46 Runs (7)
47 Sandwich dressing, familiarly (4)
48 Taking food at midday (8)
51 Guided (7)
54 Rubs clean (6)
55 Intense blue (5)
57 Mongrels (4)
58 Long hard journey, usually on foot (4)
59 Showery (5)
60 Violent quarrel (4-2)

DOWN

1 Arranged or done exactly (4,2)
2 Single-horned beast (10)
3 Functions (4)
4 At a higher point (5)
5 Alters to deceive (9)
6 Excellent example (6)
7 Set alight (of food) (6)
8 Regardless of the cost (2,3,5)
16 Small party explosives (7)
18 Stupidity (11)
20 Flavour-enhancing liquid eaten with a meal (5)
22 Presentation trays (7)
23 Correspondent (3-6)
26 Lodges (7)
28 Exercise influence (4,7)
29 Makes safe (a bomb) (7)
30 Starting a golf game (6,3)
33 Conundrum (7)
37 Forces (7)
38 No ___, road sign (5)
41 Piece of plastic that guarantees a bank draft (6,4)
43 Feeble reason (4,6)
44 Obscure, puzzling (9)
49 Hurls (6)
50 Slot in (6)
52 Reprimand (6)
53 Navigation floats (5)
56 Diminishes (4)

9 CROSSWORD

ACROSS

1 Of a killer, roaming loose in the country (2,5)

7 Orange-yellow (5)

8 Energy, vigour (3)

9 Union fees (4)

10 Gardener's basket (4)

12 Made a lot of money (6,2)

14 Condemns in advance (9)

15 Minor planet (8)

18 Replacement orb (5,3)

21 Print or write in sloping letters (9)

23 Trains (8)

25 One (4)

26 Male pig (4)

28 Blether (3)

29 Christmas-card bird (5)

30 Toy bears (7)

DOWN

2 Cheap alcoholic drink made from grapes (5,4)

3 Slightly wrong (4)

4 Group of people who direct a company's executive (9,4)

5 Rural painting (9)

6 Picture (5)

11 High-quality (2,4)

13 Out of the way (5)

16 Playful sexual behaviour (4,3,6)

17 Anew (5)

19 On/off device (6)

20 Cutting out the naughty bits (9)

22 Having problems (2,7)

24 Jetties (5)

27 Reproduced (4)

All solutions can be found hidden in the clues, written either backwards or forwards. Words such as 'back' or 'up' may suggest the answer is hidden backwards.

ACROSS

5 It's turning into a formal lunch, so perfectly upper class! (4)

6 Unruly behaviour in abattoirs rejected (4)

7 In rehearsals he shouts out – he astonishes everyone with his direction (5-4)

8 Place thyme, perhaps, in another basket (4)

10 Displaying sensitivity is part of an honest actor's job (4)

12 Cromwell's title some worship? Rot! EC to remove it! (9)

15 Young lady is back in town, all right! (4)

16 Commonly, food is put into a big rubbish bag (4)

DOWN

1 Turns up some antique toy, occasionally cartoon character Wile E! (6)

2 Bach attributed, to some extent, to gossip (4)

3 Reverses into some streets erratically, so take into custody (6)

4 Last opportunity to turn over, partly, these vessels (4)

9 Conflict arose from how people felt tables should be arranged (6)

11 Select a bit of each, or use the refrain (6)

13 Being in the middle of the Sahara I need a shower! (4)

14 In a panic, a gerbil kept here? (4)

11 *CROSSWORD*

ACROSS

4 Without exception (3)
8 Miming game (8)
9 Mass departure (6)
10 Stuck-up, conceited (6)
11 Projecting part (8)
13 World's largest continent (4)
15 Facial parts below the mouth (5)
16 Printing error (4)
18 Lazy and untidy (8)
20 String instruments (6)
22 Rich cake (6)
23 Decorated folds of paper for brief letters (8)
24 Breakfast food (3)

DOWN

1 Large lumps (6)
2 Three-piece band (4)
3 Lazily, without hurry or aim (4)
4 Very surprising (11)
5 Grades (6)
6 Formal headgear item (3,3)
7 Move round, whirl (4)
12 Gunge (3)
13 Small horse-like animal (3)
14 Saunters (6)
15 Elite group (6)
17 Flora (6)
19 Disclosure of secret information to the press (4)
20 Large tanks (4)
21 Greasy (4)

Each of the 26 letters of the alphabet should be entered into the grid once, and only once.

| A | B | C | D | E | F | G | H | I | J | K | L | M |
| N | O | P | Q | R | S | T | U | V | W | X | Y | Z |

ACROSS
4 Assignments
6 Soft, mouldable
7 Touched on each shoulder with a sword

DOWN
1 Mineral used in watches
2 Common insect
3 Mimic scornfully
5 Black marketeer of the war years

MINI QUICK

ACROSS
1 Body part to pierce (7)
4 Celebratory (7)
6 Behave without restraint or discipline (3,4)
9 Putting on (a play) (7)

DOWN
1 Mischievous supernatural being (3)
2 Fate, destiny (3)
3 Sloping edge (5)
5 Blow up (volcano) (5)
7 Toupee (3)
8 Turned over soil (3)

13 CROSSWORD

ACROSS

1 Women's dresses (6)
4 Stretch of road allowing unhindered travel (8)
9 Jeer (at) (3)
10 Ignited (3)
11 Fling (5)
12 Secret languages (5)
13 Galley's steering implements (4)
14 Keep for the future (5)
15 Piece of window glass (4)
18 Surpasses (6)
20 Lure (6)
23 Row of hire cars (4,4)
24 African scavenger (5)
26 Flirtatious (look) (4-6)
29 Skilful fighter pilots (4)
31 Naval spirit (3)
33 Chances (4)
34 Feeble effeminate person (5-5)
36 As the need arises (2,3)
38 Thick strong cotton fabric with a shaved pile (8)
40 Season (6)
41 More intimate (6)
44 Space or scope (4)
45 Inflamed swellings (5)
46 Eastern garment (4)
50 Regulating device (5)
51 Comic play (5)
53 Anger (3)
54 Species of snake (3)
55 Three babies (8)
56 Cinematograph films (6)

DOWN

1 Stumbled (4,4)
2 Exterior (5)
3 ___ out, clothes (4)
4 Dove's sound (3)
5 Level above a ship's hold (5,4)
6 Curve (4)
7 By no means sleepy (4,5)
8 Sycophants (3-3)
9 Unpleasant children (5)
16 Vehicles sometimes pulled by reindeer (7)
17 Fidgety (5)
19 Asserted (7)
21 Sacred chant (6)
22 Light stud (4-3)
25 Pupil (7)
27 Buzzing sound (3)
28 Preserve (a mummy) (6)
30 Perpetrates (a crime) (7)
32 Preacher of the Gospel (7)
35 Shrewd, sharp (5)
37 Masses (3,6)
38 Rich variety of pea (9)
39 Film advertisements (8)
42 Shrub used in hedges (6)
43 Drink noisily (5)
47 Defendant's plea (5)
48 Place of suffering (4)
49 Big march (4)
52 Buffoon (3)

14 _CROSSWORD_

ACROSS

6 Durable books? (9)
7 Childish word for 'stomach' (5)
8 Common bird of several varieties (3)
9 Rotters (4)
10 Bone of the arm (4)
12 Jut (8)
15 Variety of plum (8)
17 Reckoning (7,2)
18 Fully, point by point (2,6)
20 As a result of (6,2)
23 Horse with a bay or chestnut coat dotted with grey and white (4)
24 Hybrid fruit (4)
27 Freshly produced (3)
28 Board (5)
29 Settle an argument by confronting your opponent (4,2,3)

DOWN

1 Make a replica of (9)
2 Formulated (6)
3 Conforms (5)
4 Ran furtively (8)
5 Smoker's saucer (7)
11 Coaxing (3-8)
13 Failed to include (7)
14 Goggle (4)
16 Takes back possession of (7)
17 Wally (4)
19 Friendliness (9)
21 Period of very warm weather (8)
22 Brittle (7)
25 Hunter's retriever (3,3)
26 Go bad (5)

The arrows show the direction in which the answer to each clue should be placed.

Capital of Austria ▼		Unit of electricity ▼	▼	Sandwiches		▼ US hip-hop producer and rapper (2,3)	Stimulate (the appetite)
⚑				▼			▼
Very intellectual		Mixture of earth and water ▶				Apiece	
⚑			Largest of the plant forms ▶			▼	
Social insect		Squabble	Bottle-end ▶				
⚑		▼			Incantations		Followed orders
___ Gras, fête	Global fuel company		Bounced sound ▶		▼		▼
⚑	▼					Great pleasure	
Of Hebrew origin		___ Jones, singer	Record label begun in 1972 (inits)	Get older ▶		▼	
Strictly ▶		▼	▼				
⚑				Golfer's peg ▶			
Sudden increase	Avoided ▶						

16 CROSSWORD

ACROSS

1 Grouchy mood (9)
6 Higher than (5)
10 Split, divided (6)
11 Domestic (of a country) (8)
12 Music for a film (5)
13 Eye complaint (4)
15 Churchyard trees (4)
17 Planted (seeds) (5)
18 Consumer (4)
20 Soon (4)
21 Prophetic signs (5)
24 Return (4,4)
26 Deserving reward or respect (6)
27 Very deep or unfathomable gorge or chasm (5)
28 Alcoholics (9)

DOWN

2 Opens (7)
3 Bar pivoted on a fixed point (5)
4 Holy women (4)
5 Nocturnal employee, perhaps (5,6)
7 Small juicy fruit (5)
8 By way of (3)
9 Trusty mount (5)
13 Male child (3)
14 Far East currency unit (3)
16 Hauled up with a hoist (7)
17 Epic stories (5)
19 Smells awful (5)
22 ___ Sharapova, 2004 Wimbledon ladies' champion (5)
23 One of a pair (4)
25 Spherical body (3)

Try your luck with this cryptic puzzle.

ACROSS

9 Theatrical long runner and catcher (9)
10 One who gets up part of the stairs? (5)
11 Reveal your true form? (7)
12 Burnt out through having worked as a domestic? (7)
13 Not willing to give credit (9)
16 Underworld dealer at border of garden? (5)
17 The future may be crystal clear to her (7,6)
20 Prohibit company entering to get meat (5)
21 Nearly set wrong in a serious way (9)
24 Examine crawler with soft inside (7)
25 Gently touch girl on the knee (7)
27 Sticky mess from weapon, eg, being returned (5)
28 Some theatre work? (9)

DOWN

1 Foreign affairs? (6)
2 Enjoyment at start of day for Kitty (4)
3 Leave an area with insufficient water (6)
4 Green, blue or hazel flag? (4)
5 Person who hopes for market profits, he guesses (10)
6 Dud flare exploded? That's terrible (8)
7 Severe strain breaks man (10)
8 They control the horses (7)
14 Taking the spirits away (10)
15 Assembly is something widely accepted (10)
18 More gentle person made an offer (8)
19 A game to shorten in length (7)
22 Net caught in turbulent rapids (6)
23 Longs to tell stories about the east (6)
25 Look both ways just the same (4)
26 Placed clock face upside down (4)

18 CODECRACKER

This puzzle has no clues in the conventional sense. Instead, every different number printed in the main grid represents a different letter (with the same number always representing the same letter, of course). For example, if 7 turns out to be a 'V', you can write in V wherever a square contains 7. We have completed a very small part of the puzzle to give you a start, but the rest is up to you.

15	23	2	15	13	11	15	8		26	10	25	2
23		10		20		25		13		25		25
25	17	15	12	8		11	26	6	4	11	15	10
22		1		15		15		10		6		11
11	19	18	9		7	10	20	13	13	20	22	6
		15		26		16		18				12
4	25	22	11	15	8		24	6	9	24	25	9
6				7		19		11		15		
22	6	14	15	4 **S**	2	25	12		26	25	6	14
21		10		6 **I**		6		19		22		25
15	3	15	13	11 **T**	20	10		25	21	20	6	8
10		25		15		8		22		18		15
16	20	5	15		13	20	12	14	18	4	15	8

A B C D E F G H ~~I~~ J K L M N O P Q R ~~S~~ ~~T~~ U V W X Y Z

1	2	3	4 **S**	5	6 **I**	7	8	9	10	11 **T**	12	13
14	15	16	17	18	19	20	21	22	23	24	25	26

24|

CROSSWORD 19

ACROSS

1 Roof-covering (5)
4 Since (3)
6 Reasoning (9)
7 On-screen translation (8)
9 Kitchen hand protector (4,5)
10 Arrests (4)
12 Parts of the body of interest to a chiropodist (4)
14 Couple at a time (3,2,3)
17 Kept quiet (6,2)
19 Flower urn (4)
21 Large continent (4)
23 Fiction writers (9)
25 People you can call on (8)
27 US lifts (9)
28 Chap, fellow (3)
29 Slackened (5)

DOWN

1 Sped, dashed (4)
2 Salad plant with crisp leaves (7)
3 Scarcity (8)
4 In one fell swoop (2,1,6)
5 State of having tired yourself out (12)
8 Daydreams (5)
11 Wails (5)
13 Ecclesiastical building (5)
15 Looks (for custom) (5)
16 Cosmetic to use with a razor (7,5)
18 Time gap (5)
20 Age at which you can drive a car (9)
22 Décolletage (8)
24 Popular TV shows (7)
26 Pre-owned (4)

20 QUIZ

Is this a quiz? You bet it iz!

ACROSS

7 Who was Lord Protector, 1653-58? (8)

8 What is the 'shape' of an upper area in a theatre? (6)

11 Which first name is shared by guitarist May and cricketer Lara? (5)

12 What is a famous Gothic cathedral in Paris? (5,4)

13 What is an old draper's measure of 45 inches? (3)

14 From which seed does an oak grow? (5)

16 Which town lies between Stirling and Dunfermline? (5)

17 Which shrub is the source of gum arabic? (6)

19 Which John was a famous 1970s cricket commentator? (6)

21 Which birds are found in a gaggle or a skein? (5)

22 Which word may mean 'a command' or 'to arrange'? (5)

24 Alongside the id, which internal force was postulated by Freud? (3)

25 What is an economic slump called? (9)

27 What is another word for the cranium? (5)

28 Which Latin phrase means 'still at the original location'? (2,4)

29 Which surname links former Irish president Mary, *Time Team* presenter Tony and 'quizmistress' Anne? (8)

DOWN

1 Which skin infection is caused by mites? (7)

2 What are academic subjects such as economics and politics? (6,8)

3 Kigali is the capital of which African country? (6)

4 Complete the title of the BBC series starring Susan Hampshire and Tom Baker, *Monarch of the* ___ (4)

5 What is an anti-hacking computer program or a flame-resistant partition? (8)

6 Where is the European HQ of the Red Cross? (6)

9 What is a pudding of custard enclosed in sponge fingers? (9,5)

10 What may be a basis for measurement, or a regimental flag? (8)

15 What is a sacred musical work such as Handel's *Messiah*? (8)

18 Which substance derived from tar is used to preserve wood? (8)

20 In which country do Ajax play their football? (7)

21 Which small desert-roaming rodent is often kept as a pet? (6)

23 Which John was a 19th-century art critic and philanthropist? (6)

26 At which time is the sun highest in the sky? (4)

21 CROSSWORD

ACROSS

9 Seller of sweets (12)
11 Barn birds? (4)
12 Thin ___, nothingness (3)
13 Fitting (4)
14 Instruct (5)
15 Empty a suitcase (6)
16 Additional buildings (7)
18 Small brown birds (8)
20 US vagrant (4)
22 Instrument making images of internal organs (7)
24 Cradles (4)
25 Fabric, cloth (8)
26 Idle people (6)
28 Imp (3)
30 Bangers (8)
32 Supposed (8)
33 Loss of status or importance (8)
35 Building (8)
36 Throws into turmoil (8)
37 Puts at risk (8)
40 Slump (3)
41 Leaves quickly (6)
43 Solidity (8)
46 Pound (4)
47 Water ices (7)
48 Baby's biscuit (4)
49 Making great efforts (8)
52 Intoxicating liquid, often given up for Lent (7)
55 Stands up to (6)
56 Theatrical work (5)
59 Parts of drills (4)
60 Bitterly cold (3)
61 Before long (4)
62 Avoid (5,5,2)

DOWN

1 Newspaper article (6)
2 Filleted (3,3,4)
3 Singing a melody using nonsensical syllables (4)
4 Caused by a bug (5)
5 Appearing very keen (9)
6 Emotional upset (6)
7 Barrel maker (6)
8 Keep a keen eye on time while in the office (5-5)
10 Bond (3)
17 Subsequent, succeeding (7)
19 Lack of civic order (11)
21 Port of southern Japan (5)
23 Say again (7)
24 Church singer (9)
27 Railway yards (7)
29 Inflammable block used on barbecues (11)
30 Resigns (from a federation) (7)
31 Obscenity (5,4)
34 Resists (7)
38 Portable sunshade (7)
39 Inventories, catalogues (5)
42 Droning on (10)
44 Inland-waterway vessel (10)
45 Events involving death (9)
50 Create, originate (6)
51 Demand emphatically (6)
53 Alternative possibility (6)
54 Approve by a vote (5)
57 Waterproof coat (3)
58 Cobblers' tools (4)

CROSSWORD

ACROSS

1 Hardly any, virtually zilch (4,2,7)
9 Slept (6)
10 Expanding (8)
11 Functions (4)
12 Steed (5)
13 Prods (4)
14 As well (3)
15 Light afternoon meal (3)
16 Destroys, obliterates (4)
18 Keeps (5)
20 Pointed end where two curves meet (4)
22 Small vessels equipped with arms (8)
24 Italian dishes (6)
25 Stone-age art (4,9)

DOWN

2 Wicked deeds (5)
3 Keyboard operators (7)
4 Strange (3)
5 More advanced in years (5)
6 Hard hats (7)
7 Larva of a louse adhering to human hair (3)
8 Spurn (4)
12 Person held for ransom (7)
13 Spa, hot tub (7)
17 Adjoin, border (4)
19 View disappearing towards the horizon (5)
21 Colloquial language (5)
23 Long coil of feathers worn around the neck (3)
24 Cooking pot (3)

Every solution begins with one of five letters. Rearrange these letters to find a vital word.

The five-letter word is: _____

ACROSS

8 Preserve (a mummy) (6)
9 Put in order (8)
10 Act of disposal (8)
11 Soldiers (6)
12 Belligerent person (9)
13 Tired (5)
16 Oddly (7)
18 Determined (7)
20 Make up (for) (5)
21 Process to ascertain the amount of a substance in solution (9)
24 Great dread (6)
26 Political killer (8)
27 Fee paid to secure services in advance (8)
28 Cricket team (6)

DOWN

1 Having mixed feelings (10)
2 Bicycle made for two! (6)
3 In a highly respected manner (9)
4 Bet (7)
5 Pen (5)
6 Embryo's innermost layer of cells (8)
7 Shed tears (4)
14 Put in an arbitrary order (10)
15 Recipient of a letter (9)
17 Route around a town? (4,4)
19 Fierce competition (7)
22 Tuft of threads (6)
23 Amiss (5)
25 Always (4)

24 CROSSWORD

ACROSS

5 Local government districts (8)
7 Tea-making vessel (3)
8 Lively ballroom dance (5)
9 Undressed (8)
11 Choppers (4)
12 Sandwich dressing, familiarly (4)
14 View diminishing towards the horizon (5)
15 Of that ___, from the same family (3)
16 Iron ___, shavings (7)
20 Eastern commander (3)
21 Victuals (5)
23 Levels (4)
24 Swain (4)
26 Conclusiveness (8)
28 Part of the large intestine, or a punctuation mark (5)
29 Foremost, leading (3)
30 Provoked (strong feelings) (8)

DOWN

1 Concerning (5)
2 Bad temper (10)
3 Late light meals (7)
4 Giving birth (5-7)
6 Small manuals (9)
10 Gumption (5)
13 Price lists (7)
17 Instantly, very quickly (2,1,9)
18 Selflessly give up (9)
19 Consume (3,2)
22 Singly (3,2,1,4)
25 In a forthright manner (7)
27 Tatties (5)

Clue A leads to a solution beginning with the letter A, clue B to one beginning with the letter B etc. Solutions should be entered, using a little logic, wherever they fit.

A Strange absent air he's got;
Does he drink? He does not! (9)

B No room on Bligh's ship, so we hear –
Though he wasn't this generous, we fear! (9)

C In the music an allegro may
Signify a waterway (5)

D The needy rise, old 6 down at their head,
But grow weak or faint instead (5)

E Odd loner came
To register his name (5)

F Does this performer, aptly named,
Find his throat becomes inflamed? (4-5)

G Noise like a pig, eats a tea maybe –
Your grandparent's sister is she! (5-4)

H Sing wordlessly, an ending find
For a member of mankind (5)

I Into car I'd replace the light
That signals you are turning right (9)

J Late great guitarist of his day –
Did jinx ride him? In a way (4,7)

K Maybe I make plan to deal
With impulse that forces me to steal (11)

L Entice one who'll
Upset rule (4)

M Pilgrims took it to colonies new:
Will it bloom? Might do! (9)

N I go into neat new way
For discussion, maybe about pay (11)

O Circular letter to chaps that told
What the future was to hold (4)

P Cost to gain
Beatles' Lane? (5)

Q Well-known cited words suffice
As seller's estimate of price (9)

R Make a call to report
Where the boxing match was fought (4)

S Company employees could
Have a long thin piece of wood (5)

T Unofficial ticket-seller,
About right, a fishy fella! (5)

U They are all less than ten –
So fit them in your kitchen, then? (5)

V It ain't novel, new approach
To getting fresh air into coach? (11)

W Women's group lay heartless, while
Also cunning, full of guile (4)

X Take the hammers and knock on wood,
When playing this you will be good! (9)

Y At end of bay chat about
The sailing boat that one took out (5)

Z Weight back on bar, not in one piece
For this musical man of Greece (5)

26 CROSSWORD

ACROSS

1 People who believe violence is wrong (9)
6 Large jug for water (4)
10 Dispose of by auction (4,3)
11 Vindicated (a wrong) (7)
13 Large receptacles (4)
14 Keeps under wraps (10)
16 Breakfast food holder (3,3)
18 Desk accessory (2-4)
21 Container for taking home surplus food (5,3)
22 In want (5)
24 Womens' pre-wedding bunfights (3,7)
26 Reflection of sound waves (4)
29 Parents (4)
30 Autocue (5,5)
32 More sensible (5)
34 School monitors (8)
36 Pertaining to the universe (6)
37 Elevated walking poles used by clowns (6)
40 Parcels of arable council land rented to individuals (10)
41 Gape rudely (4)
44 Bath with underwater jets (7)
45 Go (7)
46 Hasten (4)
47 Woman who gives advice (5,4)

DOWN

2 Exhausted (3-2)
3 Make smooth (4)
4 Arrival in abundance (6)
5 Pounding underfoot (9)
7 Person dependent on a job (4,5)
8 Small salad vegetable (6)
9 Makes certain (7)
12 Setting upright (8)
15 Criminal who illegally enters a building (7)
17 Creaked (7)
19 Lessened (6)
20 Secondary routes (7)
23 Dark parts (of a picture) (7)
25 Summoned (6)
27 By the sea (7)
28 Items (7)
31 Right through the alphabet (4,1,2,1)
33 Very thin neckties (9)
34 Pilfering (9)
35 Mounts (7)
38 Glass fruit-preserve container (3-3)
39 Enter the fray to act as peacemaker (4,2)
42 Sage, jade or lime, eg (5)
43 Explosive star (4)

27 PIECEWORD

With the help of the Across clues only, can you fit the 35 pieces into their correct positions in the empty grid below (which, when completed, will exhibit a symmetrical pattern)?

ACROSS

1 Aspiration • Kept back • Tidal foam
3 Cry of an ass • Plagiarise
4 Servant girl • Trench coat • Walk with measured tread
5 Signalling light • South American animal

6 Sound system (hyphenated) • What person? • Food thickener from seaweed
7 Sensory organ • Catch sight of
8 Side • More lazy • Noble title
10 Energetically earthy • Implores
11 Rhythm

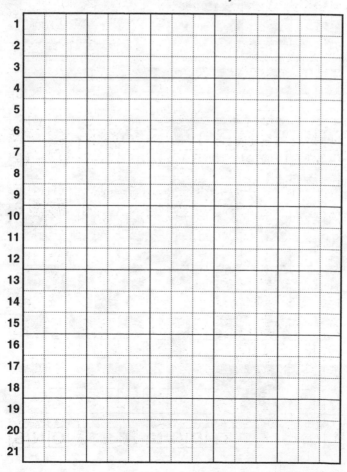

PIECEWORD

12 Part of a car engine (two words) • Adopt or advocate
14 Quartet • Food scoop • Real laugh
15 Relaxation • Cross between a grapefruit and a tangerine
16 Droplet • Travelling blanket • Heavily armoured vehicle

17 Soldier's civilian clothing • Surround (two words)
18 Sly look • Great deal • Measures of weight
19 Pen tips • Blessing
21 Deep resonant sound of a large bell • In pieces • Go into liquidation

28 CROSSWORD

ACROSS

4 Down to ___, realistic (5)
9 Knocked to the ground (7)
10 Frostily (5)
11 Natural energy (3)
12 Plant that clings to walls (3)
13 Originally called (3)
14 Short-sleeved tops (1-6)
15 14th-century poet, author of *The Canterbury Tales* (8,7)
19 Tranquillises (7)
20 Viral illness (3)
21 Branch of the armed services (inits)(3)
22 Day before a notable event (3)
23 Without money (5)
24 Pinning (down) (7)
25 Flowers with romantic associations (5)

DOWN

1 In the ___, likely soon (6)
2 Small bunch of flowers (4)
3 Style of clock (11)
4 Border (4)
5 Characteristic of country life (6)
6 Pretentious (11)
7 Acid in lemon juice (6)
8 Uncontested rounds (4)
16 Work done by a handyman (3,3)
17 Artists' stands (6)
18 Sanctuary (6)
19 Club membership payments (4)
20 Low marshy lands (4)
21 Damage beyond repair (4)

1

ACROSS
4 Vapour-like (7)
6 Only even prime number (3)
7 The lot (3)
8 Track down, look for (4,3)

DOWN
1 Self-love (7)
2 On dry land (6)
3 Keep in solitary confinement (7)
5 Skilful speaker (6)

2

ACROSS
1 Food thickener from seaweed (4)
5 Imaginary ideal country (6)
6 Spanish holiday or festival (6)
7 Biblical paradise (4)

DOWN
2 Alight or dismount (3,3)
3 Sated, full (7)
4 Fight, encounter (6)

3

ACROSS
3 Inflamed swelling on the big toe (6)
5 Uncomplaining (7)
6 Four score (6)

DOWN
1 Person who gives up easily (7)
2 Exhume (7)
4 Sugar coating (5)

ACROSS

1 Craftily (5)
5 Makes a sound like a dove (4)
6 Savoury red fruit used in salads (6)
7 Louse eggs (4)
8 Show (a film) (6)
9 Acquits without blame (8)
12 Served (6,3)
15 Fasten (3)
16 Chair carried on poles (5)
17 Stranger (5)
18 Force, thrust (3)
19 Marks made by scraping (9)
21 Local official (8)
24 Control rooms at airports (6)
25 True sound reproduction (2-2)
26 Annoy (someone) (6)
27 Vitality (4)
28 Tactics (5)

DOWN

2 Young animal which lives in a pride (4,3)
3 Remove your grip (5,2)
4 Carriers (7)
5 Schemed (8)
9 Another (10)
10 Stocking supporter (9)
11 Craftsman working with rock (10)
13 Guarantees, makes certain (7)
14 Piece of paper for stock (5,4)
20 Examining the books of (8)
21 Headache pill (7)
22 Bad luck (3,4)
23 Radio exposure of a record (7)

In this puzzle you can ignore the meaning of the clues! Instead, simply take either the first or last letter of each word in the clue to spell out your answer. For example, the W, O and E of 'Waste Of spacE (3)' would give you WOE.

ACROSS

7 Panama hat only worn outside (5)
8 Really obscene, utterly terrible programme (5)
9 Criticising Elgar Enigma Variations invites great animosity (7)
10 'Tall poppy' syndrome (3)
11 Sunday roast or Thai curry? (5)
13 Yuletide occasion; Santa Claus event (5)
15 Biodegradable carrier bag (3)
17 Americans, touring round England, visit country houses (7)
20 Absent for too long, love (5)
21 This person's ready to go (5)

DOWN

1 Reasonable idea, estimation, guesswork (4)
2 Keep off, get away, butt out! (6)
3 Galapagos creature; marine iguana (4)
4 Looking for organic grocery needs patience (6)
5 Can you wear leggings? (4)
6 Your perfume? Lingers like naff scent (6)
11 Should chew every bite thirty times (6)
12 Chill out, chaps – take life easy (6)
14 Andrew Marr tells the real story (6)
16 Ghost of Banquo appeared (4)
18 Royal corgi bites king (4)
19 Hoi polloi get rough (4)

ACROSS

1 Lady's undergarment (3)
8 Older male relatives (12)
9 Bruce ___, legendary martial-arts film star (3)
11 Futuristic genre (3-2)
12 Warm-weather seasons (7)
14 Ale (4)
15 Under control (2,4)
18 Settle cosily (6)
20 Electrically charged particles (4)
23 Lift emotionally (7)
25 Personal teacher (5)
27 Fall ill (3)
28 Hot drinks container for a picnic (7,5)
29 Finish (3)

DOWN

1 Public spectacle in Spain (9)
2 A long time (4)
3 Limited amount (6)
4 Words not scripted in entertainment (2-3)
5 Fake (5)
6 Friend (4)
7 The East (6)
10 Gathered together (9)
13 Big vase (3)
16 Moorlands (6)
17 Small cube with numbered faces (3)
19 Add-ons (6)
21 ___ of, in addition to (2,3)
22 Cram (in) (5)
24 Rocky outcrops (4)
26 Garden tool (4)

SKELETON 33

Have double the fun with this puzzle: you've got to fill in the answers and the black squares! We've given you the bare bones to start and it will help you to know that the black squares in the finished grid form a symmetrical pattern, so that every black square has at least one other corresponding black square.

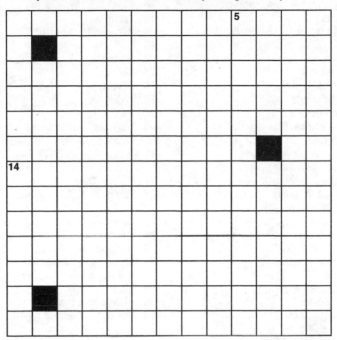

ACROSS

1 Calling differently
5 Top cook
9 Chops into squares
10 Force preventing movement
11 Brood, mope
12 Kidnap, abduct
14 Neatly
15 Indian Ocean sea cow
18 Slaughterhouse
20 Hogs
23 Roosted
24 One of a flight of treads
25 Large extinct bird
26 Leaping playfully

DOWN

1 Sways to and fro
2 Made little bites in
3 Multitude
4 Makes the noise of a horse
6 Thumb a lift
7 Crumbling
8 Extremely wicked
13 Mottled
14 Walked heavily
16 Art of paper-folding
17 Delay, obstruct
19 Brought into the open
21 Small branch
22 Enquires

34 *CROSSWORD*

ACROSS

1 Corrosive substances (5)
4 Bathes (5)
7 Objects of worship (5)
12 Made merry (8)
13 Recreational activities (8)
14 Female sheep (3)
16 Vivid figures of speech (7)
17 Advancing money (7)
19 Fur scarf (3)
21 Type (4)
23 Washed (out) (7)
24 Air passage (4)
26 Keep quiet! (5)
28 Lost animal (5)
29 Grin (5)
33 Take part in a game (4)
34 Equip (a house) (7)
36 Accomplishment (4)
37 Off the ship (6)
39 Carve, shape (3)
41 Overused saying (6)
43 Actor's starting signal (3)
44 Floating zoo (3)
45 Root vegetable (6)
48 Fellow (3)
50 Gestured assent (6)
53 Petty quarrel (4)
54 Perplex (7)
57 Snout (4)
58 Becomes threadbare (5)
59 Kiln, oven (5)
60 Extra (facility) (3-2)
63 Disclose (4)
65 Straightened (7)
67 Nimble-fingered (4)
69 Duvet warmth rating (3)
70 Soft hats tied under the chin (7)
72 Scraping (7)
74 Behind (3)
76 Big-game hunting (2,6)
77 Persistent complainers (8)
78 Large meal, banquet (5)
79 Small hollows (5)
80 Medical pictures (1-4)

DOWN

2 Strawberries' topping (5)
3 Cleared the bottom of (a waterway) (7)
5 Off target (4)
6 Wear a long face (4)
8 Thrashed (7)
9 Allowed to enter (3,2)
10 Bouquet seller (7)
11 Reasons (7)
15 Yarn (4)
16 Sort, type (3)
18 Catch (3)
19 Dark beer (6)
20 Substance that turns litmus paper blue (6)
22 Takes a breath (7)
25 Vehicle cleaning service or facility (3,4)
27 Power or right to make decisions (3-2)
30 Ordinary dress, not uniform (5)
31 Resulting in (9)
32 Depth, breadth (9)
35 Term used to indicate a married woman's maiden name (3)
38 That lady (3)
39 Garment edge (3)
40 Pallid, tired-looking (3)
42 Scoundrel (3)
46 Outer garments (7)
47 Elegant (5)
49 Fuse unit (3)
51 Ate (5)
52 Become less intense (4,3)
55 Twerp (6)
56 Doting (6)
61 Relating to the red planet (7)
62 Charmingly rustic (7)
63 Women's short hairstyle (3)
64 Small domestic fowls (7)
66 Fool (around) (4)
67 Titled widow (7)
68 Small assisting vessel (3)
71 Weight measure (5)
73 Irritable (5)
74 Military assistant (4)
75 Fool (4)

35 CROSSWORD

ACROSS

1 Political campaigner (8)
6 Took action or set off (4,1,4)
7 Goblin (3)
8 Swift, quick (5)
9 Curdle (4,4)
12 Creative skills (4)
13 Musical style (4)
16 Stayed well out of the way (4,5)
18 Having been sworn in at a court case (5,4)
19 Howls loudly (4)
20 Capsule of cotton (4)
23 New vegetation (8)
26 Muscular spasm (5)
27 Golf expert (3)
28 Peacemakers (9)
29 Simultaneously (2,6)

DOWN

1 Hobbled (6)
2 Because of a lack of opposition (2,7)
3 ___ for, desiring strongly (8)
4 Starsign (7)
5 Fresh, youthful (4)
10 Jack-knife clam (5,5)
11 Previous issue of a periodical (4,6)
14 Place of combat (5)
15 Marks on the skin (5)
17 Temper, rage (5)
21 Stepping quietly (2,7)
22 Grumble (8)
24 Gratify (7)
25 Decline (6)
26 Got here (4)

Each of 25 letters of the alphabet should be entered into the grid once, and only once. Can you find which letter has not been used?

A	B	C	D	E	F	G	H	I	J	K	L	M
N	O	P	Q	R	S	T	U	V	W	X	Y	Z

ACROSS
- **4** Plane figure with six sides
- **6** Peculiarity of behaviour
- **7** MI5 agent

The missing letter is: _____

DOWN
- **1** Pack of cards
- **2** Door posts
- **3** Very tall
- **5** Anarchic comic originating in Newcastle

MINI QUICK

ACROSS
- **1** Bowler-hatted Bond villain (6)
- **5** Relating to noise (5)
- **6** Push forward (5)
- **7** Motor shed (6)

DOWN
- **2** Stylish (7)
- **3** Berries used to flavour gin (7)
- **4** Accumulation of uncompleted work (7)

37 CROSSWORD

ACROSS

1 Recreational activity (5)
4 Timber which is relatively easily cut (8)
9 Expressing differently (9)
10 Musical drama such as *Carmen* (5)
11 Over-the-top camp trashiness (6)
13 On paper (2,5)
16 Raw mineral (3)
17 Early evening meal (4,3)
19 Approve, sanction (6)
22 Take the lid off (5)
24 Flake off (9)
26 ___ of, threw away (8)
27 Deprived (5)

DOWN

1 Heed (4)
2 Loud crying (7)
3 Enclosed places near buildings (5)
4 Glide over snow (3)
5 More misty (7)
6 Enthusiastic yell (5)
7 Singular (3)
8 Open pies (5)
12 Malicious pranksters (7)
14 Blow up (7)
15 Raise your voice (5)
18 Replenish (3,2)
20 Bird's claw (5)
21 Refuse to admit (4)
23 T'ai ___, martial art (3)
25 Passing craze (3)

The answer to each of these clues begins with a different letter of the alphabet. The clues are not numbered, so you must work out where each answer fits in the grid.

A Disciple (7)	**N** Noxious (7)
B Have children (5)	**O** Tender (5)
C Statement of beliefs (5)	**P** Occurring before expected (9)
D Small coffee cup (9)	**Q** Given to arguing (11)
E Infuriated (11)	**R** Logic (6)
F Bonded (5)	**S** Gap (5)
G Potter's substance (5)	**T** Sinew (6)
H Scavenging carnivore (5)	**U** Expression of disgust (3)
I Laboratory particle (3)	**V** TV tape (5)
J Fair (4)	**W** Neigh (6)
K Cutting implements (6)	**X** Yellow substance in plants (7)
L Owed feudal allegiance (5)	**Y** Pull sharply (4)
M Repairs (5)	**Z** Fanatical (7)

39 *CROSSWORD*

ACROSS

1 RAF officer (4,9)
10 Fought in an affair of honour (7)
11 Tatty, unkempt (7)
12 People to admire and imitate (4,6)
14 Rung (4)
16 Holiness (8)
18 Large group of fish swimming together (5)
21 Determined individualists (9)
22 Frenzy (5)
23 State of owing money to the bank (2,4)
25 Use seniority to obtain privileges (4,4)
28 Brown relish poured onto Chinese food (3,5)
29 Get free, gain freedom (6)
31 Chose (5)
33 Delegated (6,3)
35 Advances (5)
36 Enraged (8)
40 Yokel (4)
41 Included in a list of members (2,3,5)
44 Meringue dessert (7)
45 Is quietly angry (7)
46 Stirrers (13)

DOWN

2 Perfect (5)
3 Prospector (4,5)
4 Long in the tooth (3)
5 Principles of conduct (6)
6 Forbidden (2,2)
7 Result of too much reading? (3,6)
8 Worshipped (6)
9 Slim girl (5)
13 Discover the existence or presence of something (6)
15 Finger protectors when sewing (8)
17 Brilliantly (7)
19 Debatable point (5)
20 Position in the rear (4,4)
21 Advertising material sent through the post (8)
24 Weaving strands together (8)
26 Perplexed (2,1,4)
27 Scrape mark on a shoe (5)
30 Grind (with the teeth) (6)
32 Holed up (4,5)
34 Fair chance (4,5)
37 State of not being employed (6)
38 Sea-going vessels (5)
39 Give rise to (6)
42 Different (5)
43 Soya-bean product (4)
45 ___ Browne, military belt (3)

40 CROSSWORD

ACROSS

1 Ancient floor designs (7)
7 Added alcoholic spirit (5)
8 Pull (3)
9 Old dye (4)
10 Vessel with cabins (4)
12 Detested thing (8)
14 Fines (9)
15 Formally give up office (8)
18 Marshes, swamps (8)
21 Doing OK under the circumstances (7,2)
23 Conceded (8)
25 Related (4)
26 Look at (4)
28 Trench coat (3)
29 Spectator's cry of approval (5)
30 Support (a cause) (7)

DOWN

2 Yet another time (4,5)
3 Helps (4)
4 Performed to a required standard (3,3,7)
5 Decorators' flaming implements (9)
6 Switches (5)
11 Variety of capsicum (6)
13 Dots of land (5)
16 Miscellaneous items (4,3,6)
17 Mops (5)
19 Pleas of elsewhere (6)
20 Routine preparation (9)
22 Nerve (9)
24 ___ to, becomes more interested (5)
27 Radio operators' code word before foxtrot (4)

The arrows show the direction in which the answer to each clue should be placed.

Conclude (3,2) ▼ / Felt pain ▶		__ colour, unwell ▼		Musical group ▼		Dame __ Everage, megastar ▼
Spouted milk container ▶		Knight's glove ▼	Tropical shrub ▶	Cramped ▼		Swindler ▼
Set of two ▶				What Katy __, book ▼		__ Kelly, Aussie outlaw ▼
Enjoyable ▶	Extortionate money-lender ▼	Supreme Norse god ▶				
		Sensible ▶				
Riveted ▶ / __ Brynner, actor ▶						
		Intention ▼		__ Amin, Ugandan dictator ▼		Verily ▼
Cheerfully ▶						
			Jack __, comic ▶			
Himalayan bigfoot	__ Stuart, news-reader ▶					

42 CROSSWORD

ACROSS

1 Leave quickly (5)
4 Fishes often packed in tins (8)
11 Operating smoothly (4,5)
12 Encouraged (5)
13 Wood often used in shipbuilding (4)
14 Danced (6)
16 Add a new soundtrack to (3)
18 Garden tool (3)
19 Mixed cold dishes (6)
22 As well as (4)
24 Theatrical piece (5)
26 Journal and magazine kiosk (4-5)
27 Biblical ship (5,3)
28 Rubbish (5)

DOWN

2 Artwork made up of fragments (7)
3 Double-reed instrument (4)
5 Find the total of (3,2)
6 Ancient Celtic priests (6)
7 Derogatory term for a horse (3)
8 Abreast (4,2,4)
9 Alert, comprehending (8-2)
10 Range of singing voice (4)
15 Green vegetable (3)
16 US currency (7)
17 Written compositions (6)
20 Of the Moon (5)
21 Soft covering of fluffy hair (4)
23 Title of the emperor of Russia (4)
25 ___ Khan, title of a Muslim leader (3)

1

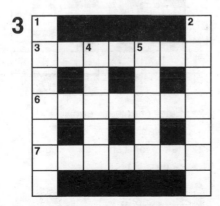

ACROSS
1 Handle clumsily (3)
3 Bridge call (3)
5 Subject to duty (7)
6 Type of bet (4-3)
9 Churchyard tree (3)
10 Flit around (3)

DOWN
1 Articles of baked clay (7)
2 Candle substance (3)
3 Front part of overalls (3)
4 Having an expression like Bambi's? (3-4)
7 Female whale (3)
8 Hairpiece (3)

2

ACROSS
1 Meadow's main plant (5)
5 Cardboard beverage container (4,3)
6 Expert, able (7)
8 Furrow the brow (5)

DOWN
2 Regret (3)
3 Decelerate (4,2)
4 Argue (6)
7 Litigation (3)

3

ACROSS
3 Inconsiderate driver (4,3)
6 Be subjected to, suffer (7)
7 Fortress protecting a town (7)

DOWN
1 Defeat decisively (7)
2 Dishonourable (7)
4 Examination of accounts (5)
5 Chartered (5)

44 CROSSWORD

ACROSS

- **6** Downgrades or derides (9)
- **7** Ill fate (5)
- **8** Term used to indicate a married woman's maiden name (3)
- **9** Loosen (4)
- **10** Seal (off) (4)
- **12** Citrus drink (8)
- **15** Preparing (a pack of cards) for cheating (8)
- **17** Idiot (9)
- **18** Stranded traveller (8)
- **20** Large crested parrot (8)
- **23** Is the freeholder of (4)
- **24** Aid (a criminal) (4)
- **27** Cycle of the internal combustion engine (3)
- **28** Aim (5)
- **29** Getting hotter (7,2)

DOWN

- **1** Clearly (9)
- **2** Nut often used in trout recipes (6)
- **3** Heavy ropes on a sailing ship (5)
- **4** Went pale (8)
- **5** Concurs (7)
- **11** Small household ornaments (5-6)
- **13** Dignified older women (7)
- **14** Ripened (4)
- **16** Approximate (7)
- **17** Fund (4)
- **19** Audible paces? (9)
- **21** Eater of animals and vegetables (8)
- **22** Takes for a short time and then returns (7)
- **25** Conveys (6)
- **26** Break up (5)

Every solution begins with one of five letters. Rearrange these letters to find small residential road.

The five-letter word is: _____

ACROSS

8 Too energetic (10)
9 Per person (4)
10 Magic potion (6)
11 Subatomic particle (8)
12 Medieval instrument (4)
14 Old exam (6-4)
16 Printed headings on missives (11)
20 End of a dispute (10)
22 Acid to the taste (4)
23 Apprentices (8)
25 Bend low (6)
27 American coin (4)
28 Put out (10)

DOWN

1 Nasty look (4,3)
2 Most essential point (of the matter) (4)
3 Most frightening (8)
4 Small parasitic insects (4)
5 Harsh (6)
6 Many-legged creepy-crawlies (10)
7 Sea creature with eight tentacles (7)
13 Those with the vote (10)
15 Eagle's nest (5)
17 Alluring (8)
18 Young hare (7)
19 Social reject (7)
21 Devon city (6)
24 Location (4)
26 Responsibility (4)

46 CROSSWORD

ACROSS

1 House built in sections (6)
5 Natural, innate (6)
9 Substance obtained from olives (3)
11 Mediterranean variety of wild marjoram (7)
12 Expose (a secret) (3,4)
13 Uncomplicated (4)
15 Flower stalks (5)
16 House linked to another (4)
17 Water outlets (4)
19 Smiles broadly (5)
20 Alexander Graham ___, telephone inventor (4)
24 Absent-minded musing (7)
25 Highest (7)
26 High card (3)
27 Give evidence (6)
28 Turns outwards (6)

DOWN

2 Coral formations (5)
3 Baby horse (4)
4 Extra cushion on a chair for a child (7,4)
5 Lights up (11)
6 Coastal inlets (4)
7 Make joyful (5)
8 Ambitious people (2-7)
10 Make new rules (9)
14 Absolutely! (3)
16 Advance payment (3)
18 Fulcrum (5)
21 Black wood (5)
22 Agreeing with fact (4)
23 Off-white gemstone (4)

All solutions can be found hidden in the clues, written either backwards or forwards. Words such as 'back' or 'up' may suggest the answer is hidden backwards.

ACROSS

5 Turned over content of fridge – no cream in ice-cream container! (4)

6 On holiday in Kenya, waiting to return (4)

7 Although turning piece of metal, it never let fresh air in (9)

8 Formerly residing in Congleton, certainly (4)

10 Very unusual for a restaurant to feature such a lightly cooked steak! (4)

12 Put up the visor – rockets are partially like acid (9)

15 Boast about being involved in the return of Shergar, but not true (4)

16 One might be included in a shipping alert (4)

DOWN

1 Control some of the water going over Niagara (6)

2 Undershirt turns up in the washing-basket several times (4)

3 Clothes manufacturer is acquired as part of the retail organisation (6)

4 Quick, come back in perfect safety (4)

9 Extract from the Garnetts' dialogue crops up to make you angry (6)

11 Rise up, rise up in support of cricket-lovers everywhere! (6)

13 Shrek, for example, is up amongst the better goblins (4)

14 A wise man will get in his agent (4)

48 CROSSWORD

ACROSS

9 Erase (marks) (3,3)
10 Country or holiday home (5)
11 Swear (4)
12 Used to be (4)
13 Physician (5)
14 Grieves (6)
15 Root vegetables (7)
17 Two hanging pieces of material on winter hats (3-5)
19 Glance through (4)
21 Cooking (7)
23 Prepare food (4)
24 Abrasive mass used for cleaning (4,4)
25 Fail to penalise (3,3)
27 Alehouse (3)
29 No good whatsoever! (4,4)
31 Preserve (a right) (8)
32 Become gradually less acceptable (4,4)
34 Trapped (8)
35 Asks earnestly (8)
36 Provider (8)
39 Undertake a winter sport (3)
40 Reels for yarn (6)
42 Separates grain from (corn) (8)
45 ___ for, chooses (4)
46 Rapid succession of chirping sounds (7)
47 Danger (4)
48 Sounding like a frog (8)
51 Authors' credits (7)
54 Ceremonial (6)
55 Prickly shrub (5)
57 Scoffs (4)
58 Middle of the leg (4)
59 Inept fool (5)
60 Grooms the feathers (6)

DOWN

1 Writing-desk (6)
2 Control, authority (10)
3 Flower support (4)
4 Shirk (5)
5 Punched your card to start work (7,2)
6 Tool for banging in nails (6)
7 Offhand (6)
8 Make (a building) resistant to noise (10)
16 High-pitched musical instrument (7)
18 Charming immaturity in a female (11)
20 Offence (5)
22 Joins up (7)
23 Yell like a feline in pain (9)
26 Non-batting cricketer (7)
28 Make unavoidable (11)
29 Those who search for underground water (7)
30 Photographers' workplaces (9)
33 Pair of earphones (7)
37 Describe (7)
38 Levels (5)
41 Popular money-earner for teenagers (5,5)
43 People in the armed forces (10)
44 Lotto-players' venue (5,4)
49 Military land forces (6)
50 People related by marriage (2-4)
52 Elongate (6)
53 Kills (with a sword) (5)
56 Barks sharply (4)

49 CODECRACKER

This puzzle has no clues in the conventional sense. Instead, every different number printed in the main grid represents a different letter (with the same number always representing the same letter, of course). For example, if 7 turns out to be a 'V', you can write in V wherever a square contains 7. We have completed a very small part of the puzzle to give you a start, but the rest is up to you.

	17		22		24		19		10		14	
21	8	3	9 C	17	6		13	24	8	18	6	2
	26		8 U		24		25		20		7	
22	18	13	2 T		16	18	6	13	9	17	6	15
	3				6		16		2		15	
8	20	11	13	2	26	3	5	2	3	9		
	19		3					5			22	
	11	26	5	24	3	22	3	20	19	18	1	
	22		9		6		2				13	
22	9	13	26	9	6	18	1		17	13	14	6
	5		13		4		18		13		6	
16	5	7	23	8	18		8	11	12	13	26	15
	11		2		1		22		4		1	

A B C̶ D E F G H I J K L M N O P Q R S T̶ U̶ V W X Y Z

1	2 T	3	4	5	6	7	8 U	9 C	10	11	12	13
14	15	16	17	18	19	20	21	22	23	24	25	26

Each of the 26 letters of the alphabet should be entered into the grid once, and only once.

A	B	C	D	E	F	G	H	I	J	K	L	M
N	O	P	Q	R	S	T	U	V	W	X	Y	Z

ACROSS

3 Unruly groups
5 Spouted milk container
7 ___ *Do Fools Fall in Love?*, Diana Ross single
8 Lead-up to Christmas

DOWN

1 Person who acts for another
2 Give up on a task
4 Far from strict
6 Hat worn by Tommy Cooper

MINI QUICK

ACROSS

1 Reflection (in a mirror) (5)
5 Mollusc with a fan-shaped shell (7)
6 Dried raisin (7)
8 Psychiatrist's sofa (5)

DOWN

2 Scale copy, dummy (4-2)
3 Hairstyling substance (3)
4 Fine French brandy (6)
7 In addition, as well (3)

51 CROSSWORD

ACROSS

1 Ledge (5)
4 Fastener (3)
6 Private compartment on a train (9)
7 Large party (8)
9 Simple plan of an area (6,3)
10 Body parts which perceive sound (4)
12 Ultra (4)
14 Lined up in uniform (2,6)
17 Admitting guilt (6,2)
19 Approach (4)
21 Stand-in worker (4)
23 Directs (a boat) (9)
25 Meaning (8)
27 Just, fair (9)
28 Bring charges against (3)
29 Hibernated (5)

DOWN

1 Old-style window frame (4)
2 Issue (from) (7)
3 Information offered in reaction to a query (8)
4 Television show (9)
5 Metal panels attached to the front and back of a vehicle (6,6)
8 Blockheads (5)
11 Disagreement (3-2)
13 Meticulous care (5)
15 Cause merriment (5)
16 Formal wedding garments (7,5)
18 Twitch (5)
20 Thrilling experience (9)
22 Stirs up (8)
24 Defensible (7)
26 Polite and considerate chap, in short (4)

Try your luck with this cryptic puzzle.

ACROSS

8 Attack fee (6)
9 Circle round every one, getting there (8)
10 Sword with three points keeping quiet (4)
11 Useless purpose, sea fogs (10)
12 Flower in autumn – it's developing round river (10)
14 Fighting unit mad without leader (4)
15 Airport desk where payment received, they say (5,2)
17 Soft soap for cloth (7)
20 Sounds like the animal is naked (4)
22 The box I've stolen, I destroyed (10)
24 That lacier embroidery, dramatic (10)
26 Old cloth on table finally brings anger (4)
27 Horses' discipline to put on clothes on time (8)
28 Number going into seventy, ten indeed, when reversed (6)

DOWN

1 Neck injury clean round joint at top of leg (8)
2 Religious type with unusual stripe (6)
3 Sweet hot stuff, perfect (10)
4 Burglary to interrupt conversation? (5-2)
5 Mexican crisp in coat, ruined (4)
6 Religious type wanting tea without milk or sugar? (8)
7 County of Northern Ireland where social worker on edge (6)
13 Man with new novel given time to become spiteful (10)
16 Five in creases, smoothed out crack (8)
18 Nothing in a gentle, moving stretch (8)
19 Elks can somehow become loose (7)
21 Stick poster in this place (6)
23 Season to jump (6)
25 Papers are wrong over head of Mafia (4)

53 CROSSWORD

ACROSS

1 Stretches the neck (6)
4 Fatten up (5,3)
9 Couple (3)
10 Shelled fruit (3)
11 Insect's poisonous weapon (5)
12 Police officer (5)
13 Mischievous kids (4)
14 Soft thread (5)
15 Highest male voice (4)
18 Arouse affection (6)
20 Exempt (6)
23 Small hamlets (8)
24 Remove a fleece from (5)
26 Person who shows the way (10)
29 Become larger (4)
31 Period of light, from sunrise to sunset (3)
33 Abets (4)
34 Estate worker (10)
36 Object worn by a small baby (5)
38 Links (8)
40 Central glass-roofed hall (6)
41 Objected to (6)
44 Gaze (4)
45 Run away (3,2)
46 Land unit (4)
50 More unfavourable (5)
51 Portents (5)
53 T'ai ___, martial art (3)
54 Large container (3)
55 Baubles (8)
56 Being lazy (6)

DOWN

1 Plots (8)
2 Misbehave (3,2)
3 Relieve (4)
4 Jollity (3)
5 Co-ordination of a complex business operation (9)
6 Club membership payments (4)
7 Taking everything into consideration (2,7)
8 Younger male lover (3,3)
9 Selects telephone numbers (5)
16 Decrease (4,3)
17 Break to bits (5)
19 Floated (7)
21 Schedule (6)
22 Furniture compartments (7)
25 Muscular wrenches (7)
27 Embankment to restrain water (3)
28 Watching (6)
30 Generally supposed (7)
32 Daydream (7)
35 Habitual sceptic (5)
37 Fragrant dried petals (3-6)
38 Bivouacked (6,3)
39 Giving support (to) (8)
42 Fluff your chances (4,2)
43 Ill-tempered woman (5)
47 Plants associated with arid climes (5)
48 Sudden movement (4)
49 Accustomed (4)
52 Woman's title (3)

54 PIECEWORD

With the help of the Across clues only, can you fit the 35 pieces into their correct positions in the empty grid below (which, when completed, will exhibit a symmetrical pattern)?

ACROSS

1 Biased • Charged
2 Express, state
3 Groups of vehicles travelling together • Plucked (a string)
4 Possesses
5 *Charlotte* ___, 2002 film • Body organs that perceive sound

6 Prevents, obstructs
7 Kindled • Clamour
8 Become worn away • Adjust feathers
9 Polygonal church recess • Adjoining
10 Drippy behaviour

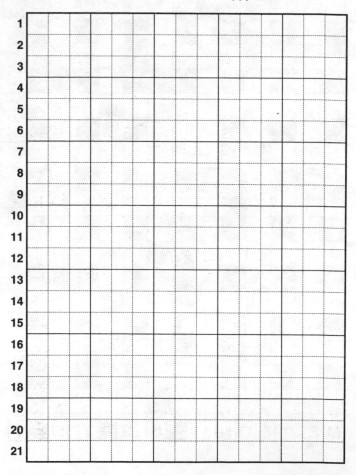

PIECEWORD

11 Steer clear of • Commonly used coin
12 Courier
13 Apple centre • Reflected sound
14 Traditional saying • Body
15 Nervous mannerism • Guided
16 Attired

17 House linked to another • Electrically charged particles
18 Bow in the middle
19 Cold infusion (two words) • Imagining, supposing (two words)
20 Small, in Scotland
21 Marches • People who go about naked

55 CROSSWORD

ACROSS

4 Took (an exam) (3)
8 Top secret (4-4)
9 Pay no attention to (6)
10 Gazed (6)
11 Moving (the hips) (8)
13 Butterfly-like creature (4)
15 Took part in an election (5)
16 Wholly engrossed (4)
18 Becoming friends again after an argument (6,2)
20 Bodies of soldiers (6)
22 Fix in the mind (6)
23 Publicity (8)
24 Knight's title (3)

DOWN

1 Arranged or done exactly (4,2)
2 Scorch (4)
3 One pound sterling (4)
4 Performance receiving prolonged applause (4-7)
5 Slightly coloured (6)
6 Fisherman (6)
7 Elderly female relative (4)
12 Intestine (3)
13 Female parent (3)
14 Armed hold-ups (6)
15 Night watches (6)
17 Scottish musicians (6)
19 Father's sister (4)
20 Finishing line in a race (4)
21 Forcibly remove (4)

ANoffGRAMS 56

Unscramble the anagrams before entering the answers. It may be possible to make more than one word from the letters. Make sure you enter the right one!

ACROSS
1 A BLOWGUN (8)
6 ATE TRY (6)
9 GO SEMI (6)
10 THE PLANE (8)
11 CANNIEST (8)
12 BE STAN (6)
13 THE CREATORS (11)
16 PRIM DAHLIAS (11)
20 CAMPED (6)
22 BRAIN SET (8)
24 BEERS FIT (8)
25 AIR GUT (6)
26 SHERPA (6)
27 RING TIER (8)

DOWN
2 GET RUN (6)
3 DRIEST LEG (9)
4 MELON (5)
5 WAS HERE (7)
6 HAS SUTURE (9)
7 THOSE (5)
8 NET TAN (6)
14 ICIER HEAP (9)
15 TRIERS HIT (9)
17 RAREBIT (7)
18 ARCHES (6)
19 AN EDIT (6)
21 A NEAR (5)
23 THING (5)

ACROSS

5 Stringed instrument (8)

7 Ox-like antelope (3)

8 Annoy (5)

9 Tiny cardboard container (8)

11 Stage departure (4)

12 Esplanade (4)

14 Squeeze (5)

15 Small hotel (3)

16 Nest eggs (7)

20 Feel sorrow (3)

21 Deals (5)

23 Inhabitant of southern Scandinavia (4)

24 Atop (2,2)

26 Small cylindrical containers (8)

28 Transmitter of sensation (5)

29 Hurry (3)

30 Breathes life into (8)

DOWN

1 Final Greek letter (5)

2 Hatching (of eggs) (10)

3 Thicket (7)

4 Getting off a boat (12)

6 Scrutinise again (2-7)

10 Assists (5)

13 Small children (7)

17 Stunning (3-9)

18 Fabricating (9)

19 Famous racecourse (5)

22 Render sacred (10)

25 Buildings for relics (7)

27 Grind the teeth (5)

Clue A leads to a solution beginning with the letter A, clue B to one beginning with the letter B etc. Solutions should be entered, using a little logic, wherever they fit.

A Land of Vienna, Salzburg too,
Where gold art is fashioned anew (7)

B '50s hippie (never a Ted)
Thrashed old devil, so it's said (7)

C To these rolling hills let's go,
Though chilly surroundings for
poor Stow! (8)

D Hilda developed a plant that's now a
Prize-winning garden flower (6)

E To beget or sow the seeds
Points to male or female needs! (8)

F One won't win fair lady, yet
The RAF ain't upset! (5,5)

G Number at match
Might be held by a catch? (4)

H From here on I become
The principal female role for some (7)

I Where sheep and cows may be found,
Forming part of cricket ground? (7)

J My jam is evil, but mix it,
For he once used to say he'd fix it! (5,6)

K Symbol returns and I log in
To find the weight that's clued within (8)

L One who comes from Preston gains
From new canal, and
different trains (11)

M Cool men maybe sport
Visual aid of this sort (7)

N Musical sound it might be –
A, B, C, D, F or G! (4)

O From endless Sahara I became
A famous star with Egyptian name (4,6)

P Sneak a look around the east
For quarry sought by wild beast (4)

Q New Iraq rule? I depart
Before this dispute can start! (7)

R Salesman has ceramic square
With snake or lizard pictured there? (7)

S In the north and south cry out;
It's deadly poison, there's no doubt! (10)

T In new estate you'll see the whole
Of cups and saucers, jug and bowl (3,3)

U UN left Yemen port
With no load of any sort (7)

V Source of annoyance, which is strange,
Since I've no tax to arrange! (8)

W For towns in Somerset, Shropshire too,
See this chap at Waterloo! (10)

X Maybe fix the French to see
This sci-fi series on TV (1-5)

Y In Tokyo gaze in some surprise
As people take this exercise (4)

Z To get old Ford like one of these
Might it really be a breeze? (6)

59 CROSSWORD

ACROSS

4 Stopped (5)
9 Seethed, swirled (7)
10 In need of a scratch (5)
11 Shape of a rainbow (3)
12 Annoy (3)
13 Large deciduous tree (3)
14 Fashionable circle (2-5)
15 Circus balancer (9,6)
19 Bouquet seller (7)
20 Beaker with a handle (3)
21 ___ Geldof, Band Aid organiser (3)
22 Before now (3)
23 Dim (5)
24 Tennis game with one player per side (7)
25 Very long time (5)

DOWN

1 Printed text of a play (6)
2 Thick slab (of bread) (4)
3 Doubt (11)
4 Round red-rinded cheese (4)
5 Placid (6)
6 Releasing (from a contract) (11)
7 Word for expressing the time (6)
8 Artificially coloured (4)
16 Malevolent spirits (6)
17 Acquire (6)
18 Strong, sturdy (6)
19 Disgusting (4)
20 Kate ___, supermodel (4)
21 Courageous (4)

Have double the fun with this puzzle: you've got to fill in the answers and the black squares! We've given you the bare bones to start and it will help you to know that the black squares in the finished grid form a symmetrical pattern, so that every black square has at least one other corresponding black square.

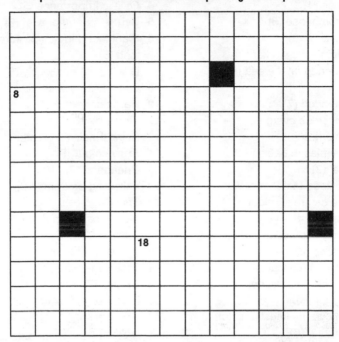

ACROSS

7 Declared to be illegal
8 ___ of July, US Independence Day
9 Repair clumsily
10 Deduced
13 Young goats
15 Large brown seaweed
16 Agility
17 Suggestive
19 Dark arts
21 More and more

DOWN

1 Ask for money or favours
2 Seaside jetty
3 Failed to make a decision
4 Jagged hook designed to catch fish
5 Wrong, in error
6 Net
11 Gives authority to
12 Yellow spring flower
14 Shows publicly
17 Nuisance
18 Calendar's duration
20 Place for confining a beast

ACROSS

9 Church penitence booth (12)
11 Circle (4)
12 Electrically charged atom (3)
13 Ellipse (4)
14 Recompense (5)
15 Boasts of (6)
16 Building site worker (7)
18 Bordering on the sea (8)
20 Flay (4)
22 Pretended (7)
24 Coniferous evergreens (4)
25 Unworried (8)
26 Deliveries of babies (6)
28 Steal (3)
30 Subsided (4,4)
32 Care centre for elderly people (4,4)
33 Animal reputed to have a long memory (8)
35 Watched (critically) (8)
36 Act with great enthusiasm (2,2,4)
37 Spend the night (4,4)
40 Remove the intestines from (3)
41 Leftovers (6)
43 Detailed (knowledge) (8)
46 Alluring (4)
47 Talk louder (5,2)
48 Children's playthings (4)
49 Nipping (8)
52 Twirls (7)
55 Small prawn (6)
56 Crouches (5)
59 Toss (a coin) (4)
60 Sticky substance (3)
61 Round door handle (4)
62 Twin blow (6,6)

DOWN

1 Use a vacuum cleaner (6)
2 Liquor store (3-7)
3 Large continent (4)
4 Of little importance (5)
5 Usurp the authority of (9)
6 Plant found in rich pasture-land (6)
7 Display ostentatiously (6)
8 Long military walk (5,5)
10 Hard drinker (3)
17 Fierce blaze (7)
19 Being inactive in winter (11)
21 Army colour (5)
23 Cheapens (7)
24 Following on from (7,2)
27 Thin (7)
29 Modes of transport for witches (11)
30 Clears mud from (a river bed) (7)
31 Tact, sensitivity (9)
34 Excites (7)
38 Post-mortem examination (7)
39 Going in (5)
42 Holding dear (10)
44 Reached a compromise with (3,7)
45 Owner of an adjoining property (9)
50 Ascends (6)
51 Obstruct (6)
53 Puzzling riddle (6)
54 Intersection of two straight lines (5)
57 Female rabbit or deer (3)
58 Scatters (seed) (4)

CROSSWORD

ACROSS

1 Joined metal links (5)
5 Very audible (4)
6 Survive on the inadequate means available (4,2)
7 Twisted threads that hold a candle flame (4)
8 Small particular (6)
9 Make a tour of (4,4)
12 Imagine (9)
15 ___ and feather, punish severely (3)
16 Drains from (5)
17 Plucky competitor (5)
18 Stately tree (3)
19 Musicians found in churches (9)
21 Is in cahoots (8)
24 Divided by two (6)
25 Eye greedily (4)
26 Disturbance (6)
27 Honest, sincere (4)
28 Daisy-like flower (5)

DOWN

2 Sound made while pulling an extremely big load (5-2)
3 Chilled bag put on the skin to reduce swelling (3,4)
4 Swifter (7)
5 Of relatively little importance (3-5)
9 Suspension in the air (10)
10 Watching (9)
11 Gloomy people (10)

13 Loser (4-3)
14 Grew (9)
20 Compos mentis (3,5)
21 Eccentric old men (7)
22 Loosens (a Victorian corset) (7)
23 Inflict capital punishment on (7)

Every solution begins with one of five letters. Rearrange these letters to find a conjunction.

The five-letter word is: _____

ACROSS

9 Fragrant smoke (7)
10 From Jerusalem, perhaps (7)
11 Push with the elbow (5)
12 Where items of the element Fe are made (9)
13 Three-sided figures (9)
16 Slack (5)
17 Type of acid in tired legs? (6)
18 Caught (6)
22 Workers' association (5)
24 Tennessee town (9)
25 Serious actor (9)
27 Of birth (5)
29 Most unsightly (7)
30 Ideal (7)

DOWN

1 Finches (7)
2 Covered (a cake) (4)
3 Cyberspace source of information (8)
4 Hebrew patriarch (4)
5 Stretch cars (10)
6 Gardening implement (6)
7 Lazy and irresponsible person (4-2-4)
8 Racing expert offering hints (7)
14 Possible (10)
15 Qualified person (10)
19 Edison, for example (8)
20 Period of five years (7)
21 Significant (7)
23 Wanted (6)
26 Naming word (4)
28 Pare (4)

This puzzle has no clues in the conventional sense. Instead, every different number printed in the main grid represents a different letter (with the same number always representing the same letter, of course). For example, if 7 turns out to be a 'V', you can write in V wherever a square contains 7. We have completed a very small part of the puzzle to give you a start, but the rest is up to you.

17		18		13		6		13		13	
23	16	14	24	10	11	13	17	12	6	1	
21		11		15		13		6		16	
7	14	5	13	13	16		5	24	22	16	6	20
	15		20		3		15				25	
15	16	2	17	21	9	1	16		19	5	16	1
		12							14			
18	16	15	2		16	1	14	26	5	16	21	20
										E	N	T
	4				8		17		21		14	
3	10	16	21	12	16		1	6	20	16	13	20
	14		6		21		12		6		17	
	15	16	8	6	1	5	6	20	17	14	21	
	20		11		11		21		21		23	

A B C D E̷ F G H I J K L M N̷ O P Q R S T̷ U V W X Y Z

1	2	3	4	5	6	7	8	9	10	11	12	13
14	15	16	17	18	19	20	21	22	23	24	25	26
		E				T	N					

HEADS AND TAILS 65

In this puzzle you can ignore the meaning of the clues! Instead, simply take either the first or last letter of each word in the clue to spell out your answer. For example, the W, O and E of 'Waste Of spacE (3)' would give you WOE.

ACROSS

7 Piece for one viola, excruciating (5)
8 Aspirations, wishes; all pointless hope (5)
9 Marie chooses peach; Elsa likes Ogen melon (7)
10 Enjoy your supper (3)
11 Gas halts rioting unruly mob (5)
13 'Just too bad,' said Daddy (5)
15 Fantastic, amazing, dazzling (3)
17 Imbibing Guinness must have made you sloshed (7)
20 All the actors seem happy (5)
21 Fans love Ringo Starr always (5)

DOWN

1 Ashley Peacock misses Maxine (4)
2 Big bingo night held here regularly (6)
3 Wimbledon expelled ball girl (4)
4 Beckham attacked goal in extra time (6)
5 Fleas attended *Antz* premiere? (4)
6 Sad how toothache ruins your holiday (6)
11 Opus Dei; Catholics keeping Latin alive (6)
12 Barbara Windsor is renewing her contract (6)
14 Designer Stella McCartney dislikes retro fashion (6)
16 Remembered Che Guevara fondly (4)
18 Tony introduces fast food (4)
19 Pacifists grow angry worrying (4)

66 CROSSWORD

ACROSS

1 Tube carrying liquid to taps (5,4)
6 Cleaning lady (4)
10 Heavy staffs (7)
11 Venerated (7)
13 Pretty bad (4)
14 I can hardly believe it! (3,4,3)
16 Scolded (6)
18 Old-fashioned refrigerator (6)
21 Vocal party (4-4)
22 Sorrowful and serious poem (5)
24 Someone who spoils the pleasure of others (3,7)
26 Aspersion (4)
29 Part of a list (4)
30 Undertake to control (4,2,4)
32 Exuberant enjoyment or zest (5)
34 Interrupted (6,2)
36 Overland journey by big game hunters (6)
37 Boundaries (6)
40 Designers of houses (10)
41 Enormous (4)
44 Be ahead of (7)
45 Asserted in court (7)
46 Sundown (4)
47 Protesters (9)

DOWN

2 Do a sum (3,2)
3 Perpetually (4)
4 Part of a car engine (6)
5 Caricaturing (9)
7 Astrologer's forecast of the future (9)
8 Undesirable effect of flash photography (3-3)
9 Alarming (7)
12 Overlaid (8)
15 Raucous maritime bird (7)
17 Tough meat (7)
19 Eye part (6)
20 Offspring of mixed species (7)
23 Canvas covers (7)
25 Constructs (6)
27 Stacking (7)
28 ___ at, ridiculed (7)
31 Philander (8)
33 Inquirers (9)
34 Breakfast in a shell! (6,3)
35 Atolls (7)
38 Killed in a computer game? (6)
39 In the end (2,4)
42 Full of enthusiasm (5)
43 Low-heeled (4)

67 CROSSWORD

ACROSS

4 Father Christmas (5)
9 Good-natured (7)
10 Black suit in cards (5)
11 Sturdy oil-fired cooker (3)
12 Draw off (liquid) (3)
13 Deciduous tree (3)
14 Take a different path (7)
15 Giddy feeling (5-10)
19 Until the end of time (7)
20 Came across (3)
21 Spoil (3)
22 Calm area of a cyclone (3)
23 Vacant (property) (5)
24 ___ out, isolated (7)
25 Annual periods (5)

DOWN

1 Delicate soft colour (6)
2 Ineffectual person (4)
3 Quality of not being influenced by personal feelings (11)
4 Line of stitching formed by sewn-together edges (4)
5 Drew nigh (6)
6 Attributing (to) (11)
7 Time ahead (6)
8 Area of land surrounded by water (4)
16 Use a mouthwash (6)
17 Archimedes' cry (6)
18 Rips up (6)
19 Prolonged and bitter dispute (4)
20 Military food hall (4)
21 Coconut juice (4)

ARROWORD 68

The arrows show the direction in which the answer to each clue should be placed.

Main road in a town ▼		Small nails ▼		Rejoices in victory	Outdoor party	Skid smoothly	▼
Injurious ▶				▼	▼		
Added money to (an account)		(They) exist ▶				__ Falco, US actress	
▶						▼	
Silent, tight-lipped		Soft brushed leather ▶					
▶			Provides with manpower		Ascribe, attribute		Native inhabitants
Section of a dance band		Story ▶	▼		▼		▼
▶						Model married to David Bowie	
Dither		Savoury jelly ▶				▼	
▶			__ Thurman, Mia in *Pulp Fiction* ▶				
Hanukkah observers		__ *Attrac-tion*, Glenn Close film ▶					
▶			Measure-ments used in printing ▶				

69 CROSSWORD

ACROSS

1 Bodily pain (8)
6 Defended (9)
7 Immerse momentarily (3)
8 Tusk material (5)
9 Followers (8)
12 Hacks (4)
13 Object of adoration (4)
16 Of high social rank (3-6)
18 Seasonal chocolate treat (6,3)
19 Recess in a church (4)
20 Open (4)
23 Time everlasting (8)
26 At the right moment (2,3)
27 Devilish youngster (3)
28 Appendages (9)
29 Evaluates (8)

DOWN

1 Two-legged creatures (6)
2 Arose (7,2)
3 Pre-lunch drink (8)
4 Reach the intended target (3,4)
5 Lazily, without hurry or aim (4)
10 Conceit (4-6)
11 Height of fashion! (3,3,4)
14 Use a divining rod (5)
15 Samples (5)
17 Crop destroyers (5)
21 Abandons (9)
22 Disconcert (8)
24 Converts into cipher (7)
25 Tics (6)
26 Elliptic (4)

Each of 25 letters of the alphabet should be entered into the grid once, and only once. Can you find which letter has not been used?

A	B	C	D	E	F	G	H	I	J	K	L	M
N	O	P	Q	R	S	T	U	V	W	X	Y	Z

ACROSS
4 Pavilion or summerhouse
6 Parched
7 Sudden notions

DOWN
1 Picture playing-cards
2 Grassland of South Africa
3 Wily
5 Clever one-liner

The missing letter is: _____

MINI QUICK

ACROSS
1 Construct once more (7)
5 Consume (3)
6 Instrument for unlocking (3)
7 Dull stupid fellow (3)
9 In days gone by (3)
10 Tight embrace (4,3)

DOWN
1 Long-stalked plant (7)
2 Busy buzzer! (3)
3 Ruffle the feathers of (3)
4 Throughout the hours of light (3-4)
8 Offshore waters (3)
9 Burnt residue (3)

71 CROSSWORD

ACROSS

1 Police officer's authorisation to raid premises (6,7)
9 Fixed (down) (6)
10 Causing excitement in (6,2)
11 Political protest march (4)
12 Concerning the movement of the sea (5)
13 Baby's biscuit (4)
14 Try to attract (3)
15 Period of history (3)
16 Farm outbuilding (4)
18 Married women (5)
20 Flower vessel (4)
22 Area covered in trees (8)
24 Punctual, on time (6)
25 Of machinery and equipment (13)

DOWN

2 Banishment (5)
3 In weakened health (3-4)
4 Put out of sight (3)
5 Felt dull pain (5)
6 Water movements (7)
7 Affectionate name for grandma (3)
8 Small basic wooden buildings (4)
12 Canalside walkway (7)
13 Italian meat-filled pasta dish (7)
17 Swear (4)
19 Cassette film (5)
21 Colour of old photos (5)
23 Expected (3)
24 In favour of (3)

Try your luck with this cryptic puzzle.

ACROSS

8 Hard struggle, or trade (6)
9 I yell out loud for cold dessert (3,5)
10 See location (4)
11 Meat and potato dish – a piece got cooked around start of tea (7,3)
12 Irish emblem with fake diamond? (8)
13 Prize artist's returned (6)
15 Law taking time in work of sculptor (7)
16 Graduates anon getting instrument (7)
20 Declare at cricket match (6)
23 Indeed, so awfully biased (3-5)
24 Choose a flower, we hear, for spicy sauce (10)
26 Good for gibbon to yawn (4)
27 Tory with stupid contract (8)
28 A lecturer is a handsome man (6)

DOWN

1 Do sport badly, maintaining hard tennis stroke (4,4)
2 Less than an inch makes me reticent (10)
3 Shortage during period brings power cut (8)
4 I'm up on bet? That's wrong (7)
5 Mend about two (6)
6 Cheese short, shortly (4)
7 Sword hit? That is right (6)
14 US city cleaning a lot (10)
17 US in camera, suspicious (8)
18 Provide a contortionist, given too much money (8)
19 Rock sounding more courageous (7)
21 Rialto's eccentric cloth worker (6)
22 Gift gaining thanks fast (6)
25 Yield grain, we hear (4)

73 DILEMMA

These are two straightforward crosswords but we've mixed up the clues. Your task is to decide which clue belongs to which grid.

1		**2**		**3**		**4**	**5**	**6** L
7				**8**	**9**			E
								N
10			**11**					S
12		**13**		**14**				**15**
16			**17**		**18**			
19							**20**	
21				**22**				

ACROSS

7 Written or verbal attack (7) ● Washer and dryer (4-3)

9 Angry (5) ● Flick through (the pages of a book) (5)

10 Charge duty on (3) ● Jumble up (3)

11 Baby's hat worn on the beach? (3,6) ● Resilience (9)

12 Sheep-like (5) ● Place (inside) (5)

14 Freeman of a borough (7) ● Chisel, carve (7)

16 Rich sponge cake (7) ● Horned American bison (7)

18 Money recipient (5) ● Chinese gooseberries (5)

19 Having round features (4-5) ● Smash-and-grab driver (3-6)

20 Bundle (of notes) (3) ● Overweight (3)

21 Drench (5) ● Prince of Darkness (5)

22 Ten-sided shape (7) ● In weakened health (3-4)

DOWN

  1 Going against the current (8) ● Nuclear device (4,4)
  2 Pert young girl (4) ● Soldering substance (4)
  3 Kept happy (6) ● Sculptor's piece of work (6)
  4 Mighty (6) ● Shrivel (6)
  5 TV programme with contestants (4,4) ● Dilemma (8)
  ~~6 Camera's 'eye' (4) ● Help criminally (4)~~
  8 Specialist property lawyer (11) ● Of noble birth (4-7)
 13 Criticise (3-5) ● Heinous, wicked (8)
 15 Equestrian sport (8) ● House-dweller (8)
 17 Dumbfounded (6) ● Tiny child (6)
 18 Liqueur made from wild cherries (6) ● Nit-picker (6)
 19 Hazard (4) ● Carpet-like plant (4)
 20 Nourishment (4) ● Payment for work (4)

74 CROSSWORD

ACROSS

1 Small farm (5)
4 Orchestral instruments (5)
7 Rough first version (5)
12 Taken in and absorbed (8)
13 Plan of procedure (8)
14 Night before (3)
16 Conundrum of letters (7)
17 Pressurising (7)
19 Sporting arbiter (3)
21 Breeding stable (4)
23 Spun, rotated (7)
24 Powder (4)
26 Board used to file nails (5)
28 Cutlery item (5)
29 Crusts on wounds (5)
33 Sob noisily (4)
34 Swift-running feline (7)
36 Street (4)
37 Casual garment (1-5)
39 Soak (up) (3)
41 Puts onto scales (6)
43 Solid fuel cooker (3)
44 In the open (3)
45 Private discussion (6)
48 ___ talk, encouraging words (3)
50 Show unwillingness (6)
53 Nibble persistently (4)
54 Partly enclosed walkway at the side of a house (7)
57 Shipshape (4)
58 Decorate, embellish (5)
59 Hard-working students (5)
60 Characteristic mode of expression (5)
63 Tinned meat product (4)
65 Fleshy tropical fruits (7)
67 Abounding (4)
69 Mouse-coloured (3)
70 Suggestive of guilt (7)
72 Style of checked cloth (7)
74 Work steadily (3)
76 Totally disorientated (3,2,3)
77 Unprejudiced outlook (4,4)
78 Stow (5)
79 From the Orient (5)
80 Religious verse (5)

DOWN

2 Rule over a country (5)
3 Having developed plumage (7)
5 Foretell (4)
6 Besides, otherwise (4)
8 Discounted (7)
9 Criminal (5)
10 Water narrows (7)
11 Burial cloths (7)
15 Deviate suddenly (4)
16 Commercials, in short (3)
18 Fetched (3)
19 Undulate (6)
20 Leave a city via an airport (3,3)
22 Falls clumsily (7)
25 Holy day (7)
27 Jewish religious leader (5)
30 Breed of dog (5)
31 Noticeably better than (1,3,5)
32 Court case held to satisfy the public (4,5)
35 Self-confidence (3)
38 Egg-laying fowl (3)
39 Area diagram (3)
40 Fizzy drink (3)
42 Large antelope (3)
46 Admitted to making a mistake (5,2)
47 Less (5)
49 Geological period (3)
51 Given a money penalty (5)
52 Block up (4,3)
55 Move a tape back to the beginning (6)
56 Opinion (6)
61 Between (7)
62 Aims high (7)
63 Despondent (3)
64 Handbooks (7)
66 Seabird (4)
67 Systems of government (7)
68 Dutch ___ disease, tree ailment (3)
71 Assign (5)
73 Invalidate (5)
74 Cooking utensils (4)
75 System of relaxing exercise (4)

ACROSS

- **1** Coppers (7)
- **7** Put forward (5)
- **8** Large, non-flying bird (3)
- **9** Vivacity (4)
- **10** Wound with a knife (4)
- **12** In the ___, outdoors (5,3)
- **14** Censures (9)
- **15** Quartet (8)
- **18** Roughly shaped currant bun (4,4)
- **21** Tool for firing tacks? (6,3)
- **23** Regulated (8)
- **25** Swear (4)
- **26** Encouragement, especially for a horse (4)
- **28** Set age (3)
- **29** Beleaguering of a town (5)
- **30** Most near (7)

DOWN

- **2** Action not being filmed (3,6)
- **3** Public drinking places (4)
- **4** Current in your body that could kill (8,5)
- **5** Card player's unreadable visage (5-4)
- **6** Illumination devices (5)
- **11** Purer (6)
- **13** Boon (5)
- **16** Finally, just this last time (4,3,3,3)
- **17** Besom (5)
- **19** Military induction (4-2)
- **20** Austere (9)
- **22** Be printed (2,2,5)
- **24** Prepares (the way) (5)
- **27** Questions (4)

All clues marked with just an asterisk have thematically linked solutions.

ACROSS

1 Ends abruptly (6,3)
6 Person who imitates another
10 Goes back to a previous state
11 * (3)
12 Full of holes
13 * (5)
14 Conversing about business at a social event (7,4)
16 Milk bottle carriers
18 * (7)
22 From the UK's continent
23 Kitchen sandglass (3-5)
26 South American small monkey
28 Regardless
31 Actor's response to applause (7,4)
35 Capital of Western Australia
36 * (5)
37 * (3)
38 Plans
39 Fool with money
40 * (9)

DOWN

1 Just
2 Immature eels
3 Accessory for securing your hair (5,4)
4 Beginning
5 Remote and impersonal
6 Queen's favourite dog
7 Of the open sea
8 * (5)
9 Plaything
15 Story in verses
17 * (5)
18 * (5)
19 Drew near
20 Glasgow football team
21 * (4)
24 * (9)
25 Penang's country
27 Chicken intended for the oven
29 Peninsula by the Black Sea
30 Pure
32 Crucifixes
33 Alfred ___, Swedish inventor of dynamite
34 Defeated party
36 Three or four?

ACROSS

1 Only a handful (3)
8 Inability to do anything (12)
9 Regret (3)
11 Native American religious pole (5)
12 Decorative strips (7)
14 Mexico's currency unit (4)
15 ___ with, steeped in (6)
18 Sweet liquid (6)
20 Trickle or leak slowly out (4)
23 Faded celebrity (3-4)
25 Political assistants (5)
27 ___ trip, self-gratifying experience (3)
28 Act of giving someone a new position or function (12)
29 Express verbally (3)

DOWN

1 Ability to predict consequences (9)
2 Stimulate (the appetite) (4)
3 Cover in garments (6)
4 Gripping device (5)
5 Russian rulers (5)
6 Socially pretentious person (4)
7 Accompany (6)
10 Science of the celestial bodies (9)
13 Charged atomic particle (3)
16 Hits (6)
17 Female rabbit or deer (3)
19 Gentle whirlpools (6)
21 Broadcasting live (2,3)
22 Gains by work (5)
24 Sunrise direction (4)
26 Solidifies (4)

1

ACROSS
2 Money affairs
5 Overnight protest (5-2)
6 Published issue

DOWN
1 Of the nobility
3 Watchful
4 Earring for non-pierced ears (4-2)

2

ACROSS
1 Pie case
4 Springy, pliant
5 Be next to
7 Saucy view

DOWN
1 Chapel bench
2 Long and slender
3 Admonition
6 No score

3

ACROSS
3 Highly seasoned
5 Meet head-on
6 Expertise

DOWN
1 Vitality
2 Wild West bandits
4 Practitioner of nakedness

79 CROSSWORD

ACROSS

1 Fancy bumping into you! (4,4,2,3)
10 Building where beer is made (7)
11 Combats (7)
12 Eye-witnesses (10)
14 Before now (4)
16 Vipers (8)
18 Metric measures (5)
21 Troops of mounted soldiers (9)
22 Yield (to authority) (5)
23 Three-dimensional objects (6)
25 Alternative plan that may be used in an emergency (8)
28 Owing money (8)
29 Mexican garment worn as a cloak (6)
31 Pertaining to the organ of smell (5)
33 Residence on the river? (9)
35 Cautions against danger (5)
36 Voices great interest (8)
40 Darts player's starting point (4)
41 Obstreperous toddler (5-5)
44 Draw level (5,2)
45 Captures again (7)
46 Elevator operator (4,9)

DOWN

2 Very fat (5)
3 Large amount (5,4)
4 Wall-climbing plant (3)
5 Blunders (6)
6 Unseat (4)
7 Slackening gradually (6,3)
8 Ill-treatments (6)
9 Cinders (5)
13 Choice delicacy or item (6)
15 Very hot curry (8)
17 Maligned (7)
19 Commonplace (5)
20 Suddenly started (5,3)
21 Sofa pillows (8)
24 Tinkering (8)
26 Weights used to hold ships steady (7)
27 Very strong alcohol (5)
30 Little brook (6)
32 Popular Italian food (9)
34 Put on display (9)
37 Most reliable (6)
38 Skulk (5)
39 Writing-fluid vessel (6)
42 Voucher (5)
43 Make informal conversation (4)
45 Cereal crop used in the UK to feed cattle (3)

80 CROSSWORD

ACROSS

6 Avid readers (9)
7 Expending (5)
8 Travel down the piste (3)
9 Hills (4)
10 Emend (4)
12 Rings out (8)
15 Sceptical (8)
17 Becoming old or doing well (7,2)
18 Sends up (8)
20 Wild and uncontrolled (8)
23 Shoemakers' tools (4)
24 Move swiftly and smoothly (4)
27 Hump, haul (3)
28 Former (5)
29 Exposing (7,2)

DOWN

1 Kidnappers (9)
2 More sanctimonious (6)
3 Branchlets (5)
4 Was in charge (8)
5 Casual tops (1-6)
11 Hut on a farm (11)
13 Terser (7)
14 Scottish tribe (4)
16 Fantastic notion (7)
17 Spaces (4)
19 Tart sweets (4,5)
21 System of belief in higher
   powers (8)
22 Wild (7)
25 Remains close (6)
26 Month of All Fools' Day (5)

The answer to each of these clues begins with a different letter of the alphabet. The clues are not numbered, so you must work out where each answer fits in the grid.

A Arc of the horizon (7)
B Indian ball, often of onions (5)
C Range of voice (9)
D Final judgement (4)
E ___ Paige, musical actress (6)
F Fit insect? (4)
G Inedible pieces of meat (7)
H Hiker's kitbag (9)
I Say again (7)
J Pulls sharply (5)
K Rap (on a door) (5)
L Grazing land (3)
M Singer married to Guy Ritchie (7)

N Communications grid (7)
O Capsize (8)
P Derogatory term for a Catholic (6)
Q Degree or level of excellence (7)
R Football match official (7)
S Person using snow runners (5)
T As well (3)
U Inconsistently (8)
V Cleaned a car, perhaps (7)
W To what place? (5)
X Rare inert gas (5)
Y ___ log, Christmas dessert (4)
Z Sector (4)

82 CROSSWORD

ACROSS

1 Sheep's neck joint (5)
4 Socialist (4,4)
9 Retreated (6,3)
10 Explosives buried in the ground (5)
11 ___ pig, rodent (6)
13 Spur to creativity (7)
16 Be victorious (3)
17 Flower often seen in hanging baskets (7)
19 Male baptismal charge (6)
22 Lucky talisman (5)
24 Boldly displays (9)
26 Accent, stress (8)
27 Outdoor fund-raising functions (5)

DOWN

1 Fitful cries (4)
2 Add up (votes) again (7)
3 Acquire facts in small amounts (5)
4 Tony Blair's youngest son (3)
5 Dithering (7)
6 Ineffectual people (5)
7 Woman under religious vows (3)
8 The ___, cricket title contested by England and Australia (5)
12 Rouses from slumber (7)
14 Smooth over (4,3)
15 Hot and tasty (5)
18 Mythological maiden (5)
20 White ___, star at the end of its existence (5)
21 Queries (4)
23 Human limb (3)
25 Public transporter (3)

All solutions can be found hidden in the clues, written either backwards or forwards. Words such as 'back' or 'up' may suggest the answer is hidden backwards.

ACROSS

5 It's in the records, not in any other place (4)

6 Partially overturn canoe near waterfall – it's a gas! (4)

7 When back in Wilhelmshaven I ram bustling dockside with U-boat (9)

8 We sing it in church back in London, my home town (4)

10 It's lifted in a gust like a skirt worn by a man! (4)

12 Made up in columns and rows, sorcerer composes this devilish puzzle! (9)

15 Tumble back into a music hall after a few drinks (4)

16 During the trial I establish that they are not true statements (4)

DOWN

1 Sheriff's man is hiding in the stockade – put your hands up! (6)

2 Get this hairdo in a proper modern salon (4)

3 It may be worn in the cold by an Inuit man, or a keen trainspotter! (6)

4 Ripped up in a mean, rotten way (4)

9 Only some of the finest leathers make somewhere to settle comfortably (6)

11 Some policemen collar Derek in the food store (6)

13 It's an adventure, although it's partly true (4)

14 Erected in the Tate's main hall, a weird construction of bricks! (4)

ACROSS

1 Swerves (5)
4 Equal footing (3)
6 Aquatic avian (5-4)
7 Take unawares (8)
9 Guiding instance (9)
10 Swell (4)
12 Sweet juicy fruit available in many varieties (4)
14 Candied plant-stalk (8)
17 Manicure tool (4-4)
19 Opening to the mouth (4)
21 Misprint (4)
23 Person clicking heel and toe (3,6)
25 Extends (8)
27 Holding as a prisoner (9)
28 Diffuse substance (3)
29 Annoying (5)

DOWN

1 Solemn promises (4)
2 Show eagerness (7)
3 Moral doubts (8)
4 Advantage, right (9)
5 Special 24 hours (3-6,3)
8 Shoe gaiters (5)
11 Mushrooms, eg (5)
13 Gripes (5)
15 Carved decoration (5)
16 Not complimentary (12)
18 Petits ___, small fancy cakes (5)
20 Occupies (9)
22 Flat wire pin to hold curls in place (8)
24 Ministers of religion (7)
26 Repulsive in appearance (4)

Each of the 26 letters of the alphabet should be entered into the grid once, and only once.

| A | B | C | D | E | F | G | H | I | J | K | L | M |
| N | O | P | Q | R | S | T | U | V | W | X | Y | Z |

ACROSS
2 Modern watch crystal (6)
5 Groups of birds (6)
7 1950s dance style (4)

DOWN
1 Unbuttered (toast) (3)
3 Improvement, increase (7)
4 Rigid container (3)
6 Sewn edge (3)

MINI QUICK

ACROSS
3 For very little expense (7)
6 Football official (3)
7 Black liquid mineral (3)
8 Imagined object of terror (7)

DOWN
1 Sacred Egyptian beetle (6)
2 Self-assurance (6)
4 Likeness of a figure (6)
5 Cowardly colour (6)

86 CROSSWORD

ACROSS

1 Pimples (5)
4 Was distinctive (5,3)
11 Basically (2,7)
12 One of Jamie Oliver's catchphrases (5)
13 Assessment (4)
14 Skin irritations (6)
16 Section of a curve (3)
18 Newspaper inserts (3)
19 Underground channels for waste (6)
22 ___ Flanders, 1996 film (4)
24 Part of a machine that has a circular motion (5)
26 Consume (a drink) rapidly (5,4)
27 Belittling (8)
28 Slightly wrong (5)

DOWN

2 Hands over money in advance (7)
3 Elephant's tooth (4)
5 Projections on a zip (5)
6 Speak up against (6)
7 British deciduous tree (3)
8 Hypnotic (state) (6-4)
9 Having a stiff rough coat (of a dog) (4-6)
10 Fuse (4)
15 Snooker implement (3)
16 Waterproof jackets (7)
17 Into sin (6)
20 Arouse (5)
21 Uproar (4)
23 Take away the cream (4)
25 Nervous mannerism (3)

Have double the fun with this puzzle: you've got to fill in the answers and the black squares! We've given you the bare bones to start and it will help you to know that the black squares in the finished grid form a symmetrical pattern, so that every black square has at least one other corresponding black square.

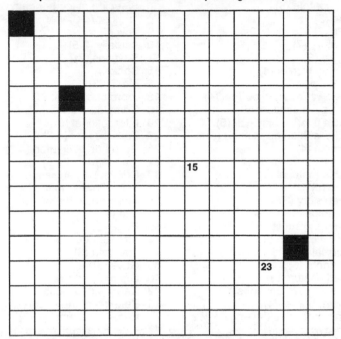

ACROSS

1 Aggressive boisterous behaviour by groups of young men
9 Enticing quality
10 Went beyond
12 Urge on
14 Attach
15 Stream
19 Sticks out
20 Supplies
22 Getting round
24 Uninvited guest

DOWN

2 Give support to
3 Worn out by age
4 Travelled by boat
5 Christmas
6 Safe place for lambs
7 Wedding attendant
8 Seize without authority
11 Self-service restaurant
13 Stops from happening
16 Force out
17 Person controlling a car
18 Custom, practice
21 Offspring of a donkey and a horse
23 Rage

88 CROSSWORD

ACROSS

1 Kills (a fly) (5)
4 Viscous drops (5)
7 Maltreatment (5)
12 Deemed (8)
13 Felt contrite (8)
14 Lout (3)
16 Eats (7)
17 Burglary (7)
19 Ciggie (3)
21 Kitchen worker (4)
23 Quavered (7)
24 Bestows a knighthood on (4)
26 Disruptive conduct (5)
28 Sticks used to play golf (5)
29 Strike with an open hand (5)
33 Remain (4)
34 Ice-cream flavouring (7)
36 Edible material (4)
37 Style (6)
39 Kitten's cry (3)
41 Worships (6)
43 Colouring substance (3)
44 Long slimy fish (3)
45 Informal name for a British banknote (6)
48 Head gesture (3)
50 Gatekeepers' cottages (6)
53 Adjoin, border (4)
54 Band that cools the engine of a car (3,4)
57 Organs of the stomach (4)
58 Appeals to a god (5)
59 Artistry (5)
60 Feel like, want (5)
63 Bulb-like underground stem (4)
65 Connected (7)
67 Mineral deposit found in hard rock (4)
69 Affectedly shy (3)
70 Turning (milk) (7)
72 Large animals hunted for sport (3,4)
74 Mineral aggregate (3)
76 Abnormal tendency to suspect and mistrust others (8)
77 Shining (8)
78 Rude (5)
79 Opted for (5)
80 Stage whisper (5)

DOWN

2 At which place? (5)
3 Leave the ground (4,3)
5 Refined woman (4)
6 Jagged hook (4)
8 Sleeping place beneath or above another (4-3)
9 Vow (5)
10 Actually (2,5)
11 Sustains (7)
15 Spoken (4)
16 Medic (3)
18 Word of consent (3)
19 Complete (a form) (4,2)
20 International (6)
22 Early supper (4,3)
25 Evade an obligation (4,3)
27 Man-made silk (5)
30 Criminal organisation (5)
31 Money owing to the bank (9)
32 Small body that orbits a larger one (9)
35 Rage (3)
38 Affectionate name for grandma (3)
39 Guys (3)
40 Get married (3)
42 Carry with difficulty (3)
46 Banning of the export of goods to certain countries (7)
47 Ingenious, well designed (5)
49 Spherical body (3)
51 Rigid point of view (5)
52 Lured, tempted (7)
55 Native of Scandinavia (6)
56 Representative figure (6)
61 Leave stranded (7)
62 Respects (7)
63 Long-leaved lettuce (3)
64 Human beings (7)
66 Grim (4)
67 Peas, beans etc (7)
68 Hook and ___, clothing fastener (3)
71 Now broadcasting (2,3)
73 Dug from the ground (5)
74 Solemn appeal to a god as witness of a truth (4)
75 Oval items with hard shells (4)

CROSSWORD

ACROSS

5 Scorn (8)

7 Romance (3)

8 Pertaining to the sun (5)

9 Compelling, effective (8)

11 Line behind which darts players stand (4)

12 Tangle (4)

14 Rabbit-like wild animals (5)

15 Charged particle (3)

16 Twines (7)

20 Day before a festival (3)

21 Sews together as a temporary measure (5)

23 Feel sore all over (4)

24 Second-class mark (4)

26 Monument commemorating war victims (8)

28 Slip-up (5)

29 Snooze (3)

30 Puffed up (8)

DOWN

1 Black look (5)

2 Either (3,2,5)

3 Unwell while travelling on a ship (7)

4 Fascinating (12)

6 Apprehending (9)

10 Scottish lakes (5)

13 Gives support (7)

17 Toy to soothe a baby (8,4)

18 Corrupts morally (9)

19 Movie award (5)

22 Miser (10)

25 Take by surprise (7)

27 Black card (5)

Try your luck with this cryptic puzzle.

ACROSS

9 Non-stop flight? (9)
10 Foreign friend I am sorry to leave (5)
11 Appearing to view Chinese porcelain (7)
12 Gadgets dig madly into stew? On the contrary (7)
13 Diana's angry outburst results in a whitewash (9)
16 Speak publicly about zero tax (5)
17 Crude description of a hooligan all keyed up? (5,3,5)
20 Attack in the television studio (5)
21 Betrayal from evil cheater by the railway (9)
24 An account running between two banks? (7)
25 Fell in an acrobatic way (7)
27 Scope needed for large movement of stock (5)
28 Where the canny soccer player should always be? (2,3,4)

DOWN

1 Poetically skilful? (6)
2 Came out top (4)
3 Fish I found in a certain spot (6)
4 Animal entering most aggressively (4)
5 Sketch game often seen crossing the moat (10)
6 Worker several find good-looking (8)
7 Team burden not astride a horse (4-6)
8 Huge mythical beast (7)
14 Lace acquired on a limited budget (10)
15 Factory turned into a cultivated area of land (10)
18 Understood it's been harvested (8)
19 Business worry (7)
22 The bend of the road? (6)
23 Sings at the top of the scale? (6)
25 A better facility, of course (4)
26 Boy holding nothing but a burden (4)

91 CROSSWORD

ACROSS

1 Plump-faced angel (6)
5 Takes fright (6)
9 Up in the ___, uncertain (3)
11 Act of reaching a destination (7)
12 Plush, luxurious (7)
13 Meat-substitute bean (4)
15 Double-reeded woodwind instruments (5)
16 Thin part of a wine glass (4)
17 Delivery vehicles (4)
19 Summer dish of cold, raw vegetables (5)
20 Occasion of taking food (4)
24 Set of kettledrums (7)
25 Obtain by succession (7)
26 Birmingham sporting and entertainment venue (inits)(3)
27 Making enquiries (6)
28 Most accurate (6)

DOWN

2 Prince William's brother (5)
3 Large illegal party (4)
4 Rotating metal machine part (4-7)
5 Working classes (11)
6 Naming word (4)
7 Family emblem (5)
8 Apathy (9)
10 Arouse the senses of (9)
14 Small horse-like animal (3)
16 Uncle ___, USA's nickname (3)
18 Titles (5)
21 British noblemen (5)
22 Of an aeroplane, move slowly along the ground (4)
23 Old-fashioned word for 'you' (4)

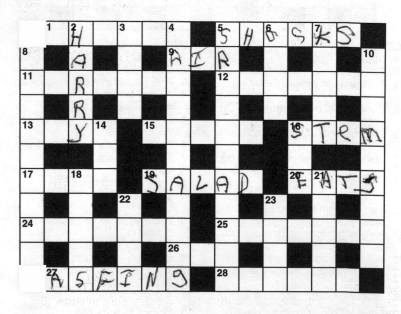

Every solution begins with one of five letters. Rearrange these letters to find a word, meaning 'to add fuel to'.

The five-letter word is: _____

ACROSS

8 Sixpence (6)
9 Written composition (8)
10 November in the order of months (8)
11 Three-legged stand (6)
12 Money held on someone's behalf (5,4)
13 Lubricated (5)
16 Mugs, fools (7)
18 One of a pair for warming the side of the head (7)
20 Nasty smell (5)
21 Laggard (9)
24 Comfort (6)
26 Joined, united (8)
27 Metric weight, around 2.2lb (8)
28 One who guards a harem (6)

DOWN

1 Blue and white clothes for a seaman (6,4)
2 Kitchen tools for cutting (6)
3 Change the shape of (9)
4 Engraving (7)
5 John ___, British poet (5)
6 Indifference to pain or pleasure (8)
7 Capital city of Norway (4)
14 Competence (10)
15 Listened in (9)
17 Marsupial such as the TV character Skippy (8)
19 Of long standing (3-4)
22 Pleasure trip (6)
23 John ___, 2004 Democratic presidential contender (5)
25 Do not include (4)

93 CROSSWORD

ACROSS

1 Nomads (6)
4 Person with long experience or standing (3-5)
9 Dread (3)
10 Cat's foot (3)
11 Casual affair (5)
12 Sailing (2,3)
13 Increases (4)
14 Gap or opening (5)
15 Con trick (4)
18 Pay out (6)
20 Being temporarily in another's possession (2,4)
23 Concession on duty owed (3,5)
24 Ornamental jars (5)
26 Chess, draughts etc (5-5)
29 18th-century dandy such as Nash or Brummell (4)
31 Loud prolonged noise (3)
33 Drunkards (4)
34 Greaseproof wrapping (5,5)
36 Detest (5)
38 Reticence (8)
40 ___ of, as a replacement for (2,4)
41 Tipster (6)
44 Hostile attack (4)
45 Become familiar (5)
46 Small car or skirt (4)
50 Stake (5)
51 Steak (1-4)
53 Drink by scooping liquid with movements of the tongue (3)
54 Great ___, extinct bird (3)
55 Ships' flags (8)
56 Contemptible (2-4)

DOWN

1 Declared null and void (8)
2 Promised (5)
3 Flat structure of logs (4)
4 Count among your possessions (3)
5 Meat joint (3,2,4)
6 Earl Grey, Darjeeling, for example (4)
7 Melody makers (9)
8 Domains (6)
9 Feature of a church (5)
16 Person unspecified (7)
17 Nail-shaped spice (5)
19 Behave in an excessively dramatic fashion (4-3)
21 Las Vegas' state (6)
22 Courtesy form of address (7)
25 Terrible, dreadful (7)
27 Associate (3)
28 Pep (6)
30 Unprotected (7)
32 Prolonged (4-3)
35 Area between the stomach and thigh (5)
37 Holding out (7,2)
38 Overthrow of a government (4,5)
39 Laid bare (8)
42 Come to a halt (4,2)
43 Ghoul (5)
47 Eskimo snow-hut (5)
48 Long song for one voice (4)
49 Prohibit (4)
52 Double-decker (3)

94 CROSSWORD

ACROSS

1 Crawling with vermin (5)
5 Be next to (4)
6 Meal outdoors (6)
7 Skein of yarn (4)
8 Highly seasoned sausage (6)
9 Letters (8)
12 Retreat from a position (5,4)
15 Long-lived tree of the beech family (3)
16 Hot contest (3-2)
17 Haughty (5)
18 Gaseous mixture comprising mostly oxygen and nitrogen (3)
19 Impregnating with perfume (9)
21 Gun-belts (8)
24 Skin indentation (6)
25 Opposed to (4)
26 Daughters of a sibling (6)
27 ___ party, pre-wedding occasion (4)
28 Wedding official (5)

DOWN

2 Japanese creative art (7)
3 Sombreros, eg (3-4)
4 Child's name for rabbits (7)
5 Accomplished (an ambition) (8)
9 Rapid cookers (10)
10 Glass vial that releases a foul smell when ruptured (5,4)
11 Supports (10)
13 Blushing (7)
14 Exclude from society, favour, and common privileges (9)
20 Referring (to) (8)
21 Large wasps (7)
22 Interferes (7)
23 Take over from (7)

The arrows show the direction in which the answer to each clue should be placed.

Persuade (5,4,3) ▼	Biblical king of Judah ▼		Defends	Wartime radio comedy series (inits) ▼	Thick piece (of bread, eg)	▼
Spiteful ►			▼	▼		
Make an enquiry	Creative skill ►				Queen's daughter	
►		Arab country ruled by a sultan ►		▼		
Sharp pain	Smelled awful! ►					
►		Ploughed land		Helicopter blades		Plant of the dock family
Page size	Land measures ► ▼			▼		▼
►					Scheming *Othello* character	
Side post of a door	Out of bed ►				▼	
►			Rowing implement ►			
Irish pirate in *Peter Pan*	Little and ___, comedy duo ►					
►			The sun personified ►			

96 CROSSWORD

ACROSS

4 Cry uncontrollably (3)
8 Disrespectful (8)
9 Telling off (6)
10 Coached beforehand (6)
11 ___ up, gathering (8)
13 Second Greek letter (4)
15 Brightly coloured and often double-headed spring flower (5)
16 Pieces of bread dipped in liquid (4)
18 Mundane (8)
20 Vagabonds (6)
22 Writing-table with drawers (6)
23 Orbs of vision (8)
24 Married woman's title (3)

DOWN

1 False (6)
2 Period of prosperity (4)
3 Look after (4)
4 Clichéd classifications (11)
5 Attractiveness (6)
6 Easily shocked people (6)
7 Scorch (4)
12 Airy matter (3)
13 Front of a boat (3)
14 Human joints (6)
15 Orchestra conductor's stand (6)
17 Scholars (6)
19 Musical composition (4)
20 Tethers (4)
21 Style of knitwear (4)

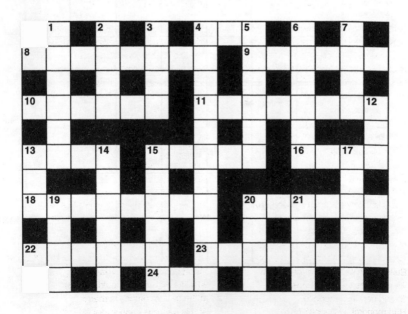

Clue A leads to a solution beginning with the letter A, clue B to one beginning with the letter B etc. Solutions should be entered, using a little logic, wherever they fit.

A In North Africa, quite surprising,
Dreadful gale, air is rising (7)

B He puts the top bits on to cars,
Working with weights on metal bars (11)

C Swindle one in court, they say,
And he'll bring magic, any day (8)

D Bird in water – or elsewhere
Might be a big one at the fair! (6)

E Half eleven: Neil messed
About, to add some spirit, zest (7)

F Suffer lanes, twisting round,
Where state of terror may be found! (11)

G There's singer Campbell, Seb as well,
Where Campbells and Macdonalds fell (7)

H In such old, archaic, inns
I shelter (so poor, for my sins) (10)

I Write me nice plot, but take care
That not every part of it is there! (10)

J To put in danger and tempt fate
I'd spare Joe, in dreadful state (10)

K Nomadic person reportedly spread,
With lemon onto toast or bread? (4)

L Buildings in which to watch a show,
As my clues bad, as I know! (7)

M Stupid person who once
Had mongrel on bonce? (10)

N Awfully sad? No way! I'm
OK at the present time! (8)

O Quiet dog caught by son, perhaps,
Then has a row, disputes and snaps (7)

P Poor English OAPs end up
With thick vegetable broth to sup (3-4)

Q Group of Status having drinks;
They're needed for the meeting, one thinks (7)

R Is it uncommon so to make
An order for this sort of steak? (4)

S Greeted military types at least,
As well as odd adults round the East (7)

T At the end it's clear,
This story one can hear (4)

U Paul, have break,
Or big disruption one can make! (8)

V East never changes, although maybe
It's just a false surface that we see (6)

W Woman ditching man has fuel That's processed,
useless as a rule (6)

X Mix 'U', an 'X', a 'D', and lo,
Its Legend topped charts for Dave Dee & Co (6)

Y Vigorous, with lots of vivacity –
Just like 14 downs should be? (8)

Z In the freezer our ice is made
At this degrees centigrade! (4)

ACROSS

1 Aiming at the intended destination (2,6)
6 Missed a chance (6,3)
7 Bother (3)
8 Tear into shreds (3,2)
9 Extra piece in a book (8)
12 Dolts (4)
13 Study intensively (4)
16 Tough challenge (4,5)
18 Secretly listen in (9)
19 Posing no difficulty (4)
20 Put out of focus (4)
23 Puts out of shape (8)
26 Congregation (5)
27 Gunge (3)
28 Realms (9)
29 Signs the back of (8)

DOWN

1 Oops! (2,4)
2 Grab (3,4,2)
3 ___ income, money from a source other than work (8)
4 Splattered (7)
5 Desist (4)
10 Car racing (5,5)
11 Give (a baby) formula milk (6-4)
14 High rubber boot (5)
15 Dignity and assurance of manner (5)
17 Exists, inhabits (5)
21 Prone to go to law (9)
22 Investigate (4,4)

24 Figures with carrot noses made in winter (7)
25 People worthy of contempt (6)
26 Transient crazes (4)

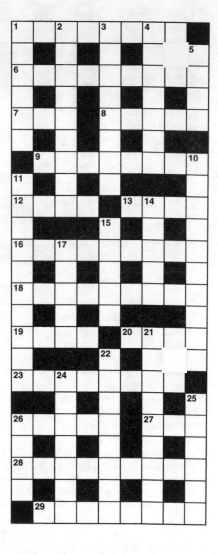

1

ACROSS
- **4** Footsloggers (7)
- **6** Bare rocky hill (3)
- **7** Mate (3)
- **8** Lend a hand (4,3)

DOWN
- **1** On edge (7)
- **2** More than one, grammatically (6)
- **3** Keep in solitary confinement (7)
- **5** Hire for a job (6)

2

ACROSS
- **1** Old (4)
- **5** Whinger (6)
- **6** Disquiet (6)
- **7** Inert gas (4)

DOWN
- **2** Reach a level of maturity (4,2)
- **3** Underground prison (7)
- **4** Very quick, in music (6)

3

ACROSS
- **3** Weight attached to a fishing line (6)
- **5** Two-pack card game (7)
- **6** Jaunty, dashing (6)

DOWN
- **1** Personal competition (7)
- **2** Barbaric (7)
- **4** Ability (5)

100 HEADS AND TAILS

In this puzzle you can ignore the meaning of the clues! Instead, simply take either the first or last letter of each word in the clue to spell out your answer. For example, the W, O and E of 'Waste Of spacE (3)' would give you WOE.

The crossword grid shows 7 ACROSS filled in with the letters: D I R T Y

ACROSS

7 Hands are not clean enough (5)
8 Luciano Pavarotti inspires Lulu? Maybe (5)
9 Wheat or maize bring on cereal allergy (7)
10 Seeing the light (3)
11 Keys, usually, can open doors (5)
13 Create mood – dim the light (5)
15 Match it totally (3)
17 Vostok, Apollo, Gemini, Mir; American, Russian spacecraft (7)
20 Remove bandage, apply antiseptic ointment (5)
21 Assist spending; lend or borrow (5)

DOWN

1 White Hart Lane – Tottenham (4)
2 Analgesics take away most acute pain (6)
3 Hopeless hecklers only boo (4)
4 Fusty old bachelor attracts girls. Strange (6)
5 Which is human being? (4)
6 Aerobics makes you feel quite fit (6)
11 Teenagers probably hate everybody; raging adolescence (6)
12 Deplore vengeance; very outdated tiresome attitude (6)
14 Most people agree; others will comply (6)
16 Tiger emerged after dark (4)
18 Flirting will annoy boyfriend (4)
19 Tonic? Only with gin (4)

ACROSS

1 Subterranean burial places (9)
6 Dirty mark (5)
10 Proclaimed (6)
11 Brings up (8)
12 Motive (5)
13 Heraldic bearing (4)
15 Repetition of sound (4)
17 Sleeveless outer garment (5)
18 Changed the colour of (4)
20 Clasped (4)
21 Consumers (5)
24 Tall garden flowers (8)
26 Imbeciles (6)
27 Swings from side to side (5)
28 Religious sceptics (9)

DOWN

2 Statistician (7)
3 American cars (5)
4 Betting term indicating inequality (4)
5 Financially supporting (11)
7 Rodent (5)
8 Monkey without a tail (3)
9 Check for concealed weapons (5)
13 Adam's ___, water (3)
14 Insane (3)
16 Religious dissenter (7)
17 Lawlessness (5)
19 Dangerous (5)
22 Flat broke (5)
23 Grain store (4)
25 Established rule (3)

102 CROSSWORD

ACROSS

9 Controlled without outside interference (4-8)
11 Ingredient of porridge (4)
12 Piece of wood (3)
13 Intertwining of rope, cord etc (4)
14 Strong string (5)
15 Later part of life (3,3)
16 Outwit (7)
18 Sensation caused by an injection (8)
20 Flowing molten rock (4)
22 Robbers (7)
24 Fuel found in Irish bogs (4)
25 Attendance check using a name register (4-4)
26 Foxes' lairs (6)
28 Large, non-flying bird (3)
30 Deep woodwind instruments (8)
32 Familiar or humorous title given to a person (8)
33 Commercial travellers (8)
35 Throughout the usual sleeping time (3-5)
36 Draws up (a list) (8)
37 Never fatigued (8)
40 Make legal claim (3)
41 Rucks in rugby football (6)
43 Nooks and crannies (8)
46 Insect found over stagnant water (4)
47 Was overcome by emotion (7)
48 Sharp little bites (4)
49 Thieving (8)
52 Presupposed (7)
55 Dark arts (6)
56 Noise of a horse (5)
59 Ears (4)
60 Expected to arrive (3)
61 Socially pretentious person (4)
62 Besides what's already been said (3,2,7)

DOWN

1 Cosy knitted hat (6)
2 Eccentric (3,3,4)
3 Otter's den (4)
4 Start (5)
5 Render in another language (9)
6 Be connected to the side of (6)
7 Stacker (6)
8 Transport held up by highwaymen (10)
10 Give your word of honour (3)
17 Erupting mountain (7)
19 Condition of being out of work (11)
21 Smell, scent (5)
23 Cut-out design (7)
24 Plant that lives longer than two years (9)
27 Private detectives (7)
29 Without wavering (11)
30 Cuts in two (7)
31 Infant's pyjamas (9)
34 Harasses (7)
38 Draws back (7)
39 Woolly animal (5)
42 Persuading (10)
44 Enjoyment of physical pleasure (10)
45 Jammy cakes (9)
50 Bread fragments (6)
51 Harmoniously (2,4)
53 Christmas drink (3-3)
54 Swimming pools (5)
57 Sticky substance derived from certain trees (3)
58 Take notice (4)

This puzzle has no clues in the conventional sense. Instead, every different number printed in the main grid represents a different letter (with the same number always representing the same letter, of course). For example, if 7 turns out to be a 'V', you can write in V wherever a square contains 7. We have completed a very small part of the puzzle to give you a start, but the rest is up to you.

2	15	13	17	10		18	9	19	8	12	13	20
12		19		19		19		7		10		23
13	19	24	18	10	12	3		4	17	10	15	12
19		18		10				22				12
13	9	19	26	26	12	26		17	9	24	12	2
20		26				23		20		22		26
	19	15	20	26	18	19 (O)	14	12	25	10	6	
26		9		17		9 (R)				22		12
20	9	12	25	2		2 (D)	12	7	17	20	12	26
9				2				15		17		26
17	10	1	17	12		7	19	25	17	25	11	17
5		25		26		15		13		20		6
12	16	15	17	20	12	26		21	17	26	18	26

A B C Ø E F G H I J K L M N Ø P Q Ø S T U V W X Y Z

1	2 (D)	3	4	5	6	7	8	9 (R)	10	11	12	13
14	15	16	17	18	19 (O)	20	21	22	23	24	25	26

Each of 25 letters of the alphabet should be entered into the grid once, and only once. Can you find which letter has not been used?

| A | B | C | D | E | F | G | H | I | J | K | L | M |
| N | O | P | Q | R | S | T | U | V | W | X | Y | Z |

ACROSS
1 Sauté (3)
3 Pledging (8)
6 Bets on (a horse) (5)

DOWN
1 Electrical cord (4)
2 Questions contest (4)
4 Electrical resistance units (4)
5 Chewing structure (3)

The missing letter is: _____

MINI QUICK

ACROSS
1 Dummy pill (7)
4 Reading desk (7)
6 Small sea fish (7)
9 Humiliated (7)

DOWN
1 Buddy (3)
2 Small bed (3)
3 Nobleman (5)
5 Fundamental character (5)
7 Infusion (3)
8 Supreme being, creator of the universe (3)

105 *CROSSWORD*

ACROSS

6 People settling an area taken over by their home country (9)

7 ___ grease, vigorous polishing and cleaning (5)

8 Image of yourself (3)

9 Voices (4)

10 First garden (4)

12 Lightens (a cargo) (8)

15 Person inflicting extreme pain (8)

17 Suspending (7,2)

18 Excess of hype or power (8)

20 Limit (8)

23 Presidential adviser (4)

24 List of computer commands (4)

27 Laid up (3)

28 Regular pounding (5)

29 Person who does unpaid housework and cooking (9)

DOWN

1 Coming to office (9)

2 Volubly (6)

3 Understands (5)

4 Rose (8)

5 Amaze (7)

11 Brown-nosing (11)

13 Move impatiently (7)

14 School work done outside lessons (4)

16 Crown, sceptre and other symbols of royalty (7)

17 ___ and eye, fastener (4)

19 (Painting) with colour-coding (2,7)

21 Ex-sweetheart (3,5)

22 Social outcasts (7)

25 Archimedes' cry of discovery (6)

26 Mystify (5)

The answer to each of these clues begins with a different letter of the alphabet. The clues are not numbered, so you must work out where each answer fits in the grid.

A Make worse, annoy (9)
B Sharp and cold (of wind) (6)
C Seats (6)
D Sediment (5)
E Lips (5)
F Small dangerous weapons (11)
G Vivid (7)
H 'Laughing' animal (5)
I Tasteless (7)
J Lively (5)
K Door opener (3)
L Making the most noise (7)
M American elk (5)

N Unfeeling (4)
O Plant which grows from an acorn (3,4)
P Chinese starter (11)
Q Tremble (6)
R Stately (5)
S Rhythmic dance (5)
T Hypothesis or conjecture (6)
U Manipulate (3)
V Female fox (5)
W Thin biscuit (5)
X Percussion instrument (9)
Y Rise and fall repeatedly (2-2)
Z Nothing (5)

ACROSS

1 Wet particles (9)
6 Large crustacean (4)
10 Flapped (at) (7)
11 Licitly (7)
13 Nullify (4)
14 What's life like for you? (4,6)
16 Dilate (6)
18 Entry places (6)
21 Indirect (8)
22 Snoops (5)
24 Go ___, end up wrong (4-6)
26 Devotional image (4)
29 Sunbeams (4)
30 Car's strap (6,4)
32 TV recording device (5)
34 Blended well (6,2)
36 Feature, facet (6)
37 Swells out (6)
40 Called together again (10)
41 Too (4)
44 Italian dish (7)
45 Gorge yourself (7)
46 Average (4)
47 Stirring (9)

DOWN

2 Bestow (5)
3 Eggs of a louse (4)
4 Cowboy contests (6)
5 Buffing up (9)
7 Moves elsewhere (9)
8 Still like a lad (6)
9 Undertakes (7)
12 Sluicing the mouth (8)
15 Loose (a dog) (7)
17 Greater importance (7)
19 Piece of music written for a solo instrument (6)
20 Remove from contact with the public (7)
23 Ratify (7)
25 Occurrences (6)
27 Supposing (7)
28 Artificially stimulated (5,2)
31 Suddenly receive as an inheritance (4,4)
33 Sheet to protect furniture while decorating (4,5)
34 Being a male parent (9)
35 Guards (7)
38 Practice session (3,3)
39 Display (3,3)
42 Prolonged stay in bed in the morning (3-2)
43 Become liquid because of heat (4)

108 *PIECEWORD*

With the help of the Across clues only, can you fit the 35 pieces into their correct positions in the empty grid below (which, when completed, will exhibit a symmetrical pattern)?

ACROSS

1 Container for flannel, toothbrush etc • Invented
2 Large, non-flying bird
3 Blow your top • Handed
4 Gentle knock • Pair
5 Cuddled

6 Small mistake • Warm and comfortable
7 Fashion, fad • Talk big
8 Person who eats
9 Chance • Belonging to you and me

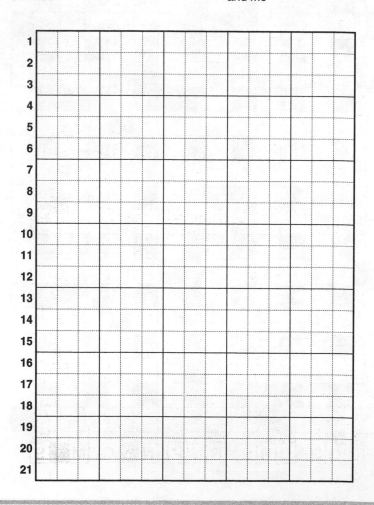

PIECEWORD

10 Clothes already worn by someone else (hyphenated)
11 Item you would wear for a slalom • Volcanic residue
12 Contemplating your own existence (hyphenated)
13 Blokes • Howl
14 Comprehensive (hyphenated)

15 Watch chains • Snoozes
16 Shoe rising over the ankle • Derelict ship
17 Rises
18 Black gold • Variety of lettuce
19 Expression • Smut
20 Regret
21 Takes back • Spanish combatant in an arena

ACROSS

4 Musical beat (5)
9 Hounds (7)
10 Sojourned (5)
11 Give voice to (3)
12 Frozen over (3)
13 Mutt, mongrel (3)
14 Smooching (7)
15 Involving lots of physical work (6-9)
19 Rouse suddenly (7)
20 Weeding tool (3)
21 Tavern (3)
22 Reverential wonder (3)
23 Pretend (5)
24 Takes short swaying steps (7)
25 Vapours (5)

DOWN

1 Towards higher ground (6)
2 Medical photograph (1-3)
3 Breaking up (text) grammatically (11)
4 Russian emperor's title (4)
5 Shopping area with stalls (6)
6 Various items (4,3,4)
7 Summertime star sign (6)
8 ___ party, all-male do (4)
16 Nut variety (6)
17 Principles (6)
18 Make a raised design (6)
19 Filter (4)
20 Sculpts (4)
21 Buddies (4)

1

ACROSS
1 Large (3)
3 Knight's title (3)
5 Waltzing (7)
6 Wounded (7)
9 Choke (3)
10 Method (3)

DOWN
1 Sheets, blankets etc (7)
2 Revolver, for instance (3)
3 Move on snow (3)
4 Stiffly, inflexibly (7)
7 Spouted milk container (3)
8 Din (3)

2

ACROSS
1 Having unusual tastes (5)
5 Knoll (7)
6 Colour of the heavens (3-4)
8 Talk foolishly (5)

DOWN
2 Laid up (3)
3 Create or cause (a fuss) (4,2)
4 Basket material (6)
7 On the contrary (3)

3

ACROSS
3 All-in-one pyjamas for infants (7)
6 Pleased, satisfied (7)
7 Cash put by (4,3)

DOWN
1 Run away (7)
2 Mail carriage fee (7)
4 Treats for the dog (5)
5 Water-bird (5)

ACROSS

1 Tidal part of a river (7)
7 Vacuous (5)
8 Not much ___, mediocre (3)
9 Behindhand (4)
10 Boast (4)
12 In a courteous manner (8)
14 House-painter (9)
15 Strict party line (8)
18 Large habitable area of the Earth's surface (4-4)
21 Bloodshed (9)
23 Fanatically devoted (8)
25 Injure by rough handling or clawing (4)
26 ___ there, done that, motto of the jaded (4)
28 Have food (3)
29 Puts into a cage (5)
30 Ornamented (7)

DOWN

2 Wiseacre (5,4)
3 Drug-dependent person (4)
4 Connections and dealings within a multi-ethnic society (4,9)
5 Multi-legged bug (9)
6 Offspring (5)
11 Hi-fidelity sound system (6)
13 Flat carrying-boards (5)
16 Wrapped up, finished (4,3,6)
17 Offhand (5)
19 Black-and-white bird (6)
20 Coarse behaviour (9)
22 Profoundly (2,3,4)
24 Implant (5)
27 Permanent wound-mark on the skin (4)

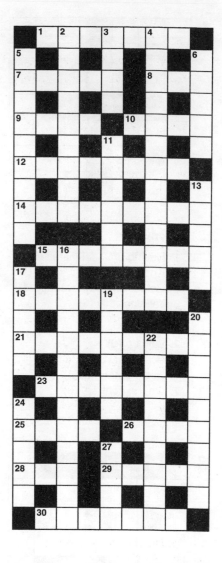

Every solution begins with one of five letters. Rearrange these letters to find someone in front of a train.

The five-letter word is: _____

ACROSS

8 Affectionate term (10)
9 Lightly cooked (4)
10 Greek island in the Ionian Sea (6)
11 Basic principle (8)
12 ___ Blyton, Noddy's creator (4)
14 Person employed to watch children (10)
16 Obsolete short musket with a flared muzzle (11)
20 Demoted (10)
22 Dull (4)
23 Lattice for training fruit trees (8)
25 Spain/Portugal peninsula (6)
27 Dramatic part (4)
28 Londoners' soap opera (10)

DOWN

1 Split second (7)
2 Letter following alpha (4)
3 Kitchen loaf container (5,3)
4 Ale (4)
5 Short musical pieces (6)
6 Made into a play (10)
7 Boozy (7)
13 Portrays precisely (10)
15 Lose vital fluid (5)
17 Duvet covers, sheets etc (8)
18 Russian ballet company (7)
19 Fencing swords (7)
21 Bombarding enemy plane (6)
24 Harsh grating sound (4)
26 Water swirl (4)

113 *CROSSWORD*

ACROSS

1 Groups looking for missing people (6,7)
9 Threw out (6)
10 In the ___, being processed (8)
11 Short note (4)
12 Holy ___, thing earnestly pursued (5)
13 Touches lightly (4)
14 Lowing sound (3)
15 Lamb's mother (3)
16 Naps (4)
18 Raised (5)
20 Recess in a church (4)
22 Opposite (8)
24 ___ out, removed from a group, or set aside (6)
25 With unaided vision (2,3,5,3)

DOWN

2 Privileged clique (5)
3 Kidnappers' demands (7)
4 Owned (3)
5 Letter before bravo and charlie (5)
6 Overbalanced (7)
7 Long fish with a smooth scaleless skin (3)
8 Ignore (4)
12 Hungarian stew (7)
13 Cul-de-sac (4,3)
17 Metal liable to rust (4)
19 Credit to your bank account (3,2)
21 Run-down (5)
23 Pair of (3)
24 Stir-fry pan (3)

Have double the fun with this puzzle: you've got to fill in the answers and the black squares! We've given you the bare bones to start and it will help you to know that the black squares in the finished grid form a symmetrical pattern, so that every black square has at least one other corresponding black square.

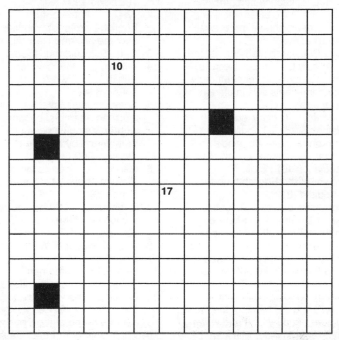

ACROSS

1 Holding more goods than is necessary
9 Egg producer
10 Very small dog
11 Circulated as an unverified story
12 Gusted
14 Derogatory 16th-century term for Catholic doctrine
16 Trough
18 Famous female singer
19 Almond-flavoured biscuit
22 Burns without a flame
23 Neither solid nor liquid
24 Aerial sport

DOWN

2 Poison
3 Legal right to demand payment
4 Followed
5 Seizure of power
6 Breathed out
7 Person who cares for feet
8 Capricious wilful behaviour
13 Became ill again
15 Dessert named after a ballerina
17 Edith ___, WWI heroine
20 Keyboard instrument with pipes
21 Jumping biting insect

115 *BEST OF BRITISH*

All that's great about Britain.

ACROSS

1. Playwright and poet considered England's greatest dramatist (11)
9. ___ House, Gloucestershire, seat of the Duke of Beaufort and location of an annual three-day equestrian event (9)
10. Native British tribe led against the Romans by Queen Boudicca (5)
11. Tim ___, tennis player seemingly in the semi-finals at Wimbledon most years (6)
12. National ___ Gallery, building in Trafalgar Square, London (8)
13. Common name of England's national sport, a corruption of 'association' (6)
15. Follower of the English founder of Methodism (8)
18. Oxfordshire palace built for the Duke of Marlborough after he won the 1704 battle of the same name (8)
19. JMW ___, English painter who left the nation nearly 40,000 works when he died in 1851 (6)
21. Creature associated in song with 8 down, and the name of the car and boat used by land and water speed record holder Malcolm Campbell (8)
23. Word that famous London road intersections Oxford and Piccadilly have in common (6)
26. Island in the Firth of Clyde famous for whisky (5)
27. Mystic sword of King Arthur, which he received from the Lady of the Lake (9)
29. English patron famous for slaying a dragon (5,6)

DOWN

1. In short, Mr Coe, who was world 800-metres champion between 1981 and 1997 (3)
2. WH ___, 20th-century English-born poet who later became an American citizen (5)
3. Queen of England, 1558-1603 (9)
4. William ___ the Younger, British Tory PM 1783-1801 and 1804-06 (4)
5. British tennis player who, after fourteen attempts, became women's singles champion at Wimbledon by beating Billie-Jean King in 1969 (3,5)
6. George ___, pen-name of eminent Victorian novelist Mary Ann Evans (5)
7. Benjamin ___, 20th-century British composer of the operas *Peter Grimes* and *Billy Budd* (7)
8. Popular singer of WWII, the 'forces' sweetheart' (4,4)
11. Letters before the name of a British naval vessel (inits)(3)
14. Buckinghamshire house, given to the nation in 1917 as the official country home of the British PM (8)
16. English author of the classic recollection of childhood *Cider with Rosie* (6,3)
17. Benjamin ___, British Conservative politician and novelist, PM in 1868 and 1874-80 (8)
18. Charles ___, 19th-century English mathematician who devised the precursor to the computer (7)
20. Initials of the organisation that organises the annual Chelsea Flower Show (inits)(3)
22. Gordon ___, England goalkeeper for the 1966 World Cup (5)
24. Pole tossed at traditional Highland Games.... (5)
25. ...by one north of the border (4)
28. Historic former port of East Sussex, one of the Cinque Ports (3)

ACROSS

1 Glass rainbow maker (5)
4 Young seal (3)
6 Financial help (9)
7 Decontaminates (8)
9 Dial showing a car's amount of petrol (4,5)
10 Place for drying hops (4)
12 Existed (4)
14 Blows up (8)
17 Ordains (8)
19 Meeting of lips (4)
21 Russian king (4)
23 Walking stealthily (9)
25 Objects that keep a row of paperbacks upright (4-4)
27 Works together (9)
28 Idol (3)
29 Nest creatures (5)

DOWN

1 ___ up, adds vigour to (4)
2 Trespass (7)
3 Places where boats are tied up (8)
4 Truism (9)
5 Bulletin to newspapers (5,7)
8 In progress (5)
11 Cock-crow (3-2)
13 Arrive by plane (3,2)
15 Hauls (5)
16 Criticising while feigning friendship (4-8)
18 Boasts (5)
20 Braced (9)
22 Self-made beer (4,4)
24 Encourages (7)
26 Employs (4)

All solutions can be found hidden in the clues, written either backwards or forwards. Words such as 'back' or 'up' may suggest the answer is hidden backwards.

ACROSS

5 Take one in the tub at home (4)
6 A greeting back in Australia: 'Hi, cobber!' (4)
7 With a bit of wood to rest each arm on, I call for this instrument (9)
8 It's turned in a very tight manner around the wheel (4)
10 For part of the year no one will get money for work (4)
12 In a move to stop arson, a general meeting is held at the priest's house (9)
15 Rough steep rock that rises up in an amazing arch (4)
16 How ordinary-looking sentences may conceal one in this puzzle! (4)

DOWN

1 Back in the pet shop, Harry ran a competition for best songbird (6)
2 Former singing duo who appeared in the show – Hammersmith Palais? (4)
3 Alteration causes some protest and much anger (6)
4 Thin circular object in the stand is compact, perhaps (4)
9 Up in the rigging is Nelson's flag (6)
11 Look at some of the people who are gardeners (6)
13 Area of land is put up in order to make a larger cattle farm (4)
14 Rising in popularity is, we note, current affairs programme (4)

ACROSS

1 Make a note of (3)
8 Lack of a fixed abode (12)
9 Maritime (3)
11 Person who accepts a bet or challenge (5)
12 Stern (7)
14 Procures (4)
15 Overrun, swarm over (6)
18 Foxes' lairs (6)
20 Dwindles (4)
23 Predator hawk (7)
25 Pang of conscience (5)
27 Wrath (3)
28 Short beige cotton coat (6,6)
29 Tiny amount (3)

DOWN

1 Ideal, perfect (4,5)
2 Take ___, 1990s re-formed pop group (4)
3 Fumigates (6)
4 Information carried on a book cover (5)
5 Prose piece (5)
6 Common insects (4)
7 Upward climb (6)
10 Counterpane (9)
13 Put into service (3)
16 Layout, structure (6)
17 Golfing peg (3)
19 Baked ___, pudding with ice cream and meringue (6)
21 Centre of thought in the body (5)
22 Whole team (5)
24 Mosque leader (4)
26 Hand cover (4)

Each of the 26 letters of the alphabet should be entered into the grid once, and only once.

A	B	C	D	E	F	G	H	I	J	K	L	M
N	O	P	Q	R	S	T	U	V	W	X	Y	Z

ACROSS
3 Satisfy (a thirst) (6)
4 Kill (by sci-fi laser) (3)
6 Be luminous (4)
7 Awkward situation (3)
8 Satellite television channel (3)

DOWN
1 React in surprise (4)
2 Pounds, pulsates (6)
5 Fervent (4)

MINI QUICK

ACROSS
1 Funny TV show based on everyday life (6)
5 Frequent (5)
6 Join forces (5)
7 Sign on (6)

DOWN
2 Done on company premises (2-5)
3 Critical (7)
4 Parents (7)

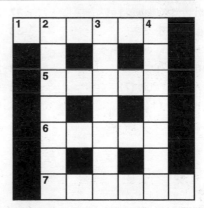

120 *CROSSWORD*

ACROSS

1 Be restless (4,5,4)
10 Advertised as being available (2,5)
11 Lowers (7)
12 Mild dairy product similar to fromage frais (4,6)
14 Muslim chieftain (4)
16 Hires (8)
18 Lay into (3,2)
21 Obliging, yielding (9)
22 Start, beginning (5)
23 Neither male nor female (6)
25 Restocked (6,2)
28 Outline (8)
29 Pressure (6)
31 More mature (5)
33 Person who is blamed for the faults of others (9)
35 Bridges (5)
36 Assumed (8)
40 Frozen confections (4)
41 Rich and satisfying in flavour (4-6)
44 Close-fitting one-piece garment (7)
45 Cover with dots (7)
46 Hoity-toity (4,3,6)

DOWN

2 Love (5)
3 Serviceable (9)
4 Jack ___, sailor (3)
5 Religious nonconformity (6)
6 Whims (4)
7 Surround (9)
8 American name for association football (6)
9 Employers (5)
13 Accessories (6)
15 Illuminated by artificial light (8)
17 Estimate (7)
19 Prim and proper (5)
20 Hurry up! (4,2,2)
21 Map's height lines (8)
24 Surrounding area (8)
26 Members of the clergy (7)
27 Robbery (5)
30 Instruction book (6)
32 Spicy beef and pork sausage (9)
34 Engaging (staff) (9)
37 Shirked (6)
38 Testaments (5)
39 Impulsive (6)
42 Data entry (5)
43 Hit (4)
45 Maths problem (3)

121 CROSSWORD

ACROSS

5 Overhead single-track train (8)
7 Fled (3)
8 Ball game played with the gloved hand (5)
9 Wizard (8)
11 Zero in tennis (4)
12 Bluish-white metallic element (4)
14 ___ up, make room for another person by moving along (5)
15 Solidified water (3)
16 Gathers in a crowd (7)
20 Tiresome chore (3)
21 Ribbons (5)
23 Gentle (4)
24 Aristocrat (4)
26 Sleeping quarters (8)
28 Abdominal pain (5)
29 Excessively (3)
30 Overnight sojourn (8)

DOWN

1 Neat (5)
2 Showing a lack of emotional commitment (10)
3 Monitor (7)
4 Bright spot in an otherwise gloomy situation (6,6)
6 Flightless birds (9)
10 Divulges secrets (5)
13 Uprisings (7)
17 Sound reproduction with little distortion (4,8)
18 Easy profit (1,4,4)

19 Supplant, take (possession) by force (5)
22 Designed to forestall (3-7)
25 Reinforced shoe tips (7)
27 Escalates (5)

ARROWORD 122

The arrows show the direction in which the answer to each clue should be placed.

US state, capital Lincoln ▼	British government of India ▼		Animal fat used for cooking	Jane Austen novel	Poor quality wine	▼
Obliterate ►			▼	▼	Ernie __, Phil Silvers character	
Cook with oil	__ jet, Boeing 747 ►				▼	
►		Tracey __, conceptual artist ►				
Timber tree of the olive family	Harass (a celebrity, eg) ►					
►		German dictator	Chris __, 1970s tennis star	Failed, of a supply (3,3)		Called for
Mouth secretion	High-nesting wader ►	▼	▼	▼		▼
►					Singer of Smooth Operator	
Coerce into action	Firm's yearly conference (inits)	Nervy, on edge ►			▼	
►	▼					
__ Sharif, actor		Musical exercise ►				
►			__ Heath, 1970s PM ►			

123 CODECRACKER

This puzzle has no clues in the conventional sense. Instead, every different number printed in the main grid represents a different letter (with the same number always representing the same letter, of course). For example, if 7 turns out to be a 'V', you can write in V wherever a square contains 7. We have completed a very small part of the puzzle to give you a start, but the rest is up to you.

14		16		4		18		16		20		20
4	6	13	9	14	18	5		14	8	7	11	14
6		13		18		14		22		14		20
7	22	1	7	8		12	7	8	15	23	8	2
8		16		7			23					17
	9	17	11	1	22	7	4	4	11	7	4	4
9		11				14				11		5
17	11	1	7	18	13	8	13	23	4	22	2	
1				8				11		14		20
16	7	22	26	14	8	7		12	23	8	19	7
								P	U	R		
7		14		21		14		22		19		8
7	3	17	22	7		4	25	23	7	7	24	2
10		1		11		6		19		8		22

A B C D E F G H I J K L M N O P̶ Q R̶ S T Ʊ̶ V W X Y Z

1	2	3	4	5	6	7	8 R	9	10	11	12 P	13
14	15	16	17	18	19	20	21	22	23 U	24	25	26

Try your luck with this cryptic puzzle.

ACROSS

8 Part of shoe creating lesion (6)
9 Desire a penny with little in France (8)
10 Military vehicle full of fish? (4)
11 This applies pressure to obtain suite (10)
12 Brad Pitt perhaps seen in centre, cooking broth (5-5)
14 Enthusiastic about drunk? Not I! (4)
15 Club concealing the broken knife (7)
17 Caustic joke offered by fellow (7)
20 Hired vehicle with levy on one (4)
22 Consider on purpose (10)
24 Young person gains social security payment during rise (10)
26 Attempt to get fired (4)
27 Cease working with kit for runner (3-5)
28 Hear when silent, surprisingly (6)

DOWN

1 Privately, American distraught (2,6)
2 Type of chair Mod disliked? (6)
3 Control said to be put in position again (10)
4 Festival northern? No! (7)
5 Knocks up box (4)
6 Keeping beds upset monarch (8)
7 Avenue for cryptic setter (6)
13 Insect seen down vessel (10)
16 Bald? Henry close! (8)
18 Element mixing neon with grit (8)
19 Railway car, one across the tracks? (7)
21 Person hooked? Did, perhaps, indeed! (6)
23 Hold out when sister in trouble (6)
25 Criticise sporting achievement (4)

125 *CROSSWORD*

ACROSS

1 Legal, lawful (5)
4 Desires (8)
9 Second in command (6,3)
10 Chess pieces of lowest rank (5)
11 Slake, satisfy (6)
13 Hostility (3-4)
16 Hole of a needle (3)
17 Cold infusion (4,3)
19 Sparkly dress decoration (6)
22 Muslims' holy city (5)
24 Strive (9)
26 Offered marriage (8)
27 Dubious (5)

DOWN

1 Loop of a chain (4)
2 Travel regularly (7)
3 Co-ordinate (3,2)
4 Large hole in the ground (3)
5 Anecdotes (7)
6 Urge on (5)
7 At the present time (3)
8 Devotional hymn (5)
12 People who cure (7)
14 Shackled (2,5)
15 Movies (5)
18 Vagabond (5)
20 Drink deeply (5)
21 Unravel (4)
23 Vehicle (3)
25 Carried out (an action) (3)

Unscramble the anagrams before entering the answers. It may be possible to make more than one word from the letters. Make sure you enter the right one!

ACROSS
1 HATE SNAP (8)
6 STIFLE (6)
9 CAN LET (6)
10 RAISED TO (8)
11 SCARE HER (8)
12 REPAIR (6)
13 BE REGARDING (11)
16 HITS TARGETS (11)
20 DORSET (6)
22 THY LAGER (8)
24 AGONISED (8)
25 CRONES (6)
26 COURSE (6)
27 SENORITA (8)

DOWN
2 A THREE (6)
3 ST MICHAEL (9)
4 CROAT (5)
5 CHEATER (7)
6 ENTER TRIP (9)
7 PARTS (5)
8 TOILER (6)
14 ORGANISED (9)
15 A BANISTER (9)
17 ALL GONE (7)
18 IN MOOD (6)
19 REGION (6)
21 REG IT (5)
23 IT CAT (5)

Clue A leads to a solution beginning with the letter A, clue B to one beginning with the letter B etc. Solutions should be entered, using a little logic, wherever they fit.

A Queen from 1702 was she,
So partly began new century (4)

B Rewrite zany bit, mostly new,
For Empire (not theatre name – a clue!) (9)

C Section of long tale in verse –
When rewritten no act is worse (5)

D Some idea needed for names
Like singer Martin or actor James (4)

E Showy effect, the French do say,
In the clattering, banging way! (5)

F Idiot Ollie who starred with Stan
Was rash, incautious, had no plan (9)

G Actor Robson looked narrowly
At one thus racked by jealousy (5-4)

H To hospital the answer to A returns,
For this reddish dye she yearns (5)

I Cruise nan arranged included cost
Of this cover, should ship be lost! (9

J Kath Jones, upset, might turn
To poet of a Grecian Urn (4,5)

K Meat and veg in pitta bread?
Maybe bake bun initially, instead (5)

L Rule women right maybe, and they
May use it on the grass each day! (9)

M It's said that many a tale is told
Of structure that parked cars does hold! (5-6)

N Tennis-court missing vital bit?
Nine players needed to deliver it! (5)

O Looking for white gemstone, you'll
Find in shop a lovely jewel (4)

P Place on tee, and knock the ball
Towards the hole, and hope it'll fall! (4)

Q Dreadfully wet, Dick quit, although
His mind was anything but slow! (5-6)

R Lion's sound returns round top of zoo –
To cut it, maybe this will do? (5)

S Maybe wander with Liszt to learn
Of country that is ruled from Bern (11)

T Could be like bitumen of a kind,
But hang about and stay behind (5)

U Here is where the milk arrived –
It was from the cud derived! (5)

V In this recording medium I trade –
I've a depot specially made (9)

W I am bereaved, like late Queen Mum;
During tomorrow I dowager become (5)

X Cross with Winstone and Charles, eg –
These photos reveal more than one may see! (1-4)

Y Twenty-four hours before you fix
Affirmative answer to 'Eat dry mix?' (9)

Z Fuss lets Zen develop anew,
With enthusiasm and gusto too (11)

ACROSS

1 Circles (5)
5 Tribulations (4)
6 Mark (6)
7 Rattles (4)
8 Divulge (6)
9 Organisation supplying cut-price literature (4,4)
12 Sally (9)
15 Chalice (3)
16 The same (5)
17 Thrusting weapon (5)
18 Nothing (3)
19 Killers (9)
21 Inspector (8)
24 Start a round of golf (3,3)
25 Ankle-length coat (4)
26 Irritate (6)
27 Toad-like creature (4)
28 Abrasive (5)

DOWN

2 At an undetermined stage (2,5)
3 Returned (3,4)
4 Office employment (4,3)
5 Pares down (8)
9 Storage place for ale (4,6)
10 People in residence (9)
11 Certain to fail (2,2,1,5)
13 Colours up (7)
14 Goal (9)
20 Anticipating (8)
21 Finger-shaped cakes (7)
22 Lack of movement (7)
23 Wraps up (7)

129 CROSSWORD

ACROSS
1 Small rodent (5)
4 Foolish person (5)
7 Not easily bent (5)
12 Maintained (8)
13 Hanging jewellery items (8)
14 Take as food (3)
16 Become caught on something (7)
17 Contents (of a sandwich) (7)
19 Passing through (3)
21 In wonderment (4)
23 Provoked (7)
24 Pooches (4)
26 Person acting on behalf of another (5)
28 Dirty mark (5)
29 Notices (5)
33 ___ up, dress attractively (4)
34 No tickets left! (4,3)
36 Catnaps (4)
37 Breathing disorder (6)
39 Tiny (3)
41 Portrays (6)
43 Leguminous vegetable (3)
44 Woman's underwear item (3)
45 Ring-throwing fairground game (4-2)
48 Small brush stroke (3)
50 Gloomy (6)
53 Cut roughly (4)
54 Authorise (7)
57 Low murmur of pain (4)
58 Take as your own (5)
59 Centre of thought in the body (5)
60 Tracks (5)
63 Publicity (4)
65 Boasted (7)
67 Skirting along a wall (4)
69 ___ and cry, public uproar (3)
70 Large wooden containers (7)
72 Outdoor blaze (7)
74 For what purpose? (3)
76 Treat which includes scones and jam (5,3)
77 In custody (2,6)
78 Came out of slumber (5)
79 Halts (5)
80 Venomous snake (5)

DOWN
2 Atlantic, for example (5)
3 Attacked ferociously (7)
5 Move through water (4)
6 Engrossed (4)
8 Fished with a drag-net (7)
9 Gel with the rest of a group (3,2)
10 Climbing, mounting (7)
11 Slowly relaxes (7)
15 Enthusiastic (4)
16 Expanse of water (3)
18 Domestic fuel (3)
19 Chaste, pure (6)
20 Rabbit with pink eyes (6)
22 Shakes (7)
25 Deteriorate through neglect (2,2,3)
27 Beautiful maiden (5)
30 One of Jamie Oliver's catchphrases (5)
31 Light-hearted capers (9)
32 Party decorations (9)
35 Reach the end of life (3)
38 Furthermore (3)
39 Bundle (3)
40 Wane, recede (3)
42 Pigeon's call (3)
46 School's occasion for visitors (4,3)
47 Photograph of a celebrity (3-2)
49 Hassle (3)
51 Latin-American dance (5)
52 Stowed (7)
55 Social outcast (6)
56 Complain peevishly (6)
61 Know-how (7)
62 Break off, suspend (7)
63 Cooker top (3)
64 Note for future reference (7)
66 Cascade (4)
67 Damaged the reputation of (7)
68 Be in debt (3)
71 Pointed missile (5)
73 Light wash (5)
74 Wish for (4)
75 March heavily laden (4)

CROSSWORD

|157

130 *CROSSWORD*

ACROSS

1 Accessory (3-2)
4 Award for very high record sales (4,4)
11 Place of refuge (4,5)
12 Roman home (5)
13 Ovine females (4)
14 Locked (6)
16 Infant (3)
18 Rest your legs (3)
19 Small (6)
22 Hindu spiritual leader (4)
24 Slang for 'head' (5)
26 No longer broadcasting (3,3,3)
27 Called across the mountains (8)
28 Store away (5)

DOWN

2 Ricochet (7)
3 Standing spot in darts (4)
5 Public (5)
6 Share out (6)
7 Under the weather (3)
8 Seaside watchman (10)
9 Apparently (10)
10 Concerning cars (4)
15 Enter into a record book (3)
16 Tropical birds with coloured beaks (7)
17 Also (2,4)
20 Hole ___, golfer's dream (2,3)
21 In a ___, annoyed (4)
23 Lead pellets (4)
25 Move your head in agreement (3)

Every solution begins with one of five letters. Rearrange these letters to find a work of art.

The five-letter word is: _____

ACROSS

9 Extreme greed (7)
10 Disquiet (7)
11 Stamp or photograph book (5)
12 Books custodian (9)
13 Cheating spouse (9)
16 Butcher's protective front (5)
17 Chaotic devastation (6)
18 Unusual occurrence (6)
22 Make a remark (5)
24 Emphasise again (9)
25 Highest ranking spirit in heaven (9)
27 Person in power (5)
29 Lasting many years (7)
30 Futile (7)

DOWN

1 Hand-held percussion instruments (7)
2 Meat from a young sheep (4)
3 Unsuitable pairing (8)
4 Factual (4)
5 Arboreal producer of latex (6,4)
6 Turkey's capital city (6)
7 Appointee to decide between two parties (10)
8 Significance (7)
14 Without connections (10)
15 Borrow more from a building society (10)
19 Person keen on institutional change (8)
20 Fugitive (7)
21 Old name for Hansen's disease (7)
23 Power of thought (6)
26 Ruffian (4)
28 Vegetable and Welsh emblem (4)

132 *CROSSWORD*

ACROSS

1 Keeps company (with) (8)
6 Strictly according to rules (2,3,4)
7 Spike of corn (3)
8 Captured and removed (5)
9 Of the weather (8)
12 Cameo gemstone (4)
13 Extreme pleasure (4)
16 Con man (9)
18 Up a gum tree (2,3,4)
19 In Scotland, a church (4)
20 Momentous (4)
23 People who accept things as they are (8)
26 Speed-setter (5)
27 Boating steersman (3)
28 Parts of a whole (9)
29 Moulds a raised design on wood (8)

DOWN

1 Wire ropes (6)
2 In a lifelike manner (9)
3 Extra work (8)
4 Set of implements (4,3)
5 Surface layer (4)
10 Choose the best from a selection (6-4)
11 Obsequious person (10)
14 Abandon inhibition (3,2)
15 Lofts (5)
17 Entomb (5)
21 Communicate (an idea) (3,6)

22 Book containing the words of an opera (8)
24 Praise (7)
25 Has being (6)
26 Breathe heavily (4)

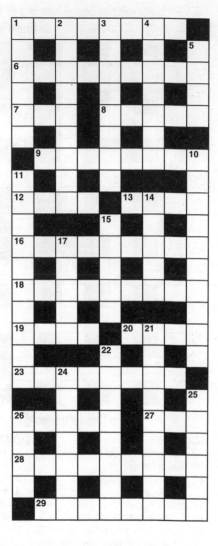

In this puzzle you can ignore the meaning of the clues! Instead, simply take either the first or last letter of each word in the clue to spell out your answer. For example, the W, O and E of 'Waste Of spacE (3)' would give you WOE.

ACROSS

- **7** Ballerina wears frilly tutu. Lovely (5)
- **8** Acid indigestion; feeling quite ill (5)
- **9** Funding will assist teachers to improve results (7)
- **10** Roman pizza parlour (3)
- **11** Cover your eyes – shocking sight (5)
- **13** Nothing equals our valiant navy (5)
- **15** Cutting the mustard (3)
- **17** Mongolian plateau is desert and named Gobi (7)
- **20** Antique dealer assesses sale value (5)
- **21** Walkers reach Lake Windermere late (5)

DOWN

- **1** Wrath, anger, vengeful fury (4)
- **2** The stuff of any child's nightmare (6)
- **3** Brian Sewell – outrageous toff (4)
- **4** Throw away your remaining cigarette – now! (6)
- **5** Aimlessly wandering around Manchester (4)
- **6** Kids, like older people, sleep soundly (6)
- **11** Cassius Clay gave Parkinson endless trouble (6)
- **12** Collect alms money; help the poor (6)
- **14** Peter Ebdon always plays excellent snooker (6)
- **16** Meet the awkward squad (4)
- **18** Summer temperature below normal (4)
- **19** Fling, affair, immoral liaison (4)

134 CROSSWORD

ACROSS

1 Adversaries (6)
4 Assured (8)
9 Shelter (3)
10 Theatre area for the orchestra (3)
11 Animals, collectively (5)
12 Mawkish (5)
13 Eye covers (4)
14 Strips the skin from (5)
15 Having similar characteristics (4)
18 Trimming (6)
20 Garden pests (6)
23 Laugh at (8)
24 Italian food (5)
26 Metal instrument similar to a recorder (3,7)
29 Makes a request (4)
31 Lavatory (3)
33 System (4)
34 Initially (5,2,3)
36 Unoccupied (5)
38 Amply rewarded (8)
40 Detaches (6)
41 Neglected (to) (6)
44 ___ my word, goodness me! (4)
45 Hilltops (5)
46 Exploiter (4)
50 Hardwood tree (5)
51 Put on (5)
53 Ailing (3)
54 Catch in a mesh (3)
55 Tip for service (8)
56 Slow-moving garden pests (6)

DOWN

1 Fought off (8)
2 Took part in a ballot (5)
3 Roof space (4)
4 Pig's enclosure (3)
5 Prepared in advance (5-4)
6 Large cups (4)
7 Barriers of upright posts (9)
8 Respected people (6)
9 Periods of respite (5)
16 Deep understanding (7)
17 Parliamentary ushers (5)
19 Showed amusement (7)
21 Healthy breakfast dish (6)
22 Lasses (7)
25 With an obstacle blocking progress (7)
27 Hill (3)
28 Casualties (6)
30 Murdering (7)
32 Container popularly associated with a wayside orator! (7)
35 Wheel rings (5)
37 Occurrences (9)
38 Sharp-eyed (9)
39 Alarms (8)
42 Boiled sweet (6)
43 Very fast bird? (5)
47 Futuristic genre (3-2)
48 Old second person singular pronoun (4)
49 Bullocks (4)
52 Affected, whimsical (3)

135 _CROSSWORD_

ACROSS

1 Military drama with Tamzin Outhwaite (3,3)
5 Plump game bird (6)
9 Grass similar to wheat (3)
11 Able to be read (7)
12 Funnel-shaped hurricane (7)
13 Edge of a square (4)
15 Dress in (3,2)
16 Alluring, elegant (4)
17 Dip (a biscuit) (4)
19 Watches secretly (5)
20 Spoken exam (4)
24 Operatives (7)
25 Lasted (4,3)
26 Nightfall (3)
27 Expression of surprise (2,4)
28 Garbage (6)

DOWN

2 ___ on, incited (5)
3 Small strong horses (4)
4 Taken as read (11)
5 Social occasion (3-8)
6 Boat-steering blades (4)
7 Will (5)
8 Cease trading (5,4)
10 Devise (9)
14 Largest of all living deer (3)
16 Gunk (3)
18 Bad-tempered (5)
21 Crow-like birds (5)
22 Right to reject a bill (4)
23 Musical notation symbol (4)

Each of 25 letters of the alphabet should be entered into the grid once, and only once. Can you find which letter has not been used?

| A | B | C | D | E | F | G | H | I | J | K | L | M |
| N | O | P | Q | R | S | T | U | V | W | X | Y | Z |

ACROSS
- **5** Maple tree with winged fruits (8)
- **6** Vitality (4)

DOWN
- **1** For what purpose? (3)
- **2** Plant from which linseed is obtained (4)
- **3** Position in paid employment (3)
- **4** Maintained (4)
- **5** Ink-squirting sea creature (5)

The missing letter is: _____

MINI QUICK

ACROSS
- **1** Choice steak (1-4)
- **5** Fan-shaped edible shellfish (7)
- **6** Sly (7)
- **8** Digging implement (5)

DOWN
- **2** Give support to (4,2)
- **3** No goals (3)
- **4** Having antlers (6)
- **7** Pinch (3)

137 CROSSWORD

ACROSS

1 Put aside for a rainy day (5,2)
7 Important school tests (5)
8 Painful or evil (3)
9 Pieces of timber (4)
10 Obtain by deception (4)
12 Tarnish (8)
14 Returns earth to the hole it was dug from (9)
15 Unwavering, perennial (8)
18 Describes in detail (8)
21 Interrupting (7,2)
23 Fundamentally (2,6)
25 Hoist (4)
26 Short tail (4)
28 Feathery scarf (3)
29 Moved by the wind (5)
30 Person who does not believe in God (7)

DOWN

2 Pain reliever (9)
3 Orient (4)
4 Unborn baby's lifeline (9,4)
5 Childlike sweet? (5,4)
6 Old proverb (5)
11 Twaddle (6)
13 Employment (5)
16 Expression emphasising the truth of a statement (2,5,2,4)
17 Compassion (5)
19 Agreement, harmony (6)
20 Giving life to (9)
22 Say in a way that others will understand (3,6)
24 Boors (5)
27 ___ seaman, rank of sailor (4)

Try your luck with this cryptic puzzle.

ACROSS

8 Run headlong into work (6)
9 One isn't a strange Baltic native (8)
10 Catch section returning (4)
11 Completely? Yes! (10)
12 Managed to back sneak, or one tells (8)
13 Scarcity of woven thread (6)
15 Meeting for students remains disrupted (7)
16 Still figure retains right height (7)
20 Subject to be important (6)
23 Vegetables with average cuts (8)
24 Resort to cornmeal, perhaps (5,5)
26 Land measure in Australia created (4)
27 Irresponsible, else otherwise in vehicles (8)
28 Leech is a fool (6)

DOWN

1 Match – spoil one during storm (8)
2 Riddle perfect for flavouring (10)
3 Macerate half-baked scones etc (5,3)
4 Pudding with hair brought up (7)
5 Emotionless time, entering hard (6)
6 One's tied, given speed at sea? (4)
7 Tray for everyone held by favourite (6)
14 Those present at 22:00 do the foxtrot? (10)
17 One so slow educated us, we hear (8)
18 Newspaperman on subject of carrier (8)
19 Keep down work for the newspapers (7)
21 Before midday, exam is without principles (6)
22 Illegal enterprise creating clamour (6)
25 Dainty model, little (4)

139 CODECRACKER

This puzzle has no clues in the conventional sense. Instead, every different number printed in the main grid represents a different letter (with the same number always representing the same letter, of course). For example, if 7 turns out to be a 'V', you can write in V wherever a square contains 7. We have completed a very small part of the puzzle to give you a start, but the rest is up to you.

25		25		1				9		9		4
11	2	10	9	22	26	5		25	16	25	8	23
19		10		2		2		2		20		19
25	19	23	26	9		21	17	3	3	2	11	23
15		16				25		12				26
21	17	5		18	17	26	13	25	5	3	23	
23		3		25		5		9		25		10
	4	23	25	26	10	17	16	23		16	25	14
10				24		15				2		15
6	23	26	10	17	15	25		5	25	15	7	17
25		23		26		9		23		25		15
10	23	25	26	10		23	20	25	21	9	3	14
16		11		23				13		23		16

A B C D E F G H I J K L M N O P Q R S T U V W X Y Z

| 1 | 2 | 3 | 4 | 5 B | 6 | 7 | 8 | 9 | 10 | 11 | 12 | 13 |
| 14 | 15 N | 16 | 17 O | 18 | 19 | 20 | 21 | 22 | 23 | 24 | 25 | 26 |

168

All clues marked with just an asterisk have thematically linked solutions.

ACROSS

1 * (9)
6 Social class in India (5)
9 Bertie ___, Taoiseach (5)
10 Calculating (9)
11 Sticking on some point? (8)
12 Hot pepper (6)
13 Town between Birmingham and Leicester (8)
16 * (6)
18 * (6)
19 Emblems of monarchy (8)
22 Score four times? (6)
24 So on and so forth (2,6)
27 Waterway connecting the Mediterranean and the Red Sea (4,5)
28 * (5)
29 Mobile-phone company (5)
30 Browned off? (9)

DOWN

1 * (7)
2 Startling event (3-6)
3 Cancel (5)
4 Paolo ___, 1 down football player (2,5)
5 Showed up (4)
6 Medicated lozenge (5,4)
7 Talent (5)
8 * (7)
14 US female singer (9)
15 UK's largest employer (inits)(3)
17 * (9)
18 Jackie ___, US TV comedian (7)
20 * (7)
21 Stored secretly (7)
23 * (5)
25 Heather genus (5)
26 Obligation (4)

ACROSS

4 Fish whose liver yields an oil rich in vitamins A and D (3)
8 Fragrant flowering bulb (8)
9 Violently discharges (6)
10 Acquire a loan (6)
11 Little chance (3,1,4)
13 True to life (4)
15 Area of open or wooded countryside (5)
16 Passed away (4)
18 Traditional ditty (4,4)
20 Rummage (6)
22 Fine, delicately woven, cotton fabric (6)
23 Current affairs studio (8)
24 Prevent from speaking (3)

DOWN

1 From past times (6)
2 Trace of a wound (4)
3 Be informed about (4)
4 Having a gossip (11)
5 Pushed in, dimpled (6)
6 Very tired (6)
7 Prevent (4)
12 Draw to a close (3)
13 Umpire (3)
14 Prone (to) (6)
15 Paying court to (6)
17 Drink of yolk, beer and spirit (3-3)
19 Responsibility (4)
20 Bird (4)
21 Unusual (4)

Have double the fun with this puzzle: you've got to fill in the answers and the black squares! We've given you the bare bones to start and it will help you to know that the black squares in the finished grid form a symmetrical pattern, so that every black square has at least one other corresponding black square.

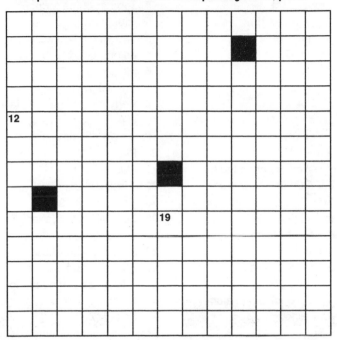

ACROSS

1 Horse soldiers
5 Floating waste matter
10 Choose
11 Riddle
12 Temporary doctor
13 Witch's curses
15 Entertain, amuse
17 Exchanges
18 Kneel before
20 Social blunder
23 Part
24 On strike
25 Cyclic rise and fall of the sea
26 Hiring

DOWN

2 Space within the top of a house
3 Amassed amount
4 Finger ornaments
6 Turned sour (of milk)
7 Silent acting
8 Shouts loudly
9 Cross-examines
14 Declares positively
16 Brushed (a horse)
19 At which place?
21 Gone by air
22 Person from Glasgow, eg

143 CROSSWORD

ACROSS

9 Be used up (of supplies) (3,3)
10 Amount charged (5)
11 Slightly wrong (4)
12 Unattractive (4)
13 Branch of a tree (5)
14 Programme (6)
15 Most chilly (7)
17 Sailor's dance (8)
19 Indecent humour (4)
21 Small chocolate cake (7)
23 Makes a sound like a dove (4)
24 Clears off (8)
25 Ballerina (6)
27 Cake ingredient added to the creamed fat and sugar (3)
29 By the ___, using dishonest means (4,4)
31 Bouts of self-centred behaviour (3,5)
32 Style of hit in tennis (8)
34 Added up to (8)
35 Charged particle in an atom (8)
36 Person working for someone else (8)
39 Retch (3)
40 Liverpudlian, familiarly (6)
42 Sets apart (8)
45 Be anxious (4)
46 Scoffed at (7)
47 Decomposes (4)
48 Trivial (8)
51 Changed (7)
54 Local council regulations (6)
55 Motorway departure points (5)
57 Painting, ballet etc (4)
58 Cut socially (4)
59 Smells (5)
60 Purifies (6)

DOWN

1 Over-enthusiastic (4-2)
2 Proof-reader (4,6)
3 Wound with a knife (4)
4 Tube or chute for pouring out liquids (5)
5 Two vowel-sounds pronounced as one syllable (9)
6 More costly (6)
7 Put behind bars (4,2)
8 Early form of record player (10)
16 Below freezing (3-4)
18 Pony-trekking, eg (5,6)
20 Place of pilgrimage for Muslims (5)
22 Terminal, last (7)
23 Voice range (9)
26 Substance left (after processing) (7)
28 Big kind man (6,5)
29 Shock absorbers (7)
30 Add up as you go along (4,5)
33 Unventilated (7)
37 Poked (7)
38 Thing that happens or takes place (5)
41 Confirming in a statement (10)
43 Flying machines (10)
44 Made uneven (9)
49 Without muscle, sagging (6)
50 Safeguard against loss (6)
52 Consuming food (6)
53 Slightly drunk (5)
56 Unwell (4)

144 CROSSWORD

ACROSS

6 Items of hall furniture (9)
7 Halley's ___, heavenly body (5)
8 Trough for bricks (3)
9 Pass the tongue
   over (something) (4)
10 Domain, sector (4)
12 Cattle rush (8)
15 Shellfish that clings (8)
17 Making a Horlicks of (7,2)
18 Of pure breeding (8)
20 Judicial reviews (8)
23 Creative studies (4)
24 Large continent (4)
27 Decompose (3)
28 Wept (5)
29 Fuel-carrying vessel (3-6)

DOWN

1 Inventory (9)
2 Pertaining to nuclear energy (6)
3 Condition (5)
4 Overdrawn (2,3,3)
5 Second-hand motor (4,3)
11 Prolonging (8,3)
13 Compiled, collected (7)
14 Fibre used in making rope (4)
16 Swans' offspring (7)
17 Charts (4)
19 People living surrounded by
   sea (9)

21 Don't mention it! (3,2,3)
22 Credit where credit is due (4,3)
25 Prowls (6)
26 Get lost! (5)

1

ACROSS
2 Restaurant where meat is sliced in front of you
5 Fierce wind
6 Horse's tuft of hair

DOWN
1 Persuade by flattery
3 Record-making material
4 Make smaller

2

ACROSS
1 Second-in-command
4 Riddle
5 Caress
7 Sponge and cream dessert

DOWN
1 Perish
2 Dog used for hunting game
3 Recreation period (4,3)
6 Organ of sight

3

ACROSS
3 Paralyse with terror
5 Feminine
6 Slander

DOWN
1 Hat with a curled brim
2 Imagine (5,2)
4 Grave crime

146 *CROSSWORD*

ACROSS

4 Implores (5)
9 Has relevance to (7)
10 Come up against (5)
11 Shelled food item (3)
12 Pledge (3)
13 As ___, in accordance with (3)
14 Flashed (7)
15 Rejuvenation (1,3,5,2,4)
19 Weaker (7)
20 Falsehood (3)
21 Slang name for a police officer (3)
22 Woodcutter's tool (3)
23 Small but starring role (5)
24 Pays in full (7)
25 Paper money (5)

DOWN

1 Petty quiz facts (6)
2 Breathe hard (4)
3 Demand, requirement (11)
4 Drug addict (4)
5 Collective term for geese (6)
6 Secondary actions (of a drug) (4,7)
7 Large prawns, fried in batter (6)
8 ___ Pitt, Hollywood heart-throb (4)
16 Puzzle, riddle (6)
17 Total and utter (6)
18 Unmask (6)
19 Front part (4)
20 Take away (4)
21 Frosty (4)

The answer to each of these clues begins with a different letter of the alphabet. The clues are not numbered, so you must work out where each answer fits in the grid.

	Clue			Clue
A	Stranded in shallow water (7)		N	Naming word (4)
B	Indian ball, often of onions (5)		O	Untypically shocking (5)
C	Hasty (7)		P	Dummy pill (7)
D	Mark with rounded spots (6)		Q	Cut into four equal parts (7)
E	Sizzling with atmosphere (8)		R	Crimson (3)
F	Full of bubbles (5)		S	Walk arrogantly (7)
G	Joy (4)		T	US state (5)
H	Hawaiian location (8)		U	Loosen (4)
I	Treat with a vaccine (9)		V	Token (7)
J	Device propelling an aircraft (3,6)		W	Affection (6)
K	Actions of a cad (7)		X	Copies (7)
L	Untruth (3)		Y	Arabian peninsula country (5)
M	Lake (4)		Z	Moves fast (5)

148 *CROSSWORD*

ACROSS

1 You must be joking! (4,3,2)
6 Cosmetic powder (4)
10 Prominent (7)
11 Fuss (7)
13 Indicates agreement (4)
14 Someone who works jointly on a TV programme, for example (2-8)
16 Remove the packaging from (6)
18 Nincompoops (6)
21 Table tennis (4-4)
22 Blowy (5)
24 Resulting from (2,6,2)
26 Aid in a crime (4)
29 Scoundrels (4)
30 Scrounger (10)
32 Make mention of (5)
34 Eloquent persuasive language (8)
36 Use sparingly (6)
37 Swivels (6)
40 Not likely to succeed (plan) (10)
41 Fierce giant (4)
44 Popular showy shrub (7)
45 Brutal, fierce (7)
46 Prescribed amount (4)
47 Attributing (9)

DOWN

2 Stared at (5)
3 Organs of sight (4)
4 Nautical measure (6)
5 Conveying (9)
7 Pleads for (9)
8 Minders (6)
9 Consuming completely (5,2)
12 Boarding-house (8)
15 Aisle, passage (7)
17 Spun fast (7)
19 Turn red (6)
20 Pearl carriers (7)
23 Vague (7)
25 Unfolded (6)
27 Auction (7)
28 Try your best (2,3,2)
31 Skilled craftsmen (8)
33 Cope with reality (4,5)
34 Counter-attacks (9)
35 Claims (7)
38 Rode the waves on a board (6)
39 Bird family to which the lapwing belongs (6)
42 Reap, gather (5)
43 Foolish mistake (4)

149 *PIECEWORD*

With the help of the Across clues only, can you fit the 35 pieces into their correct positions in the empty grid below (which, when completed, will exhibit a symmetrical pattern)?

ACROSS

1 Cardboard coaster (two words) • Concentrated (on)
2 Division of time
3 Politically correct (hyphenated) • Placed, located
4 Brandy measure

5 Engrave with acid • Mischievous children
6 Cricketers
7 The Ladies • Pub
8 Assorted, varied • River's drainage area

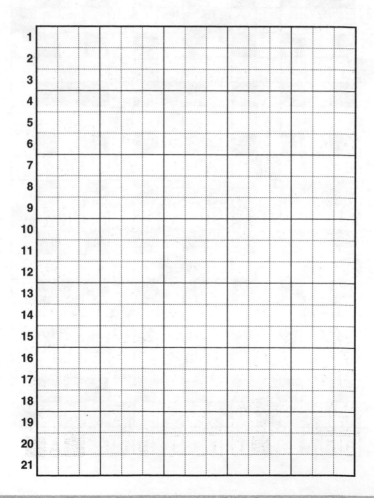

PIECEWORD

9 (We have) existed • Recent information
10 Flaunted (two words)
11 Three-piece band • Car
12 Abodes
13 Bedrock • Be worthy of
14 Applying • Astray
15 Woman secluding herself in a religious house • Clumsy boat
16 Cleaning cloths
17 Apex • Rocky outcrops
18 Domestic fuse unit
19 Circlets of flowers and foliage • Partial or total memory loss
20 Know, in Scotland
21 Lays bare, uncovers • Act of betrayal

150 CROSSWORD

ACROSS

1 Cylinders (5)
4 Commercials, in short (3)
6 Large pipe supplying taps (5,4)
7 Winter precipitation (8)
9 Hat worn by professional riders (6,3)
10 Showed up (4)
12 Put up with (4)
14 Loosen (a garment) (8)
17 Frank quality (8)
19 Classical piece (4)
21 Extravagant publicity (4)
23 Vulgar, flashy (9)
25 Delights (8)
27 Exasperated (9)
28 Little shaver (3)
29 Handsome (5)

DOWN

1 Pulls (4)
2 Concerning plants (7)
3 Sat untidily (8)
4 Hurtling mass of snow and rock descending a mountain (9)
5 Solo mum or dad (6,6)
8 Cast out (5)
11 Ground-up beef (5)
13 Five siblings born at the same time (5)
15 Bad-tempered (5)
16 Act decisively to achieve success (2,3,3,4)
18 Topical (5)
20 Of a loan, not set against an asset (9)
22 Denied (a belief) (8)
24 Areas of housing (7)
26 Tense (4)

All solutions can be found hidden in the clues, written either backwards or forwards. Words such as 'back' or 'up' may suggest the answer is hidden backwards.

ACROSS

5 Small group of performers back in the choir to entertain us (4)

6 Famous golf competition in which Nick Faldo penalty shot was seen? (4)

7 Decide to spend some of sixth-grade term in each class (9)

8 Song raised up in worship in my house of prayer (4)

10 In a canal it helps boats go back into the dock, collecting cargo (4)

12 From New England rugs to reindeer hides in American chemist's shop (9)

15 Having no job, gets back into the welding business (4)

16 Poverty contributes to a genuine education problem (4)

DOWN

1 Return of Tory peer could conceal something a bit frightening! (6)

2 Amount administered goes up in price, so don't waste it (4)

3 It's customary to be a bit malign or malicious (6)

4 In time, a noble spirit becomes stingy (4)

9 Lump of gold turns up in a gilt egg, unusual for Fabergé (6)

11 Lift up some quite practical floor covering (6)

13 Turning my steed, I rein it in and show I can do this! (4)

14 Military vehicle returns in the dark, naturally (4)

152 FOOD & DRINK

Don't make a meal of it!

ACROSS

8 Tubular pasta (8)
9 Organism, no part of which will be eaten by a vegetarian (6)
10 Yellow-skinned tropical fruit (6)
11 Frozen confection (3,5)
13 Drinks added to spirits, such as tonic or dry ginger (6)
15 Cut of 21 across from a young sheep (4,4)
16 Dutch cheese (4)
17 Toast before drinking (6)
19 ___ onion, salad ingredient (6)
21 Flesh as food (4)
22 Sandglass used as a boiling aid (3-5)
24 Boil to thicken or concentrate (a sauce, perhaps) (6)
26 Tree-fruit of which the sweet or Spanish variety is edible (8)
29 Thousand ___, tangy salad dressing (6)
31 Bread producers (6)
32 ___ Angus, breed of cattle prized for its 21 across (8)

DOWN

1 Highly seasoned Italian sausage (6)
2 Rum ___, small cake soaked in rum spirit (4)
3 Thick treacle that drains from sugar (8)
4 ___ fruit, edible green fruit of the Chinese gooseberry (4)
5 Fruit of the palm tree (4)
6 ___ acid, substance which gives lemons and limes their sourness (6)
7 Almond-flavoured biscuit (8)
12 Edible American shellfish (4)
14 Seed-bud of a potato (3)
15 Type of beer (5)
18 Measure of capacity equal to 54 gallons of beer (8)
19 Device that filters, such as a sieve or colander (8)
20 Stick for catching fish to eat (3)
21 Bill of fare (4)
23 Type of salad where the leaves have been turned in dressing (6)
25 Preserved in tins (6)
27 Slang word for 'food' (4)
28 Beast 'in the hole' in a traditional dish? (4)
30 Pink ___, cocktail (4)

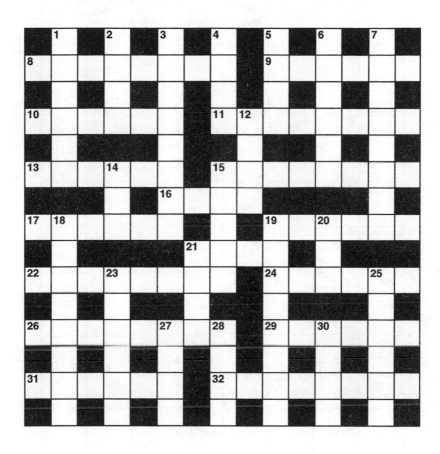

153 ARROWORD

The arrows show the direction in which the answer to each clue should be placed.

Completely identical ▸	▼	Sprang upwards	Jamie __, Klinger in M*A*S*H ▼	Eastern religion adherent ▼	Containing a hidden message ▼	Providing abundant nourishment	▼
Hand-held glittering firework ▸		Be sickly ▸				Among others (Latin) (2,2) ▼	
Weird ▸		__ Butler, Clark Gable character ▸					
			Parasitic insects	__ Gordons, Scottish dance ▸			
Billy __, US singer/ composer ▸	Off-white gemstones ▼	Airhead ▸	▼				Scottish minister's house ▼
				Ice-skating venue ▼		Sleeveless garment ▼	
Nationality of Bob Marley ▸		Girl's name, or heather					
Superpower (inits) ▸		Cracks ▸					
▸			Swiss abstract painter ▸				

186

ACROSS

5 Stairway support (8)
7 Little (3)
8 Nastier (5)
9 Torrent of abuse (8)
11 Current (4)
12 Dash, life (4)
14 Broaden (5)
15 Gardening tool (3)
16 In a doomsday scenario (2,5)
20 Seeing organ (3)
21 Chum (5)
23 Long tube (4)
24 Zenith (4)
26 Zealots (8)
28 Frequency selector (5)
29 Time past (3)
30 Carpet-securing bar (5,3)

DOWN

1 Displays or exhibitions (5)
2 Pending (10)
3 Scarves (7)
4 Statement of the privileges of a people (4,2,6)
6 Extended novels split into three distinct parts (9)
10 Gushes (5)
13 Uncertain (2,5)
17 Entangle (3,2,2,5)
18 Do a risky or dangerous act (5,4)
19 Uses an office keyboard (5)
22 Folding seaside seats (10)

25 Illuminated by twinklers (7)
27 Pleats (5)

155 CROSSWORD

ACROSS

9 Shrink back (6)
10 String instrument (5)
11 Lamented (4)
12 Interweave (4)
13 Weight unit for precious stones (5)
14 Blood fluid (6)
15 Dense (7)
17 Armed vessels (8)
19 Cross between a grapefruit and a tangerine (4)
21 Buccaneers (7)
23 Arrogance, pomposity (4)
24 Pursuing relentlessly (8)
25 Lissom, lithe (6)
27 Substance obtained from olives (3)
29 Fish, source of caviar (8)
31 Voting into office (8)
32 Continued existence (8)
34 Convincing (8)
35 Close vigilance (5,3)
36 Beat out (corn) (8)
39 Visualise (3)
40 Old writer (6)
42 Current affairs studio (8)
45 Hovered (4)
46 Compress (7)
47 Ornamental stone (4)
48 Drinking small quantities frequently (8)
51 Showed ambition (7)
54 Trapped (6)
55 Lorry (5)
57 Acquires (4)
58 Insects that can lift loads fifty times their own weight (4)
59 Daft and sentimental (5)
60 Stirs up (6)

DOWN

1 Makeshift shelter propped against a wall (4-2)
2 Easier alternative (4,6)
3 Smart ___, know-all (4)
4 Periods of bowling at cricket (5)
5 Immediately (9)
6 More moist (6)
7 Circlet of flowers (6)
8 Willingness to work with others (4,6)
16 Kept as a prisoner (7)
18 Insects with large wings (11)
20 Show malicious satisfaction (5)
22 Female siblings (7)
23 Openings (9)
26 Busy (7)
28 Coinage in current use (5,6)
29 Techniques (7)
30 Whirling (9)
33 Spectators (7)
37 Unrefined quality (7)
38 Very hard dark wood (5)
41 Warning (10)
43 Finding and getting rid of (7,3)
44 Torment (9)
49 Look through (6)
50 Moored (of a ship) (2,4)
52 Degree, range (6)
53 Landing places (5)
56 Thrill (4)

156 *CROSSWORD*

ACROSS
1 Delegated to the regions (13)
9 Liverpudlian dialect (6)
10 Tendering (8)
11 Give the game away (4)
12 Ballroom dance (5)
13 Spheres (4)
14 Toilet (3)
15 Quick bite (3)
16 Mist (4)
18 Course of a spacecraft around a planet (5)
20 Desire (4)
22 Grumpy person (8)
24 Vibration (6)
25 Simultaneously (2,3,4,4)

DOWN
2 Surpass (5)
3 Word meaning 'even-tempered' (7)
4 Part of a foot (3)
5 Cupped tree seed (5)
6 Leading (2,5)
7 Sound-sensitive organ (3)
8 Arrogant person (4)
12 Excess (3,4)
13 Ostentatiously rich (7)
17 Medicinal plant (4)
19 Military supply centres (5)
21 Darkness (5)
23 Go mouldy (3)
24 Male domestic cat (3)

Each of the 26 letters of the alphabet should be entered into the grid once, and only once.

| A | B | C | D | E | F | G | H | I | J | K | L | M |
| N | O | P | Q | R | S | T | U | V | W | X | Y | Z |

ACROSS
2 People in Jamie Oliver's profession (5)
5 Polish monetary unit (5)
6 Wet soil (3)
7 Triangular sail (3)

DOWN
1 Nark (3)
2 Sob (3)
3 Brave woman? (5)
4 Elbowing (6)

MINI QUICK

ACROSS
1 Part of a scrum (4,3)
5 Jazz band instrument (3)
6 Garbage can (3)
7 Heavy mist (3)
9 Hailed vehicle? (3)
10 Pining, yearning (7)

DOWN
1 Modest (7)
2 Boating steersman (3)
3 Chafe (3)
4 Someone who rambles on (7)
8 Spirit flavoured with juniper (3)
9 T'ai ___, martial art (3)

158 CROSSWORD

ACROSS

1 Glimpsed (5)
5 Excursion made on foot (4)
6 Brief swimsuit (6)
7 Mediocre (2-2)
8 Police officers' code word for the letter of the alphabet between India and kilo (6)
9 Got the hang of (8)
12 Rink user (3-6)
15 Abridge (3)
16 Rant (5)
17 Painful sore (5)
18 Cricketer's implement (3)
19 Tiny plants (9)
21 Complete changes of direction (8)
24 Served (soup, eg) (6)
25 Top sound reproduction (2-2)
26 Spanish fortified wine (6)
27 Score with acid (4)
28 Pulls along (5)

DOWN

2 Small flower (7)
3 Favouring a select group (7)
4 Showed briefly (7)
5 Ornamental climbing plant (8)
9 Part of a meal that comes after a starter (4,6)
10 Entertaining sight (9)
11 Tragedians (10)
13 Small falcon (7)
14 Brass instruments (9)

20 Satanic (8)
21 Give off (energy or light) (7)
22 Common stag (3,4)
23 Facial feature raised to express disapproval (7)

Try your luck with this cryptic puzzle.

ACROSS

9 Go in and upset a tin to amuse others (9)
10 Terribly vain up to a point, but innocent (5)
11 Extremist vandalised car dial (7)
12 It's no good to cut down on consumption (7)
13 Its charms vary as an annual event (9)
16 Rang round after hollow instrument (5)
17 Exaggeration of the bowling analysis? (13)
20 Bulb surprisingly lit up (5)
21 One surrounded by difficulty shows courage (9)
24 Short passage from old pamphlet (7)
25 Substitute agent demanding fine material (7)
27 Free to unfasten (5)
28 Certain to be self-assured (9)

DOWN

1 System is partly symmetrical (6)
2 Breeding-farm boss? (4)
3 Brawl over monk returning little bag (6)
4 Shout for the second boring tool (4)
5 Spanish questioner quit, or is in for review (10)
6 Waiting here where gambling takes place? (8)
7 Deviation brings CID revenge, possibly (10)
8 Vegetables social worker has for poor countryman (7)
14 Spinning round to make a drastic change (10)
15 It's boxed and flares up when struck (10)
18 Stated once again fossil fuel found in the long grass (8)
19 Pets Lee exercises round spire (7)
22 I'm leading a couple to cause damage (6)
23 Seat is prepared for a nap (6)
25 Darn foreign currency (4)
26 Jumble-sale refreshments (4)

160 *CROSSWORD*

ACROSS

1 Questions in court (5-8)
10 Withdrew (7)
11 Assaults (7)
12 Balderdash! (10)
14 Field, sphere (4)
16 Emerges (8)
18 Gave off a bad odour (5)
21 Electric cables for recharging a car battery (4,5)
22 Part of a step (5)
23 Make unwanted advances towards (6)
25 Boring (8)
28 Whenever required (2,6)
29 Queasiness (6)
31 Balanced (5)
33 Sugar snap peas (9)
35 Dote on (5)
36 Tanning lotion (3-5)
40 Belonging to you and me (4)
41 Cutting grooves in wood or stone (10)
44 Bartender's accessory (3,4)
45 Bête noire (3,4)
46 Crushed emotionally (6-7)

DOWN

2 Appraised (5)
3 Crazy person (9)
4 Terminate (3)
5 Female warrior (6)
6 Tiniest amount (4)
7 Forms a ring around (9)
8 Estimates (6)
9 Treatise (5)
13 Room for manoeuvre (6)
15 Portable shelter (8)
17 Tousled (7)
19 Old Russian rulers (5)
20 Expecting a baby (8)
21 Long-haul aircraft (5,3)
24 Embroidery practice pieces (8)
26 On a shop's shelves (2-5)
27 Dwarf-like creature (5)
30 Animals' noses (6)
32 Lingerie (9)
34 Moving staircase (9)
37 Waylaid (6)
38 Phrase always uttered by park-keepers in comics (3,2)
39 Agitated (6)
42 Annoyed (5)
43 Snooker ball colour (4)
45 Crusted dish (3)

161 *CROSSWORD*

ACROSS

1 Jockey, jostle (3)
8 Dim-witted quality (12)
9 Domestic canine (3)
11 Inhale (5)
12 Mollify (7)
14 Monetary penalty (4)
15 Propulsive force (6)
18 Looked after, cared for (a patient) (6)
20 The ___, annual fillies race at Epsom (4)
23 Enthusiasm (7)
25 Set of wives (5)
27 Skating surface (3)
28 Really, to tell the truth (2,6,4)
29 Go wrong (3)

DOWN

1 TV cassette (9)
2 Essential items to make a soufflé (4)
3 Results (of labour) (6)
4 Deceive by pretending to have a strong position (5)
5 Native of the largest continent (5)
6 Break suddenly (4)
7 School compositions (6)
10 Pay attention (4,2,3)
13 Small enclosure for animals (3)
16 Object to (6)
17 As well (3)
19 Of a book, not yet opened (6)
21 Abolish (5)
22 Snail's home (5)
24 Need to scratch (4)
26 Tiny being (4)

Have double the fun with this puzzle: you've got to fill in the answers and the black squares! We've given you the bare bones to start and it will help you to know that the black squares in the finished grid form a symmetrical pattern, so that every black square has at least one other corresponding black square.

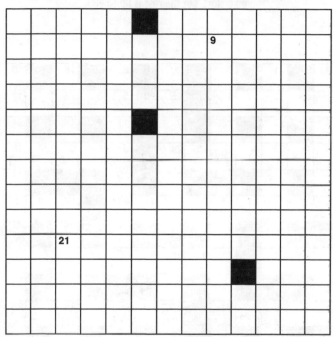

ACROSS

8 Ethically
9 Food from Heaven
10 Large passenger-ship
11 Cuddling
12 Painting (a building) with a lime-and-water mixture
16 Allocate in a new way
20 At an angle
23 Major invention in transport
24 Communicate by computer
25 Deflects

DOWN

1 Little
2 Ate noisily
3 Cauliflower sprig
4 Legendary tale
5 Pictures, visions
6 Strongly against
7 Traveller's cases
13 Struggle between nations
14 Daring
15 Compresses
17 End (a dispute)
18 Arbours
19 Pour clumsily
21 On holiday
22 Deceive

163 *CODECRACKER*

This puzzle has no clues in the conventional sense. Instead, every different number printed in the main grid represents a different letter (with the same number always representing the same letter, of course). For example, if 7 turns out to be a 'V', you can write in V wherever a square contains 7. We have completed a very small part of the puzzle to give you a start, but the rest is up to you.

20		21		8		20		2		15		10
5	23	19	18	5		25	20	5	3	18	19	17
15		17		17		2		11		1		24
3	18	20	6	17	12	24		9	5	20 A	22 P	15 T
17		5				17		20				17
25	20	24	24	17	2	24	17	24		17	12	12
		17		5				17		25		
9	15	24		24	5	18	4	26	12	9	7	15
5				19		2				24		18
24	17	22	9	20		24	13	2	20	24	3	23
17		17		16		15		12		9		9
15	12	20	22	17	14	17		1	12	18	4	5
24		8		26		26		17		5		1

A̸ B C D E F G H I J K L M N O P̸ Q R S T̸ U V W X Y Z

1	2	3	4	5	6	7	8	9	10	11	12	13
14	15 T	16	17	18	19	20 A	21	22 P	23	24	25	26

Every solution begins with one of five letters. Rearrange these letters to find a vital word.

The five-letter word is: _____

ACROSS

8 Party (6)
9 Spiritual (8)
10 Relating to lending at exorbitant rates (8)
11 Horn (6)
12 Northants town (9)
13 Set (5)
16 Tetanus (7)
18 Be subjected to (7)
20 Jane Fonda film (5)
21 Adjusted minutely (4-5)
24 Set alight (of food) (6)
26 Picky people (8)
27 Type of coffee (8)
28 Sheen (6)

DOWN

1 Cricket bat lubricant (7,3)
2 Vivacious quality (6)
3 Workers' celebration (6,3)
4 Teaching periods (7)
5 Military cloth (5)
6 Town dweller (8)
7 Portuguese resort (4)
14 Whiskers! (3-7)
15 Valued at too low a price (9)
17 Label of quality (8)
19 Person's sphere of operation or control (7)
22 Full of yourself (6)
23 Smallest amount (5)
25 Fail to win (4)

165 CROSSWORD

ACROSS

1 Preparation used to clean wool (5-3)
6 Deeply (9)
7 Viral cold (3)
8 Kept for later (5)
9 Ran out of control (8)
12 Ovine females (4)
13 Smart ___, wise guy (4)
16 Inherit the characteristics of (4,5)
18 Severe (weather) (9)
19 Flip a coin (4)
20 Bullets (4)
23 Zestful character (8)
26 Game of chance (5)
27 Afflict (3)
28 Footwear for Arctic regions (9)
29 Comes before (3-5)

DOWN

1 Breathes (6)
2 People attending an important person (9)
3 Imposed a penalty on (8)
4 Frost up (3,4)
5 Artificially coloured (4)
10 Adornment (10)
11 Brewery's finest beer? (4,6)
14 Wood-turning machine (5)
15 Stirs (5)
17 Thrills (5)
21 Fool around (4,5)

22 Supported (8)
24 Line on a map (7)
25 Glass containers (6)
26 Stuff and nonsense (4)

Clue A leads to a solution beginning with the letter A, clue B to one beginning with the letter B etc. Solutions should be entered, using a little logic, wherever they fit.

A A common sailor returns for maps, Bound up in a book, perhaps (5)

B Radiant smile, I surmise, To get someone on the Enterprise! (4)

C Is able, and did, upset tea On one running for the Presidency (9)

D Poor ad-men cry out to see Factual programme on TV (11)

E Great lake is under Eastern head, Exciting a strange fear and dread (5)

F Of course I changed and became Savage, wild, much less tame! (9)

G Such a train moves only freight; Not bad to precede head of state! (5)

H For one who writes about the past, Hot Rain is given altered cast (9)

I Instinctive perception of the mind Found in teaching of a kind? (9)

J We hear singer Michael gets teeth in To those who hoped James Stuart would win (9)

K Dan hit Derek badly – a sign He's not this friendly and benign (4-7)

L Charging Brigade of Horse For illumination, or its source (5)

M New 'routes to get into chart, As 'Longest-running play', for a start! (9)

N Deep in mine, one has Atmospheric gas (4)

O Admits, though, It's dreadful snow (4)

P Make quite sure PC word – 'Pretty and scenic' might be preferred (11)

Q Question and answer – what surfaces roads? Which Arab sheikdom has oil in loads? (5)

R Conservatives collectively Would be starboard if at sea (5)

S Less a scramble, a riot more When these events are held in store? (5)

T Royal house inspected for Department head in brand new tour (5)

U Goes up and down like waves at sea, As endlessly dull tune, maybe (9)

V View spread out in front? OK, It's spread out in V&A! (5)

W Do they throw coins in hole to show That all are healthy, they'll want to know? (4-7)

X New English phone-box for One who foreign things does abhor! (9)

Y In theory out hunting for a wife During this time of early life (5)

Z Enthusiasm one may feel Extracting it from lemon peel? (4)

The arrows show the direction in which the answer to each clue should be placed.

Running side by side	Tiny units of matter	Legitimate	▼	__ Zavaroni, 1970s singer	Dancer and pantomime actor (6,5)	Elegant	▼
▶	▼			▼	▼		
Game played with spotted tiles		Hawaiian garland	▶			Slippery fishes	
▶					▼		
Serpent that killed Cleopatra		Natives of Copenhagen	▶				
▶			Greek author of fables	Cathedral town	▶		
Apex	Is excessively sweet	Afflicts	▶ ▼				Sham
▶	▼			Horse breed		Tiny car	▼
Train service for cars		__ Hayek, Mexican actress	▶ ▼			▼	
▶							
Exploit		Sufferings	▶				
▶			French cheese				

1

ACROSS

4 Stirring (7)
6 Bed for a baby (3)
7 Chum (3)
8 Ballroom dance (3-4)

DOWN

1 Nail to a cross (7)
2 Additional levy (6)
3 Suppleness (7)
5 Buy from abroad (6)

2

ACROSS

1 Guitar run (4)
5 Nerd (6)
6 Divulge (6)
7 Stomach-churning (4)

DOWN

2 Disregard (6)
3 Animal's front limb (7)
4 Person who slides over ice (6)

3

ACROSS

3 Old-style soccer forward (6)
5 Patella (4-3)
6 Spread in many
   directions (3,3)

DOWN

1 Ennoble (7)
2 Invent, imagine (5,2)
4 Concerned about the
   environment (5)

ACROSS

1 (Drug) addicts (5)
4 Use of your own efforts (4-4)
11 Players on the same side (4-5)
12 Junior to (5)
13 Choler (4)
14 Darkened (6)
16 T'ai ___, martial art (3)
18 Take food (3)
19 Financial institution executive (6)
22 Strong foul odour (4)
24 Strangely (5)
26 Desirable hunk! (9)
27 Set to rights (8)
28 Rotten, awful (5)

DOWN

2 Young and inexperienced actress (7)
3 Batters with force (4)
5 Slackened (5)
6 Watery substances (6)
7 Finale (3)
8 Excessively fussy (10)
9 Entrance with an upper section which can be opened separately (6,4)
10 Artistically engrave (4)
15 Noah's vessel (3)
16 Printed betting forms (7)
17 Did as told (6)
20 Touch lightly with the elbow (5)
21 Woolly farm animals (4)
23 Bullets, shells etc (4)
25 Vague (3)

This puzzle has no clues in the conventional sense. Instead, every different number printed in the main grid represents a different letter (with the same number always representing the same letter, of course). For example, if 7 turns out to be a 'V', you can write in V wherever a square contains 7. We have completed a very small part of the puzzle to give you a start, but the rest is up to you.

	13		2		15		16		5		25	
26	4	3	13	15	17		25	11	16	21	14	8
	8		25		25		14		20		9	
13	15	25	22		10	12	5	4	17	17	15	11
	21				15		17		15		11	
22	5	17	22 P	21 O	17 R	3	15	8	11	24		
	3		15						11		1	
	4	17	17	15	1	5	3	25	20	11	24	
	10		18		19		14				21	
1	11	21	5	14	2	15	8		2	21	23	11
	21		17		15		5		25		15	
5	22	6	15	15	22		11	4	7	15	17	24
	15		17		3		24		15		24	

A B C D E F G H I J K L M N Ø P̶ Q R̶ S T U V W X Y Z

1	2	3	4	5	6	7	8	9	10	11	12	13
14	15	16	17 R	18	19	20	21 O	22 P	23	24	25	26

ACROSS

5 Rare phenomenon indeed (4,4)
7 Image of oneself (3)
8 'Received and understood' in radio jargon (5)
9 Ran flat out (8)
11 Muslim prayer leader (4)
12 Tie (4)
14 Final Greek letter (5)
15 Electrically charged atom (3)
16 Ropes (7)
20 Lolly (3)
21 Petits ___, small fancy cakes (5)
23 Be resentful of (4)
24 Accustomed (4)
26 Setting like blood (8)
28 Fragrant shrub (5)
29 Shed (3)
30 Came about (8)

DOWN

1 Wind instruments (5)
2 Inappropriate for the circumstances (3,2,5)
3 Involve in a quarrel (7)
4 Established (4-8)
6 Acknowledging (9)
10 Metric weights (5)
13 Schedules of charges (7)
17 Midday or midnight (6,6)
18 Chronological concept (9)
19 Words spoken directly to a theatre audience (5)
22 One whose achievements go unrecognised (6,4)
25 Pile (5,2)
27 Breeding stallions (5)

In this puzzle you can ignore the meaning of the clues! Instead, simply take either the first or last letter of each word in the clue to spell out your answer. For example, the W, O and E of 'Waste Of spacE (3)' would give you WOE.

ACROSS

7 Comb fine hair really carefully (5)
8 See lovely foliage in autumn (5)
9 Eliminated smallpox; tackling influenza now; chickenpox next (7)
10 Roman Polanski directing (3)
11 Alfred Brendel frequently plays Schumann (5)
13 Photographer Annie Liebovitz – old snapper (5)
15 Aristotle met Aesop? (3)
17 Your outside loo looks grim, old chap (7)
20 Blue cheeses smell awfully pungent (5)
21 Fashionable literati interest Melvyn Bragg (5)

DOWN

1 Ad lib – like, improvise (4)
2 Ginger beer is great; totally tangy (6)
3 Conflict – Yorkist against Lancastrian (4)
4 Grow like lime trees; ever higher (6)
5 Acrimonious tiff after affair (4)
6 Older men attract girls like her (6)
11 Appalling new American teak furniture – nasty (6)
12 Cats? Dust? Or another wheat allergy? (6)
14 Klutz, or maybe bungling idiot – either (6)
16 Playing ludo all evening (4)
18 Leisure time, free time (4)
19 Clap, applaud, give praise (4)

ACROSS

1 Spirit drink (6)
5 With no resemblance (6)
9 Grecian vessel (3)
11 Coming (7)
12 Academic qualification (7)
13 Embrace (4)
15 Booth (5)
16 *Abide With Me*, eg (4)
17 Record in writing (4)
19 Scoop (liquid) with the tongue (3,2)
20 Friendly (4)
24 Spurs (7)
25 Prying person (7)
26 Number (3)
27 Act as a substitute (4-2)
28 Mournful pieces of music (6)

DOWN

2 Giants (5)
3 Sea force (4)
4 Climax (11)
5 Overt, blatant (11)
6 Severs (4)
7 Eccentric (5)
8 Crazy goings-on (9)
10 A nod's as good as a wink to a blind horse! (3,2,4)
14 Prosecute (3)
16 Hedgerow fruit (3)
18 Contaminate, infect (5)
21 Adam's ___, lump in the throat (5)
22 Place for rubbish (4)
23 Even number (4)

Have double the fun with this puzzle: you've got to fill in the answers and the black squares! We've given you the bare bones to start and it will help you to know that the black squares in the finished grid form a symmetrical pattern, so that every black square has at least one other corresponding black square.

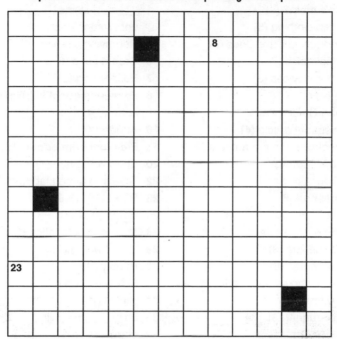

ACROSS

1 Trifles (with)
5 Moves across snow
9 Hives
10 Popular arcade game
11 Imperial measure
12 Wall scrawlings
14 Precise person
15 Appertain (to)
18 Eating at midday
20 Metal containers
23 Preserving
24 One pace up
25 Miniatures
26 Pestering

DOWN

1 Piquant
2 Underwrote
3 Verve
4 Specialist, ace
6 Yellowish-brown colour
7 Sediment build-up
8 Breathed sharply through the nose
13 Let loose
14 Wild ferret
16 Japanese craft of making shapes with paper
17 Baffling riddle
19 Childminder
21 Gesture of indifference
22 Applications

175 CROSSWORD

ACROSS

9 Leave by plane (3,3)
10 Very, extremely (5)
11 Style of knitwear (4)
12 Mum's mum? (4)
13 Civilian clothing (5)
14 Authoritative commands (6)
15 Undesirables (7)
17 Suction devices (8)
19 Rile (4)
21 Young Guide (7)
23 Newspaper article (4)
24 One of two or more authors (2-6)
25 Arab leader (6)
27 Deciduous tree (3)
29 Impressive (8)
31 Large South American snake (8)
32 In the outer areas of a city (8)
34 Fact verifiers (8)
35 Major routes (8)
36 Person who seeks to influence a politician (8)
39 Snow-runner (3)
40 Anxious (6)
42 Almost an accident (4,4)
45 Unruly child (4)
46 Spins (7)
47 Convent residents (4)
48 Petty (8)
51 Says yes (7)
54 Coincided (6)
55 Fully fledged (5)
57 Black marketeer (4)
58 Rusty old ship (4)
59 Doorway (5)
60 Sleeved garments for the torso (6)

DOWN

1 ___ Swanson, US actress (6)
2 Committee member (10)
3 Part of a wine glass (4)
4 ___ out, ejects unceremoniously (5)
5 Removing clothing (9)
6 Cream cake (6)
7 Possessing (6)
8 Female garment held up by a strap (6,4)
16 Abode (7)
18 Freedom from error (11)
20 Spicy fragrance (5)
22 Take into forced labour (7)
23 Rink sport (3,6)
26 Earphones (7)
28 Male characteristics (11)
29 Eye shading (7)
30 Bubbly (9)
33 Bricklayer, eg (7)
37 Stews (7)
38 Lazy ___, revolving condiment stand (5)
41 Paying grudgingly (7,3)
43 Man's evening dress (6,4)
44 Prenuptial all-male shindig (4,5)
49 Mutants (6)
50 Truly (6)
52 Sullies (6)
53 Wharfs (5)
56 Throw up in the air (4)

ACROSS

6 Coaxes (9)

7 Belly (5)

8 Extreme annoyance (3)

9 Place for drying hops (4)

10 Encourage (4)

12 Romantic song (8)

15 Clear, obvious (8)

17 Acting together (7,2)

18 Upholds (8)

20 Patches of hard skin (8)

23 Old land measure equivalent to a quarter of an acre (4)

24 Unusual fruit, which is trademarked (4)

27 Craft (3)

28 Mental derangement (5)

29 Settle by means of an argument (4,2,3)

DOWN

1 Barbecue on a spindle (4-5)

2 Edgings (6)

3 Floating markers (5)

4 Spoke off the cuff (2-6)

5 Claims (7)

11 Fit for occupation (11)

13 Feels contrition (7)

14 Tread (4)

16 Power units (7)

17 Flurry (4)

19 Wannabes (9)

21 Fruitless (8)

22 Gulps of air (7)

25 Retriever (3,3)

26 Modern message (5)

Try your luck with this cryptic puzzle.

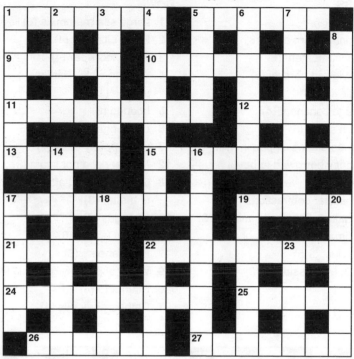

ACROSS

1 Orchestra given time for dressing (7)
5 Odd desire to live in a certain place (6)
9 Look around in the river (5)
10 Grandiose display arranged (9)
11 Manner of dealing with a complaint (9)
12 Spooky eastern lake (5)
13 Current strength (5)
15 Cunning English sort is an original model (9)
17 Get involved in moving vine tree round the point (9)
19 Super sort of wallet (5)
21 Meeting socially acceptable class outside (5)
22 Women who will eventually succeed (9)
24 Illuminate the small vessel inside (9)
25 Lazy person awfully riled (5)
26 Rewrite a score with no refinements (6)
27 Produce Edward surrendered (7)

DOWN

1 The point of waiting for transport (3,4)
2 Racket, one entertained by runner? (5)
3 Accomplice has a chance to repent, initially (7)
4 In the past one would assess and free from blame (9)
5 Correct custom, it's said (5)
6 Seeing that engineers are without deceit (7)
7 Warship besieged city in reeds, perhaps (9)
8 Stick the notice in this place (6)
14 A game of pool? (5,4)
16 Couple's mutual attraction in laboratory work? (9)
17 Soak for flavour in electrical device (6)
18 Hiker runs in front of slow walker (7)
19 Recipes concocted should be exact (7)
20 Guaranteed no doubt in the finish (7)
22 A huge foreign city (5)
23 I traded outside firm (5)

178 CROSSWORD

ACROSS

4 Medic (3)
8 Kidnap, spirit away (8)
9 Not competent (6)
10 Reviewed harshly (6)
11 Thieving (8)
13 Large continent (4)
15 Torn scrap (5)
16 Bread pieces dipped in milk (4)
18 Money borrowed to buy a house or flat (4,4)
20 Muscular contractions (6)
22 Small short-haired canine (3,3)
23 Ultimate consumers of a product (3-5)
24 Is in possession of (3)

DOWN

1 Large sea mammals (6)
2 Small biting fly (4)
3 Given footwear (4)
4 Ways in which things are unalike (11)
5 Looped (6)
6 Exchanges for money (6)
7 Open pastry case (4)
12 Neither solid nor liquid (3)
13 Dust remaining after the burning of matter (3)
14 Changes (6)
15 Muddy hollow (6)
17 Broadsheets (6)
19 Work, especially of music (4)
20 Bounders (4)
21 Cathedral recess (4)

The answer to each of these clues begins with a different letter of the alphabet. The clues are not numbered, so you must work out where each answer fits in the grid.

A Feeling of dread (5)
B Supports financially (9)
C Tin (3)
D More profound (6)
E Spread out (7)
F Pleat (4)
G More verdant (7)
H 'Laughing' beast (5)
I Clumsy (9)
J Losing control of a large vehicle (4-7)
K Martial art (6)
L Gain knowledge (5)
M Range (6)

N ___ Campbell, supermodel (5)
O Eggs (3)
P Type of virus (5)
Q Hard rock (6)
R Type of cheese (7)
S Sword (5)
T Greek bistro (7)
U Total (5)
V Female fox (5)
W Damage from ordinary use (4,3,4)
X Woody tissue (5)
Y Cede (5)
Z Region (4)

180 *CROSSWORD*

ACROSS

1 Spot or blot (7)
7 Vented (5)
8 Time past (3)
9 Villainous (4)
10 Style of bowling in cricket (4)
12 Be quiet! (6,2)
14 Car's small lamp (9)
15 Scythed (4,4)
18 Hitches (8)
21 Implementing (9)
23 Puts away (a knife) (8)
25 Full duration (4)
26 Emancipate (4)
28 Fur scarf (3)
29 Form words from letters (5)
30 Sadden (7)

DOWN

2 Authorised (9)
3 Chances (4)
4 Climbing aid comprising iron
   claws attached to a rope (9,4)
5 Attempt something new (4,1,4)
6 Security-force thugs (5)
11 Gnome (6)
13 ___ broke, skint (5)
16 Ineligible (3,2,3,5)
17 Courtroom official (5)
19 Performed high above the
   ground (6)
20 Residue from making
   omelettes? (9)
22 (Working) together (2,7)
24 Spills the beans (5)
27 Manipulator (4)

Each of 25 letters of the alphbet should be entered into the grid once, and only once. Can you find which letter has not been used?

A	B	C	D	E	F	G	H	I	J	K	L	M
N	O	P	Q	R	S	T	U	V	W	X	Y	Z

ACROSS
- 4 Male sponsor to an infant (9)
- 6 Wisecracks (5)

The missing letter is: _____

DOWN
- 1 Cut (grass) (3)
- 2 Sponsors (5)
- 3 Added tax (4)
- 5 Unlucky influence (4)

MINI QUICK

ACROSS
- 1 Dreamed (7)
- 5 Globe with a cross (3)
- 6 Opening device (3)
- 7 Old washing vessel (3)
- 9 In days gone by (3)
- 10 Numbing blow to the lower limb (4,3)

DOWN
- 1 Iced-up (7)
- 2 Writing point of a pen (3)
- 3 Fluid used for writing (3)
- 4 From dawn till dusk (3-4)
- 8 Padded lingerie item (3)
- 9 The lot (3)

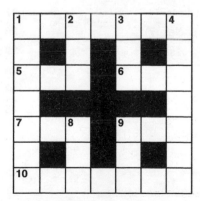

ACROSS

1 Criticise (4,5,4)
10 Makes accessible (7)
11 Doolally! (7)
12 Ladies' horse-riding style (4-6)
14 Peak, apex (4)
16 Means of back-up (8)
18 Stockpile (3,2)
21 Boiled sweets with a sour taste (4,5)
22 External ring on a target (5)
23 Binding (6)
25 Source of protein for vegetarians (4,4)
28 Roofed balconies (8)
29 Shrub genus (6)
31 March (5)
33 Market lad (6-3)
35 Songs of thanksgiving (5)
36 Doomed, unlucky (3-5)
40 Scottish woollen plaid (4)
41 Master, authority (10)
44 Pacifier (7)
45 Tentacles (7)
46 Engrossing (book) (13)

DOWN

2 Loafed (5)
3 Long short-legged dog (9)
4 Newspaper inserts (3)
5 Defames (6)
6 Knowing gesture (4)
7 Supernatural practices and phenomena (3,6)
8 Ship's officer (6)
9 Residue of a fire (5)
13 Nightclubs (6)
15 Vista (8)
17 Cutter (7)
19 Famous racecourse (5)
20 Sumptuous (8)
21 Hustle and bustle (8)
24 Skittles game (8)
26 Put on show (7)
27 Splatters (5)
30 Caper (6)
32 Unaccompanied (2,4,3)
34 Out of shot (3,6)
37 Hate intensely (6)
38 Break (5)
39 Treated mercifully (6)
42 Notion of perfection (5)
43 Holier than ___, overly pious (4)
45 Three or four? (3)

ACROSS

4 Futuristic genre (3-2)
9 Quality conveyed by touch (7)
10 Magnetic direction (5)
11 Umpire (3)
12 Organise (3)
13 Small fairy said to help Santa at Christmas (3)
14 Sea ___, tentacled marine creature (7)
15 Act like a victim (4,3,8)
19 Aground (7)
20 Closed pastry-case (3)
21 Tiny (3)
22 Scheduled (3)
23 Sadness (5)
24 Defrauded (7)
25 Go kaput (5)

DOWN

1 Mix thoroughly (4,2)
2 Yoked bovine animals (4)
3 Broadly accurate principle (4,2,5)
4 Feudal slave (4)
5 Notoriety (6)
6 Oral translator (11)
7 Sample (3,3)
8 Frying medium in Indian cookery (4)
16 Female warrior (6)
17 Conundrum (6)
18 Admits defeat (6)
19 Swamps (4)
20 Quick kiss (4)
21 Mental faculties (4)

The arrows show the direction in which the answer to each clue should be placed.

Tropical shrub ▼	Resin-producing tree ▼		Soiled	▼	Musical entertainment	Become outmoded
►			▼			▼
Stinted	Repent of ►			Horse breed		
►		Minced oath ►		▼		
Brilliant flyer	Fish-eggs	Pluck up courage				
►	▼		The __ of John and Yoko, song		Finds out	
__ Gras, festival	Traditional knowledge	Fades ►	▼		▼	
►	▼			Makers of the Quattro car		
__ Jackson, Labour MP	Frequently, in poems	US R&B singer	Viva __ Vegas, Elvis Presley film ►	▼		
Legendary twin suckled by a wolf ►	▼	▼				
►			__ Edmondson, comic actor ►			
Disobey	Time machine in Doctor Who ►					

185 *CROSSWORD*

ACROSS

1 Open disobedience (8)
6 Help yourself! (2,2,5)
7 Unit of thermal insulation (3)
8 Abolishing, putting a stop to (5)
9 Fit and active (8)
12 Cryptogram (4)
13 Geometrical shape (4)
16 Precluding (6,3)
18 Lounge furniture item (4,5)
19 Smooth (clothes) (4)
20 Folklore giant (4)
23 Succeed at university (8)
26 Lean person or animal (5)
27 Ex-Beaver (3)
28 Means of overcoming problems (9)
29 Vaulting, somersaulting, indoor athletes (8)

DOWN

1 Monies due (6)
2 Cleansed (9)
3 Moot (point) (8)
4 Live in harmony (2-5)
5 All-male party (4)
10 Boxing Day leftovers? (4,6)
11 Leaving in a hurry! (10)
14 Orchestral instrument (5)
15 Jumper with a triangular head opening (1-4)
17 Rope with a noose, thrown to catch cattle (5)
21 Say in a way that others will understand (3,6)
22 Rare metal used in lamps (8)
24 Radio exposure of a record (7)
25 Instances of mistreatment (6)
26 Passable (2-2)

1

ACROSS
1 Mesh (3)
3 Cry (3)
5 Doing a foxtrot or a waltz (7)
6 Constitutive (2-5)
9 Attain (3)
10 Soft leather (3)

DOWN
1 Soft substance used as stuffing (7)
2 Tight coil of hair (3)
3 Snow footwear item (3)
4 Narrow-minded (7)
7 Other than (3)
8 Sort, kind (3)

2

ACROSS
1 Rich pungent coffee (5)
5 Slot for a broadcast (7)
6 Armed robbery (5-2)
8 Hang in loose folds (5)

DOWN
2 On loan (3)
3 Middle Eastern dip (6)
4 Cold period of the year (6)
7 US policeman (3)

3

ACROSS
3 North African country (7)
6 Have a change of heart (7)
7 Muffling gadget (7)

DOWN
1 Make tidy (7)
2 Charge made for serving a customer's own wine (7)
4 Chopper blade (5)
5 Make cold (5)

This puzzle has no clues in the conventional sense. Instead, every different number printed in the main grid represents a different letter (with the same number always representing the same letter, of course). For example, if 7 turns out to be a 'V', you can write in V wherever a square contains 7. We have completed a very small part of the puzzle to give you a start, but the rest is up to you.

1	21	8	13	9	12	14	■	18	2	21	10	10
12	■	13	■	6	■	26	1	11	■	17	■	12
26	18	12	20	2	21	18	■	2	26	1	2	25
16	■	26	■	20	■	16	21	1	■	21	■	25
25	19	21	13	■	10	■	2 L	26 A	6 G	■	4
■	13	11	13	26	2	2	20	■	11	5	25
3	■	■	5	■	21	■	21	■	26	■	12
26	8	8	■	18	12	26	15	21	17	6	■
17	■	25	22	9	■	■	25	■	1	12	26	14
21	■	24	■	12	21	23	■	18	■	9	■	11
13	12	9	8	13	■	21	17	7	9	22	26	17
11	■	25	■	2	21	25	■	21	■	23	■	25
12	25	2	26	20	■	1	25	18	26	20	25	1

A̶ B C D E F G̶ H I J K L̶ M N O P Q R S T U V W X Y Z

1	2 L	3	4	5	6 G	7	8	9	10	11	12	13
14	15	16	17	18	19	20	21	22	23	24	25	26 A

ACROSS

1 Surgery comprised of several doctors (5,8)
9 Involuntary diaphragm contraction (6)
10 Sprinkled (8)
11 Preposition indicating movement (2,2)
12 US general-purposes vehicles (5)
13 Stoles (4)
14 South African antelope (3)
15 Exceedingly (3)
16 Units of electrical resistance (4)
18 Deadens (5)
20 Rodents (4)
22 Squirms (8)
24 Enclose in a paper covering (4,2)
25 Absurd poems (8,5)

DOWN

2 Period of rule (5)
3 Frees from obstruction (7)
4 Whelp (3)
5 Large enough (5)
6 Office staff often in a 'pool' (7)
7 On ___, at the right moment (3)
8 Carry (4)
12 Dense tangled forests (7)
13 On offer (3,4)
17 Deer (4)
19 Worker in stone (5)
21 Racecourse spies (5)
23 Sentimentality (3)
24 Heartache (3)

189 _QUIZ_

Is this a quiz? You bet it iz!

ACROSS
1 Which Latin phrase suggests that when drunk you tell the truth? (2,4,7)
9 Which projection transmits motion in a car's engine? (6)
10 What was cookery writer Mrs Beeton's first name? (8)
11 What is a drinking toast in Scandinavia? (4)
12 Which Brian is a well-known _Daily Mirror_ columnist? (5)
13 Which queen of England succeeded William III? (4)
14 What is the trunk-like nose on some animals called? (9)
16 Which Stevenson was US ambassador to the United Nations in the 1960s? (5)
19 Which wind instrument is played by James Galway? (5)
20 What is a piece of plastic used for financial transactions? (5,4)
23 In the Bible, who was the second son of Adam? (4)
25 What is the name of an energetic Cuban dance? (5)
26 Which impaler was often considered the real Prince Dracula? (4)
27 What are Muslim veils called? (8)
28 What is an anagram of 'Dorset'? (6)
29 What is a syrupy blackcurrant liqueur from Burgundy? (5,2,6)

DOWN
2 What is the homeland of the Gurkhas? (5)
3 What is a premium paid for the use of money? (8)
4 What is a paper-folding art, from Japan? (7)
5 What substance makes up the outer layer of a tooth? (6)
6 What was the nationality of former _Mastermind_ quizmaster Magnus Magnusson? (9)
7 Irish comedian Dave, who was always pictured perched on a stool, has which surname? (5)
8 Which fish gives its name to a skyline dappled with small fluffy clouds? (8)
15 Which town south of Jerusalem is Christ's reputed birthplace? (9)
17 What attacks took place during the Blitz? (3-5)
18 Which US state lies north of Louisiana? (8)
21 Steve Race hosted which old radio quiz programme? (2,5)
22 A Guildford theatre was named after which French actress Yvonne? (6)
24 Which dancer Lionel starred on the quiz show _Give Us a Clue_? (5)
26 Which Italian composed the opera _Aida_? (5)

190 *CROSSWORD*

ACROSS

1 Covers with slabs (5)
4 Lemonade (3)
6 Company of musicians (9)
7 Brilliant master of musical technique (8)
9 Underground fighter (9)
10 Cleft (4)
12 Arrange for publication (4)
14 Openly (2,6)
17 Entered into official documents (2,6)
19 Of that kind (4)
21 Printing error (4)
23 Rising up (9)
25 Religious sceptic (8)
27 Supplies water to (9)
28 Cut (the grass) (3)
29 More delightful (5)

DOWN

1 After-part of a ship (4)
2 Preparation aiding immunity (7)
3 Perceive flashing lights after a blow to the head (3,5)
4 Walked the beat (9)
5 Way to manage a problem (4,2,6)
8 Violent behaviour (5)
11 Less coarse (5)
13 Prompt to act (5)
15 Delivery vehicle (5)
16 Opposition to liberal reform (12)
18 Unpleasant odours (5)
20 Air stewards (5,4)
22 Photographic device providing light (8)
24 Really silly (7)
26 Old Russian leader (4)

228|

Every solution begins with one of five letters. Rearrange these letters to find a vital word.

The five-letter word is: _____

ACROSS

8 From Hanoi, perhaps? (10)
9 Part of a plant (4)
10 Perpetrate (6)
11 Five-line poem (8)
12 Operatic melody (4)
14 Cannot be beaten (10)
16 Ability to adapt (11)
20 Tissue in the throat (5,5)
22 One hundredth of a dollar (4)
23 Disposal of refuse by burial (8)
25 Provoke (6)
27 Hebrew patriarch (4)
28 From Vilnius, perhaps? (10)

DOWN

1 Amounts of strength (7)
2 Thing (4)
3 Skippers (8)
4 Face mask (4)
5 Rats etc (6)
6 Unselfish (10)
7 Shrill whistle of disapproval – miaow? (7)
13 Egyptian port (10)
15 Enfranchised person (5)
17 Rich and sweet (8)
18 Traveller (7)
19 However (7)
21 Cold (6)
24 Old stringed instrument (4)
26 Slang term for the nose (4)

192 *CROSSWORD*

ACROSS

1 Human breast (5)
4 Conducting yourself (8)
9 Stand at a fête or market, selling novels, hardbacks eg (9)
10 Cleaning cloths (5)
11 Go to bed late (4,2)
13 Hostile attitude (3-4)
16 Public house (3)
17 Occasion for confetti (7)
19 Alight (3,3)
22 Fulvous (5)
24 Predominantly (2,3,4)
26 Form one mass (8)
27 Stilettos (5)

DOWN

1 Drops a curtsy (4)
2 Revised (for exams) (7)
3 Saunter (5)
4 Lady's undergarment (3)
5 Clumsy (7)
6 E or O, eg (5)
7 Bite, peck (3)
8 Old Testament devotional song (5)
12 Childish name for toes (7)
14 Bloat (7)
15 Bats down (5)
18 Scene of innocent, usually rustic, pleasure (5)
20 Machinery cogs (5)
21 Common insects (4)
23 Try to win the affection of (3)
25 Bind (3)

Unscramble the anagrams before entering the answers. It may be possible to make more than one word from the letters. Make sure you enter the right one!

ACROSS

- **1** NO HAREMS (8)
- **6** BIN OFF (6)
- **9** AS MILD (6)
- **10** MISS COLE (8)
- **11** RILE RAIN (8)
- **12** TINSEL (6)
- **13** DERAILMENTS (11)
- **16** SNUB ARTICLE (11)
- **20** IS CAMP (6)
- **22** NO CRADLE (8)
- **24** A BAD SEAT (8)
- **25** LAMINA (6)
- **26** HIS AGE (6)
- **27** EATEN END (8)

DOWN

- **2** IGOR IN (6)
- **3** NO LIMPETS (9)
- **4** LEMON (5)
- **5** TOM'S RUN (7)
- **6** LEARN BAIL (9)
- **7** OF LAC (5)
- **8** IT'S SIN (6)
- **14** HIDE CANAL (9)
- **15** INELEGANT (9)
- **17** LACE NUN (7)
- **18** ACT ONE (6)
- **19** RAW BEE (6)
- **21** MANSE (5)
- **23** A MALL (5)

ACROSS

7 Commissionaire (5)
8 Specialism of treating eye problems (9)
9 Fabulous, great (6)
11 Practise (a stage show) (8)
12 Unexpectedly (12)
15 Device used to inject or withdraw fluid (7)
16 Codes of ceremony (7)
18 Power transmission network (8,4)
20 Squandered (8)
22 Tribute paid at a funeral (6)
23 Great plenty (9)
24 Remote-controlled machine (5)

DOWN

1 Fictitious name assumed by an author (9)
2 Commonplace (10)
3 Common garden bird (7)
4 Worldly person (12)
5 Second Greek letter (4)
6 Teenage infatuation (5)
10 Make up leeway (6,3,3)
13 Junior members (5,5)
14 Large bat (6,3)
17 ___ lenses, vision correctors (7)
19 Edge of hell (5)
21 Kitchen basin (4)

ACROSS

1 Severe (5)
4 Weapon which fires bolts (8)
11 Fluorescent lamp (4,5)
12 Vegetation (5)
13 Long historical film (4)
14 Religious (6)
16 Child's bed (3)
18 Undivided (3)
19 Windscreen cleaners (6)
22 By mouth (4)
24 Contribution (5)
26 Register of visitors' comments (5,4)
27 Person who tends horned ruminants (8)
28 Grudge (5)

DOWN

2 Deceive (a lover) (3-4)
3 Move on wheels (4)
5 Evocative of a style from the past (5)
6 ___ belt, securing strap in cars or aeroplanes (6)
7 Jeer (at) (3)
8 Ghostly (10)
9 Far from flattering (10)
10 Look at with amorous intentions (4)
15 Jockey, jostle (3)
16 Open garage (7)
17 Sample cloth cutting (6)
20 Bleeper (5)
21 Smell strongly (4)
23 Part of a staircase (4)
25 Tiny vegetable (3)

ACROSS

1 Sat upon (7)
7 Famous (5)
8 Jazz band instrument (3)
9 Sob (4)
10 Spoils (4)
12 Value too highly (8)
14 Facade of an emporium (9)
15 Relating to scientific methods for solving crime (8)
18 Barring (8)
21 Covered (9)
23 Movement under the force of gravity only (4,4)
25 Unwrap (4)
26 Giant of folklore (4)
28 Offer at an auction (3)
29 Slash (5)
30 Unsightly building (7)

DOWN

2 Inflamed (3,4,2)
3 Travel (4)
4 Person only vaguely related (7,6)
5 Arctic bird (4,5)
6 Survive, live (5)
11 Small amount (6)
13 Gun handle (5)
16 Lacking chemicals that are destructive to the atmosphere (5-8)

17 Concerning (5)
19 Breakfast fish (6)
20 Cheating spouse (9)
22 Boaster (9)
24 Devices for neatening hair (5)
27 Plays (4)

ACROSS

1 Congregation's answer to a minister (8)

6 Humility (9)

7 Cut the ends or top off (3)

8 Brash (5)

9 Broad-ridged tooth (8)

12 Stone resembling marble (4)

13 Sporting occasion (4)

16 Fragrant petals (3-6)

18 Seasonal chocolate treat (6,3)

19 Chilled (4)

20 Sudden loud noise (4)

23 Storyteller (8)

26 Spicy Cajun soup (5)

27 European moose (3)

28 Siren to warn of conflagration (4,5)

29 Study of coats of arms (8)

DOWN

1 Truly (6)

2 Prenuptial all-male shindig (4,5)

3 Be victorious (8)

4 Outline drawing (7)

5 Hold, restrain (4)

10 Child's competence in perusing (7,3)

11 General character (10)

14 Share an opinion (5)

15 Corset stiffeners (5)

17 Discernment (5)

21 As already mentioned (9)

22 Scenic view (8)

24 Bitter regret (7)

25 Inadequate (6)

26 Talent (4)

198 CROSSWORD

ACROSS

1 Kings of the jungle (5)

4 Assistance (3)

6 In a rage (9)

7 Green or red pepper (8)

9 Spicy sausage often used on pizzas (9)

10 Door-opening devices (4)

12 Low marshy lands (4)

14 Chance upon (4,4)

17 Nervous feeling (8)

19 Large-horned mountain goat (4)

21 Funeral heap (4)

23 Give and take (9)

25 Doom-monger (8)

27 Crafty (9)

28 Give the go-ahead silently (3)

29 In a minute (5)

DOWN

1 Part of the ear (4)

2 Kerosene light (3,4)

3 Unmarried woman (8)

4 Vegetable which occurs in globe and Jerusalem varieties (9)

5 Withdraw from service (12)

8 Sharp metal point (5)

11 Of few years (5)

13 Tip over (2-3)

15 Prying (5)

16 Process of making weak and infirm (12)

18 Blue-green gemstone (5)

20 Disaffected (9)

22 Felonious (8)

24 Be unsuccessful (4,3)

26 Old Russian emperor (4)

The black squares have to be filled in as well as the words. For a start, four black squares and four numbers have been inserted. The black squares form a symmetrical pattern.

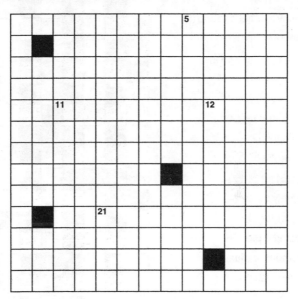

ACROSS

- **1** Promotion in rank
- **9** Clerk, officer worker etc
- **10** Stress
- **12** Dog's bay
- **14** Sarcastically
- **15** Small lizard
- **19** Plaid formerly worn by shepherds
- **20** Accessory for your tresses
- **22** Chronologically back to front
- **24** Keeping under control

DOWN

- **2** Rather dark
- **3** Every twelve months
- **4** Blackcurrant flavouring
- **5** Dark, gloom
- **6** Person who uses contacts for professional advantage
- **7** Rattled
- **8** Honestly
- **11** Balletic turn
- **13** Busby
- **16** Stain
- **17** Chinese tower
- **18** Rapidity
- **21** Improvised jazz singing
- **23** Pub

200 CROSSWORD

ACROSS

5 Difficult to grasp (8)

7 Consume (3)

8 Stretchy synthetic fabric (5)

9 Computer run-off (8)

11 Laundry appliance (4)

12 Momentarily daze (4)

14 Finicky (5)

15 Lamb's mother (3)

16 Fawn upon (7)

20 Deprive (3)

21 Gruff (5)

23 Solemnly swear (4)

24 Arab leader (4)

26 Hatching a plot (8)

28 Movement to music (5)

29 Brownies team (3)

30 Florid (8)

DOWN

1 Small land mass in water (5)

2 Feeling of kinship among women (10)

3 Fishing with harpoons (7)

4 Halloween activity (5,2,5)

6 Cockney (4-5)

10 Moment (5)

13 Velocipedist (7)

17 Sum lost in gambling (4,2,6)

18 Vanilla pop (5,4)

19 Hotel where guests can take different types of treatment (5)

22 Pre-Gothic (architecture) (10)

25 Expose to danger (7)

27 Seep (5)

ACROSS

1 South African boy had the best part of the dressing (5,5)
6 Frozen like a cake (4)
9 Bizarrely claims riot is to do with ethics (10)
10 Early outsize book (4)
12 Besides being doubly superior (4,3,5)
15 It's acceptable when board accepts Leo moving to the right (9)
17 Tedious insect? (5)
18 Model, it takes a name from a giant (5)
19 Name part of character in play (5,4)
20 Rose addressed meeting and started to dance (4,3,5)
24 Circle left with no work (4)
25 One finding Beccles is surprisingly within reach (10)
26 Express a desire, well sometimes granted here (4)
27 One might turn up and put one in (10)

DOWN

1 Nothing added to the total in Japanese wrestling (4)
2 Game bird (4)
3 Birth certificate? (8,4)
4 Step up? (5)
5 A row audibly intended, we hear, to be used in coordination (9)
7 Public space in school or college (6,4)
8 Girl's to listen to number that will sadden (10)
11 One who stirs up Serb labourer? (6-6)
13 Body of principles and rules kept in the book? (7,3)
14 Greedy lot sung out discordantly (10)
16 Flower getting prize at the dairy show? (9)
21 Belgian subject (5)
22 Veto band entering resort (4)
23 Among the best an Olympian cupbearer (4)

202 CROSSWORD

ACROSS

1 Obscureness (7)

7 Exterior (5)

8 Cheek (3)

9 Unruffled (4)

10 Wintry weather (4)

12 Breed of terrier (8)

14 Vanguard (9)

15 Person with diverse tastes (8)

18 Favour (4,4)

21 At which point (9)

23 Absolute leader (8)

25 Very small arachnid (4)

26 Small furnace (4)

28 T'ai ___, martial art (3)

29 Live, reside (5)

30 Liveliness (7)

DOWN

2 Glazed opening leading to a paved area (5,4)

3 Wool-comb (4)

4 Person scouting for gifted performers (6,7)

5 Grant (9)

6 Mass of eggs (5)

11 Suffocate (6)

13 High pile (5)

16 Tightly-contested event (5-3,5)

17 Ornamental stone (5)

19 Small earthquake (6)

20 Without hesitation (9)

22 Appropriate (9)

24 Loose protective garment worn by artists (5)

27 False image (4)

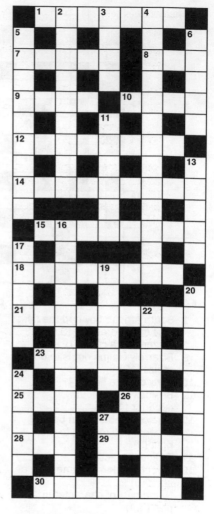

The Across clues consist of jumbled-up astronomical terms. The Down clues are straightforward.

ACROSS

- 7 EENNPTU
- 8 EIJPRTU
- 10 AELNPT
- 11 ADEIORST
- 12 ALNRU
- 14 ADEGIMNTU
- 18 EFLU
- 20 LOPTU
- 21 ARST
- 22 ACEHIPPSS
- 24 CEMOT
- 27 AAENORTU
- 30 EEMORT
- 32 ACELPSU
- 33 NOPSSTU

DOWN

- 1 Narrate
- 2 Group of lines of verse
- 3 Join
- 4 Fair
- 5 Oscillates, trembles
- 6 Abominable snowman
- 9 Facts given
- 13 Seize without legal right
- 15 Lighting gas
- 16 Male duck
- 17 Musical work
- 19 Sport played with long-handled netted sticks
- 23 Jot
- 25 Blunt
- 26 Saturate
- 28 Spherical Dutch cheese
- 29 Partner, friend
- 31 Woodwind instrument

ACROSS

1 Cease trading (5,4)
6 ___ party, all-male do (4)
10 Effusive (7)
11 Support for a temporary table (7)
13 Detail (4)
14 Not worried (10)
16 Putrid (6)
18 Workplace site of incoming mail (2-4)
21 Opposite (8)
22 Last Greek character (5)
24 Driving force (10)
26 Waterhole (4)
29 Want (4)
30 Diabolically (10)
32 Playing area for most racket sports (5)
34 Hanging sleeve at an airfield (8)
36 Openings in country walls (6)
37 Hot dish (6)
40 Haste (10)
41 Pointed nail on a bird's foot (4)
44 Small version of the flute (7)
45 In rage (7)
46 Phone (4)
47 Person who moves props in a theatre (9)

DOWN

2 Cotton yarn (5)
3 Travel by ship (4)
4 Sea cow (6)
5 Aquatic plant with floating leaves and flowers (5,4)
7 Stimulate gently (9)
8 Rapacious (6)
9 Anti (7)
12 Mathematical statement (8)
15 Longing (7)
17 Intend (7)
19 Young woman (6)
20 Outer walls of castles (7)
23 Green vegetable (7)
25 The East (6)
27 Principled (7)
28 Garish (7)
31 Dagger (8)
33 Exceptional (9)
34 Drained (6,3)
35 Organised plane routes (7)
38 Film profile of a famous person (6)
39 Performing in a play (6)
42 Extended Saturday morning snooze (3-2)
43 Mixture of meat and vegetables (4)

205 *JOLLY MIXTURES*

In this puzzle, each clue is simply an anagram of the answer – but watch out! There might be more than one possible solution to each clue. For instance, the clue 'TALE' might lead to the answer 'LATE' or 'TEAL'. You'll have to look at how the answers fit into the grid to find out which alternative is correct.

ACROSS

1	RUSTED
4	STRIPE
7	MARE
9	TIN
10	LINO
11	RENT
12	BEAT
13	ERA
14	BATTLE
17	ANGLED
20	GARDEN
23	DEARER
26	LEA
27	TRAP
28	MOPE
30	LONE
31	ATE
32	STEW
33	REVILE
34	CANTER

DOWN

1	CREDIT
2	EAST
3	TENNER
4	DEPART
5	TIDE
6	RETUNE
8	LAME
10	LANE
15	NUB
16	WEE
18	PEA
19	DOG
20	RANGER
21	LEAD
22	LATTER
23	PASTER
24	WANE
25	LUSTRE
27	PALE
29	MANE

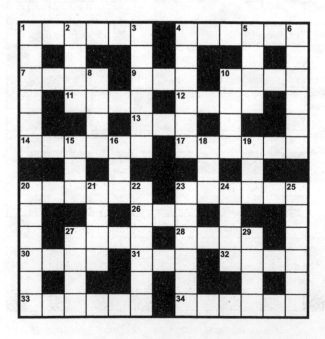

ACROSS

4 Turf chunk (3)

8 Much appreciated! (5,3)

9 Jaunt (6)

10 Enlargement (6)

11 Protection of a minor (8)

13 Rubber covering around a wheel (4)

15 Tied up (5)

16 Drug (a racehorse) (4)

18 Four-poster, for example (8)

20 Underwater swimmers (6)

22 Fancy cake (6)

23 Car flank by the kerb (8)

24 Flat-nosed dog breed (3)

DOWN

1 Merry, like a bird (6)

2 Nibble (4)

3 Legend (4)

4 Savoury steamed dish (4,7)

5 Placed at irregular intervals (6)

6 Calm, dependable (6)

7 Comfy (4)

12 Look up and down (3)

13 Small cask (3)

14 Spring religious festival (6)

15 Tea-making session (4-2)

17 Send-up (6)

19 Tough test (4)

20 Pine wood (4)

21 Undergarment (4)

ACROSS

1 Continual (9)
9 Guaranteed (7)
10 Metal fastener (3)
11 Unsuitable (5)
12 Awkward (5)
14 Horse's attendant (5)
16 Wooden blackboard support (5)
18 Fishing device (3)
19 Tree's juice (3)
21 Mournful tune (5)
22 Similar (5)
23 Dimness (5)
25 ___ pants, tapered cropped women's trousers (5)
26 Strong spirit (3)
27 Small bone in the leg (7)
28 No longer useful (9)

DOWN

1 Criticise (6)
2 Is not able to (6)
3 Low-fat dairy drink (7,4)
4 Sportsperson who does not get paid (7)
5 Make a knotted lace edging (3)
6 Act of swinging to and fro (11)
7 Genuine (4)
8 Rewrite (4)
13 Apex (4)
15 Actual (4)
17 Trod (7)
19 Mountain range in the Americas (6)
20 Valance above a window (6)
23 Yawn (4)
24 Expletive (4)
25 Limousine (3)

CROSSWORD 208

ACROSS

1 Title given by foreigners to the emperor of Japan (6)
5 List of ingredients (6)
9 Price (3)
11 Confrontation (4-3)
12 Plant with funnel-shaped flowers (7)
13 Husband of a countess (4)
15 Propeller (5)
16 Ode, eg (4)
17 Medieval stringed instrument (4)
19 Garden insect (5)
20 Yell like a baby (4)
24 Cricketer (7)
25 Flag-hoisting rope (7)
26 Human digit (3)
27 Hard, firm (6)
28 Crack (a cipher) (6)

DOWN

2 Provoke (5)
3 ___ vera, plant derivative used in cosmetics (4)
4 Social gathering at work (6,5)
5 Filled up again (11)
6 Mention, quote (4)
7 Seasonal children's play (5)
8 Form of existence following death (9)
10 Breakfast jam (9)
14 Tell falsehoods (3)
16 Tavern (3)
18 Larceny (5)
21 Presentation (5)
22 Brink (4)
23 Smart ___, know-all (4)

ACROSS

6 Street trader (6-3)

7 Worthless rubbish (5)

8 Rigid furrow (3)

9 Spick and span (4)

10 Repeated musical phrase played on a guitar (4)

12 Patron (8)

15 Impose oneself (6,2)

17 Complicated situation (5,4)

18 Postscript (8)

20 Large cask (8)

23 Birds of the night (4)

24 Smooth-talking (4)

27 Chum (3)

28 Of law cases, non-criminal (5)

29 Illegal poultry battle (9)

DOWN

1 Refusal to yield (9)

2 Fleet of warships (6)

3 Large-winged insects (5)

4 Failed (attempt) (8)

5 Perplex (7)

11 Succinctness (11)

13 Cast aspersions (7)

14 Small biting fly (4)

16 Inflict capital punishment on (7)

17 Ditch round a castle (4)

19 Fitness for consumption (9)

21 Tanker spillage outcome? (3,5)

22 Thicket of dense trees and shrubs (7)

25 Herb used to flavour liqueur (6)

26 Deride (5)

First block in some squares in a symmetrical pattern to make a crossword. Next number the squares crossword-fashion, allowing for words ACROSS and DOWN. Finally, put the correct numbers against the jumbled clues below.

A	D	I	S	H	O	N	E	S	T	Y
L	I	D	O	A	F	E	W	O	O	D
E	V	E	N	N	F	E	E	R	N	E
T	E	A	R	C	A	D	A	T	E	N
H	R	L	W	A	L	E	S	A	R	I
A	L	T	A	R	I	C	L	I	N	G
R	A	I	D	E	L	A	Y	E	A	R
G	E	M	S	T	O	Y	E	S	P	A
I	M	A	M	O	W	A	S	P	A	T
C	I	T	E	G	E	R	K	A	N	E
T	R	E	W	A	R	D	I	N	G	S

ACROSS

- Communion table
- Bounder
- Quote
- Hold tightly
- Hold-up
- Untruthful
- Sea eagle
- Regular
- Jewel
- Muslim priest
- *Citizen __*, film starring Orson Welles
- Outdoor swimming pool
- Satisfying, of work
- Health resort
- Shoe covering
- Popular brew
- Decimal base
- Plaything
- Cardiff's country
- Timber

DOWN

- Pile of banknotes
- Bridge
- Kind, type
- Cunning
- Winter sports equipment
- Male offspring
- Rot
- Disparage
- Plunge
- Eastern potentate
- Female sheep
- Shade of colour
- Notion
- Omission mark
- Chum
- Nether
- Hunger pain
- Lacking vitality
- Cat's noise
- Kidneys, liver, etc

211 *CROSSWORD*

ACROSS

4 ___ in the towel, give up (5)
9 Instrument to measure electric current (7)
10 'Laughing' wild animal (5)
11 Provide with weapons (3)
12 Homo sapiens (3)
13 Whitethorn (3)
14 Fix in the mind (7)
15 Motoring in a negligent manner (8,7)
19 One often to be seen at a certain place (7)
20 Male pig (3)
21 Characteristic sound of a cow (3)
22 Past, gone (3)
23 Garden terrace (5)
24 Treat as a celebrity (7)
25 Poor (5)

DOWN

1 Drive-surfacing material (6)
2 Augury (4)
3 Encouragement (11)
4 Waiter's tool (4)
5 Jog the memory of (6)
6 Scapegoat (8,3)
7 Summertime star sign (6)
8 Interruption (in activity) (4)
16 Deduct (6)
17 Political corruption (6)
18 Farmer (6)
19 Expectation of good (4)
20 Saintly (4)
21 Mutilate (4)

All the letters needed for the answers in each row and column are given – cross-referencing coupled with anagram skills will ensure the correct solution. To get started, locate the rarer letters first.

ACROSS

1 AABCEGLN
2 ADEEILOX
3 ADEILNP
4 AEEELMTU
5 AEHST
6 EEIRRRTV
7 EEEFIRY
8 CDINNOOU
9 KLLNNOTU

DOWN

1 CCDEEIKT
2 AEEHNORX
3 DEEINNOR
4 ALLMR
5 ABEFILTUU
6 AEELN
7 AAEGILNR
8 DEIOSTUY
9 EELNOPTV

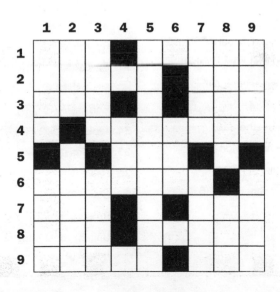

ACROSS

1 Non-aligned electorate member (8,5)
10 Publicly (7)
11 Belonging to the same family (7)
12 Drowsy feeling (10)
14 Informal photo (4)
16 Govern (8)
18 Peephole in a door (5)
21 Easily put-upon person (4,5)
22 In texture, like toffee (5)
23 Scarce object (6)
25 Framed pop group's award (4,4)
28 Highly regarded (8)
29 Number in a cricket team (6)
31 Different (5)
33 Restrained military step (4,5)
35 Conceptual (5)
36 Obsessional fear (8)
40 Meander (4)
41 Bring together (10)
44 Large jazz combo (3,4)
45 Grumbler (7)
46 Old-fashioned boat (6,7)

DOWN

2 Loyal vassal (5)
3 Device to control an aircraft by instruments (9)
4 Glacial (3)
5 Gaudy (6)
6 Sebaceous (4)
7 Weaken the force of (9)
8 Water-diviner (6)
9 Take up and use (5)
13 Umpire's decision? (3,3)
15 Self-destructive (8)
17 Try your best (2,3,2)
19 Disorder (5)
20 Fragrant flowering bulb (8)
21 Land inspector (8)
24 Means of deciding a winner (3-5)
26 Overturns (7)
27 Poetry (5)
30 Flourish (2,4)
32 Hortensia (9)
34 Tequila cocktail (9)
37 Javelins (6)
38 Delve (5)
39 Stain (6)
42 Row, quarrel (5)
43 Unit for measuring horse's height (4)
45 Clever humour (3)

ACROSS

6 Relatively unpleasant dispute (6,7)
8 Hotel reportedly came to life – that's natural (6)
9 Make hostile sergeant suffer (8)
10 Volatile little girl? (3)
11 Cockney man on the way back encounters some respect (6)
12 Tape case round badger's burrow (8)
15 One outside hospital needing treatment for this (4)
17 Some assist in eastern chapel (7)
19 They make progress rowing with each other (7)
22 Hide away model to make an impression (4)
24 A boy with wobbly gait first was excited (8)
27 Tell associate (6)
28 First person to perform language (3)
29 Invite to study first attitude of utter hatred (8)
30 Coin as turned in gaming house (6)
31 Filling station by the roadside (9,4)

DOWN

1 999 ways of acting model finds are indecent (8)
2 Class having short answer, fellow member of tribe (8)
3 Beginner at church is partly risque at first and makes a gurgling sound (7)
4 Account endlessly stuck for plant (6)
5 Make a break for the island (6)
6 Signing off at the end of a race (9-4)
7 Not a suitable punishment for one guilty of arson? (5,8)
13 A one-off time period (4)
14 A dear correspondent? (3)
16 We hear fruit of plant give up (4)
18 Girl changed from topless maid (3)
20 Toy car, it was damaged in cruel act (8)
21 Name lass becoming a rep (8)
23 Number of print run (7)
25 It was repeatedly rejected by an artist (6)
26 Most calm when morning examination was circulated (6)

ACROSS

1 Confused babble (6)
5 Muscle at the front of the upper arm (6)
9 Turkish lord (3)
11 Of earthquakes (7)
12 Domed building or hall (7)
13 Lads (4)
15 Turn outwards (5)
16 Prolonged journey from place to place (4)
17 Bird feathers (4)
19 The real ___, genuine (5)
20 In vogue (4)
24 Boundaries (7)
25 Peeled (7)
26 Score of nothing in sport (3)
27 Congregate (6)
28 Small farmers (6)

DOWN

2 Concord (5)
3 Jolt (4)
4 Rambling, hiking (11)
5 Brutally (11)
6 Urban settlement (4)
7 Irregularly marked horse (5)
8 Time by which a product must be consumed (3-2,4)
10 Crime of killing one's own father (9)
14 Wicked act (3)
16 Nervous habit (3)
18 Cost (5)
21 Pivot (5)
22 Swimming pool (4)
23 System of credit transfer between banks and post offices (4)

ACROSS

1 Snow-runner (3)
8 Unhesitating quality (12)
9 Bird associated with sagacity (3)
11 Banishment (5)
12 Bishop's district (7)
14 Person with supernatural visionary powers (4)
15 Variety of cigar (6)
18 Attest to (6)
20 Emit (oil) (4)
23 Make shiny (7)
25 Tapestry (5)
27 Decide, make a choice (3)
28 Between one body like our Sun and another (12)
29 Sensory organ (3)

DOWN

1 Die-shaped piece used to add flavour to stews (5,4)
2 Inactive (4)
3 Director's cry to start filming (6)
4 Fire residue (5)
5 Escape (5)
6 (Put) in contact with (2,2)
7 Nautically aft (6)
10 From now on (9)
13 Anger (3)
16 ___ to go, champing at the bit (6)
17 Chump (3)
19 Robustly masculine (6)
21 Aspect (5)
22 Depilated (5)
24 Notion, thought (4)
26 Tender (4)

The black squares have to be filled in as well as the words. For a start, four black squares and four numbers have been inserted. The black squares form a symmetrical pattern.

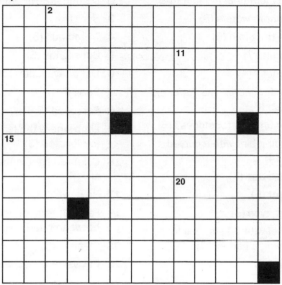

ACROSS

1 ___ Arms Park, sports ground
5 Highlander, eg
10 ___ plague, disease transmitted by rat fleas
11 Awakening clock
12 Matt ___, star of *The Bourne Identity*
13 Be excessive
15 Vitamin of the B complex
17 Uncreased
19 ___ *through the Tulips*, song
20 Stevie ___, singer with Fleetwood Mac
23 Forbid the use of
24 Madden
25 Routes
26 North Yorkshire town

DOWN

2 Book used in collecting and mounting stamps
3 Censure
4 Max ___, cosmetics company
6 ___ Abbado, Italian conductor
7 Subdue
8 Waiting
9 Art of playing to win
14 City in NW England
16 Kindly
18 Show to be false
21 West African country
22 Pack, at sea

218 _CROSSWORD_

ACROSS

1 Morse code element (3)
8 In a dictatorial manner (4-8)
9 Offshore waters (3)
11 Use the brain (5)
12 Jumble (7)
14 Harness (4)
15 Rhododendron-like flowering shrub (6)
18 Like lurid horror stories? (6)
20 Wading bird with a curved bill (4)
23 Large ape (7)
25 Grant (5)
27 Sort, type (3)
28 Panel with 64 squares for playing a game (12)
29 Close (3)

DOWN

1 Expel (9)
2 Demonstrative pronoun (4)
3 Burn (6)
4 Tremulous (5)
5 Cut slightly (5)
6 List of available dishes (4)
7 Snag (6)
10 Parboiled (3-6)
13 Limb where the femur and tibia are located (3)
16 Coloured light in the night sky (6)
17 Be unwell (3)
19 Familiar term of address between hearty types (3,3)
21 Cleanse (5)
22 Put aside to use later (3,2)
24 Blaring (4)
26 Extensive (4)

The answer to each clue is a word which has a link with each of the three words listed. This word may come at the end (eg Head linked with Beach, Big and Hammer), at the beginning (eg Black linked with Beauty, Board and Jack) or a mixture of the two (eg Stone linked with Hail, Lime and Wall).

ACROSS

1 Bank, Mouth, Yellow (5)
4 Beam, Printer, Surgery (5)
7 Forth, Side, Take (5)
9 Causing, Good, Stricken (5)
10 Organ, Signs, Statistics (5)
11 Fitting, Hang, Let (5)
12 After, Fore, So (5)
15 Calendar, Eclipse, Year (5)
18 Flower, Post, Time (3)
20 On, Park, Suit (6)
21 Fireworks, Games, Market (6)
22 Dance, Into, Room (3)
24 Gun, Parting, Sling (5)
27 Drug, Half, Whole (5)
30 Lily, Moth, Paper (5)
31 Boxing, Political, Stage (5)
32 Cover, Photo, Stamp (5)
33 Ply, Purpose, Storey (5)
34 Card, Eyed, Tongued (5)
35 Basket, Dirty, Sheets (5)

DOWN

1 All, Handed, Wing (5)
2 Box, Mail, Over (5)
3 Air, Man, Range (5)
4 Best, Crossing, Spirit (5)
5 Finish, Stitch, Wood (5)
6 Metric, Scale, Ship (5)
8 Draw, Music, Sheet (5)
13 Black, Land, Hampstead (5)
14 Beef, Potato, Sunday (5)
16 Down, Ground, Wraps (5)
17 Face, Round, Turn (5)
18 Part, Player, Two (3)
19 Sheep, Stick, Switch (3)
23 Arch, Cake, Fish (5)
24 Back, Ejector, Ministerial (5)
25 Comic, Glasses, Soap (5)
26 Duty, Out, Postage (5)
27 Blazer, Nature, Off (5)
28 Myth, Sprawl, Sub (5)
29 Being, Error, Race (5)

The arrows show the direction in which the answer to each clue should be placed.

River's edge ▼		Tie tightly ▼		Pinkish tropical fruit ▼		Capital of Egypt ▼
►						
Roman emperor		Toy (2-2)		US motor racing		Volatile gas
►		▼		▼		▼
Parachutist	Of the moon		Military alliance (inits) ►			
Kent airport ►	▼			Industrial Italian city		German region
►			__ Saint Laurent, designer ►	▼		▼
__ *Vadis*, Ustinov film		Arctic resident	Stockton's river	Division of time ►		
Change later, wrongly ►	▼		▼			US term for 'mother'
►				Unilever brand of detergent ►	▼	
Scottish hillside	Long narrow flag ►					
__ and downs, uncertainties ►				__ Johnson, aviatrix		

ACROSS

1 Excessive sentimentality (8)
6 Trifle (5,4)
7 Become tangled (3)
8 Satirical sarcasm (5)
9 Busy traffic period (4,4)
12 Place for skating (4)
13 Offshoot of a branch (4)
16 Programme with listeners giving their opinions (4,5)
18 State of immobility and stupor (9)
19 Pubs (4)
20 Round capsule of cotton (4)
23 Cosmetic (8)
26 Yellow pigment (5)
27 Outlaw (3)
28 Priest who performs a rite (9)
29 Not used (8)

DOWN

1 Open ___, magician's command (6)
2 Severe indigestion (9)
3 Throughut the hours of darkess (3-5)
4 Quivering effect in singing (7)
5 Skirmish (4)
10 By district (10)
11 ___ custody, imprisonment for your own safety (10)
14 Expand (5)
15 Jogs (5)
17 Allow to be known (3,2)

21 From a ship into the water (9)
22 Easy to get on with (8)
24 Stepwise arrangement of troops (7)
25 Joined (6)
26 Before now (4)

ACROSS

9 Effusive person (6)
10 Sides of a river (5)
11 Owned by you and me (4)
12 Dunderhead (4)
13 Scottish vicarage (5)
14 Of a pigeon, trained to return to its base (6)
15 Man or gorilla, for example (7)
17 Lawless (8)
19 Paving stone (4)
21 Exaggerate a role (7)
23 Young horse or related animal (4)
24 Variety of sugar (8)
25 Chocolate and cream pastry (6)
27 Creative skill (3)
29 Without a single pip (8)
31 Lozenge-shaped (8)
32 Cosseted (8)
34 Deserving blame (8)
35 Foe (8)
36 Interest paid on shares (8)
39 Hearing organ (3)
40 Personal effects and assets of the deceased (6)
42 Hard work (8)
45 Skin alive (4)
46 Gushing stream (7)
47 Throbbing pain (4)
48 Sporty and active (8)
51 Continuation (7)
54 ___ pig, rodent (6)
55 ___ suzette, dessert pancake (5)
57 Noble title (4)
58 Clarified butter used in Indian cooking (4)
59 Nocturnal insects (5)
60 Fissure (6)

DOWN

1 Hairdressing aid (6)
2 Benign enchantment (5,5)
3 Bleak, dreary (4)
4 Choice steak (1-4)
5 During pregnancy (9)
6 Illness that affects breathing (6)
7 Pertaining to the universe (6)
8 Shrub with fragrant white or pink flowers (10)
16 Couple (7)
18 End of a prison sentence (7,4)
20 Vast (5)
22 Clover-like plant (7)
23 Accommodation plus all meals (4,5)
26 Ginger-haired person (7)
28 Frequent customer at transport cafes (5,6)
29 Assume (7)
30 Tact (9)
33 Put back into office (2-5)
37 Stage or screen star (7)
38 Magnetic direction (5)
41 Educated on your own initiative (4-6)
43 Feline with slanting blue eyes (7,3)
44 Giftedness (9)
49 Disembarked (6)
50 Harsh experience (6)
52 Utter, out-and-out (6)
53 Discontinue (5)
56 One and all (4)

223 CROSSWORD

ACROSS

4 Gained victory (3)
8 Kidnap, abduct (8)
9 Form of print (6)
10 Sport in which the competitors go down the piste (6)
11 Charged with current (8)
13 Package (4)
15 Lathery (5)
16 Propels with oars (4)
18 Having more than you know what to do with (4-4)
20 Praying ___, insect of the cockroach family (6)
22 ___ justice, fitting retribution (6)
23 Almost an accident (4,4)
24 Witch (3)

DOWN

1 Close-fitting necklace (6)
2 Strongly against (4)
3 Make a noise like an engine (4)
4 Secretly monitoring telephone conversations (4-7)
5 Subtle refinement (6)
6 Sampler (6)
7 Tiny skirt (4)
12 Lettuce said to have originated on a Greek island (3)
13 Chinese frying pan (3)
14 Nice-looking (6)
15 Gallic (6)
17 Fanciful behaviour (6)
19 Recess (4)
20 Grumble (4)
21 Insensitive (4)

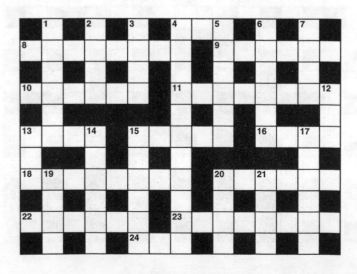

ACROSS

1 End a flight hastily (5-4)
9 Stir up (7)
10 Rower's pole (3)
11 Make into one (5)
12 Unusually small (5)
14 Keep quiet! (5)
16 Discharge (5)
18 Potato-like root (3)
19 Floating zoo (3)
21 Bucolic scene (5)
22 Extreme (5)
23 Coronet (5)
25 Small flat savoury Indian cake (5)
26 Grecian vessel (3)
27 Envisage (7)
28 Crisis (9)

DOWN

1 Picky, fussy (6)
2 Central courtyard (6)
3 Pride and arrogance (11)
4 Nimbly (7)
5 Period of one of the Earth's revolutions (3)
6 Irritating (11)
7 Band (4)
8 Fresh, youthful (4)
13 Emporium (4)
15 Locks (4)
17 Five-lobed (leaf) (7)
19 Season of the year (6)
20 Ardently (6)
23 Eatery (4)
24 Belonging to us (4)
25 Industrious insect (3)

ACROSS

4 Inlay firmly (5)
9 Ashamed (7)
10 Perform (5)
11 ___ on, encourage (3)
12 Dark-coloured fluid used for writing and printing (3)
13 Blokes (3)
14 Time free from work (7)
15 With too many options (6,3,6)
19 Skilled worker (7)
20 Be in the red (3)
21 Seed of a fruit (3)
22 Opening, break (3)
23 Give off odour (5)
24 Musical term meaning 'lively' (7)
25 Tyrolean song (5)

DOWN

1 Tooth decay (6)
2 Ramble (4)
3 Audaciously (11)
4 Paradisal garden (4)
5 Military trumpeter (6)
6 Ecstatically (11)
7 Lapis ___, decorative stone (6)
8 Eye sore (4)
16 Retail ___, shop (6)
17 Toothed (6)
18 Provide with a job (6)
19 In addition (4)
20 Iridescent precious stone (4)
21 Wedding attendant (4)

ACROSS

6 Covered with plastic (9)
7 Egg-shaped (5)
8 Lid (3)
9 Land force (4)
10 Cook pastries and biscuits (4)
12 Workman (8)
15 Finish (8)
17 Disorder (9)
18 Forefront (8)
20 Conflict in which most nations are involved (5,3)
23 Take orders from (4)
24 Mandibles (4)
27 Public transporter (3)
28 Bogus (5)
29 Shop selling writing materials (9)

DOWN

1 Legitimate (9)
2 Preserve the old Egyptian way (8)
3 Take permanent possession of (5)
4 Wooden fortress (8)
5 Took (a child) into your family (7)
11 In a self-important way (11)
13 Loose outer garment gathered to the waist (7)
14 Part of a camera (4)
16 Facial feature raised to express disapproval (7)
17 Change or cause to change position (4)

19 Shooting from both sides (9)
21 Abroad (8)
22 Grandiosity (7)
25 Teem (6)
26 Savoury jelly (5)

227 _CROSSWORD_

ACROSS

1 On loan (3)
8 Sensitive (6,6)
9 Take legal action (3)
11 Pickled musk-melon (5)
12 Studio (7)
14 Delicate (4)
15 Everyday, ordinary (6)
18 Amorous (6)
20 Otherwise (4)
23 ___ rice, long-grain rice (7)
25 Simple lock (5)
27 Creative activity (3)
28 Sealed from the breeze (7-5)
29 Rocky outcrop (3)

DOWN

1 Awaiting action (2,5-2)
2 Those people (4)
3 Schedule (6)
4 Distant, withdrawn (5)
5 Native of the largest continent (5)
6 For nothing (4)
7 Put oil on the head, usually in a religious ceremony (6)
10 Batsman or bowler (9)
13 Golf-ball pedestal (3)
16 Devotional string of beads (6)
17 Allow (3)
19 Limited amount (6)
21 Loose-limbed (5)
22 Abscond romantically (5)
24 Border, lean upon (4)
26 Axe-grip (4)

Complete the crossword and the circled letters will spell out the title of the novel by P G Wodehouse which is dedicated 'To my daughter Leonora without whose never-failing sympathy and encouragement this book would have been finished in half the time'.

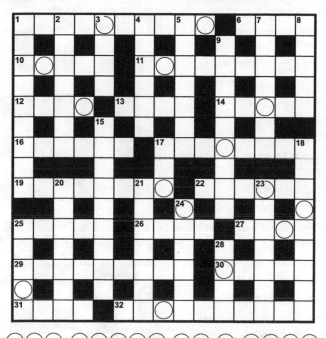

ACROSS

- **1** Unlucky Friday date?
- **6** Fifty per cent
- **10** Drive back
- **11** Driver
- **12** Location
- **13** Amaze
- **14** Tremble
- **16** Creepy-crawly
- **17** Make a pal of
- **19** Power to see
- **22** Tell
- **25** Book description
- **26** Heavy shower
- **27** Autograph
- **29** Astronaut's garment
- **30** Animal akin to the giraffe
- **31** Want
- **32** Reviving

DOWN

- **1** Revolving gate at ticket-office
- **2** Momentum
- **3** Slate
- **4** Thrill
- **5** Learner
- **7** Norm
- **8** Ludicrous situation
- **9** Children
- **15** Wrote quickly
- **17** Wager
- **18** Requiring a lot of attention
- **20** Copy
- **21** Hairy
- **23** Art of paper-folding
- **24** Sift out impurities
- **25** American buffalo
- **28** Person in charge

229 CROSSWORD

ACROSS

1 Communicate via the internet (5)

5 Anything eaten to sustain life and health (4)

6 Watery component of blood (6)

7 Irritating sensation (4)

8 Whenever you choose (2,4)

9 Cut (8)

12 Well-developed male (9)

15 Monkey without a tail (3)

16 Cover in fat before and during cooking (5)

17 Article of faith (5)

18 Australian running bird (3)

19 Amount gained, after tax (3,6)

21 Handcuffed (8)

24 Chance to succeed (4-2)

25 Census (4)

26 Balance out (4,2)

27 Watch out for (4)

28 Heat-resistant cookware (5)

DOWN

2 Body of men enrolled and drilled as soldiers (7)

3 Animate, cause to occur (7)

4 Piggish (7)

5 System that comes into operation in case of malfunction (4-4)

9 Rebuking (10)

10 Kidney-shaped snack item (6,3)

11 Thwarted (love) (10)

13 Edible crustacean (7)

14 Domineering (9)

20 Lined with wood (8)

21 Pleasant to the ears (7)

22 Narrowly (7)

23 One who is a gourmet (7)

In each of these clues, one letter has been printed incorrectly or left out entirely. Can you work out what the clues should be and solve the puzzle? 30 Down, for example, should read 'Feed', which is EAT.

ACROSS

1 Taking coal from the round (6)
4 Waiter (6)
7 Outbuilding for housing a jar (6)
9 Not harm (4)
11 Done by (3)
12 Deported (4)
13 Aches (6)
15 Arm joins (5)
17 Expansive (4)
18 Rum (4)
20 Study (5)
23 Botherhoods of employees (6)
25 Hulk (4)
27 Fort of address (3)
28 In his place (4)
29 Sable (6)
31 Young mat (6)
32 Lowest legions (6)

DOWN

1 Hitchcraft (5)
2 Nether (3)
3 Apple a lubricant to (6)
4 Sap up (6)
5 Lathe (4)
6 Ordinary curse of events (7)
8 Wall attention to (9)
10 In gloom (9)
14 Pit into service (3)
16 Segment of a tee trunk (3)
17 Europan country (7)
19 Alcoholic sprit (3)
21 Got noticed (6)
22 Thrown with farce (6)
24 Fades (5)
26 Closet (4)
30 Deed (3)

231 CROSSWORD

ACROSS

9 Police inquiry base (8,4)
11 Adjoin, border (4)
12 Clap eyes on (3)
13 Loose (4)
14 Discolour (5)
15 Scrap merchant (6)
16 Paralyse with terror (7)
18 Shoe leather (8)
20 Floor-length skirt (4)
22 Grave (7)
24 Uppermost point (4)
25 Lunar appearance (8)
26 Extravagance (6)
28 West Country mound (3)
30 Rough period in your life (3,5)
32 Suitable for marriage (8)
33 Very heavy metal (4,4)
35 Panic (8)
36 Clear soft drink (8)
37 Blabbermouth (8)
40 Slash (3)
41 Saintly (6)
43 Person who looks forward (8)
46 Had a hunch (4)
47 Raise (a siege) (7)
48 Warning sound (4)
49 High heel (8)
52 Child's word for sleep (3-4)
55 Cake decoration (6)
56 Warmed and dried (5)
59 Placed down (4)
60 Historical period (3)
61 Originate (4)
62 Process of reducing nasal blockage (12)

DOWN

1 Different from (6)
2 Scattering (10)
3 Untidy state of affairs (4)
4 Move silently (5)
5 Yoke (9)
6 Unaware of ethics (6)
7 Scottish food made from sheep (6)
8 Slightly nauseous feeling (10)
10 Snare (3)
17 Extreme right-winger (7)
19 Unbeliever (11)
21 Smell, odour (5)
23 Variety of animal etc (7)
24 Building designer (9)
27 Percolation (7)
29 Glowing fireside implement (3-3,5)
30 Started to collapse (7)
31 Defeat utterly (3,2,4)
34 Oven (7)
38 Sudsy (7)
39 Long rope with a running noose (5)
42 Voters (10)
44 Fickleness (10)
45 Personal grant (9)
50 Plant of the pea or bean family (6)
51 Hearty, outdoorsy (6)
53 Head of a newspaper (6)
54 Eccentric (5)
57 Breakfast food (3)
58 Feat (4)

232 JOLLY MIXTURES

In this puzzle, each clue is simply an anagram of the answer – but watch out!
There might be more than one possible solution to each clue. For instance, the
clue 'TALE' might lead to the answer 'LATE' or 'TEAL'. You'll have to look at how the
answers fit into the grid to find out which alternative is correct.

ACROSS

1 TIPS
6 CASK
8 SHRUB
9 RUSE
10 GORE
11 CRATE
13 SORE
15 TAPED
18 TIME
19 LANE
21 PADRE
24 DENE
25 AGREE
28 WEST
29 DEAF
30 LEASE
31 RANG
32 RITE

DOWN

2 SPOILT
3 ROT
4 TUBA
5 AUNT
6 HOES
7 COSTER
12 PAR
14 NEAR
16 DEN
17 ATE
18 MINE
20 SILENT
22 ORE
23 MELDED
25 WERE
26 TUGS
27 LYRE
29 AFT

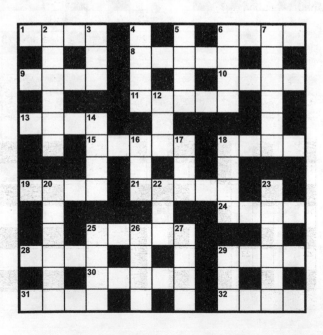

ACROSS

1 Dead ringer (8,5)
9 Dress warmly (4,2)
10 Paper money (8)
11 Bathroom powder (4)
12 Variety of birch (5)
13 Electrical resistance units (4)
14 Portion of a circle (3)
15 Broadcast (3)
16 Public room (4)
18 Man-made watercourse (5)
20 Greek letter or small amount (4)
22 Fearless (8)
24 Very white (6)
25 Annual vacation (6,7)

DOWN

2 Furry anorak with a hood (5)
3 Newsworthy (7)
4 Rascal (3)
5 Deteriorate (2,3)
6 Earth substance (7)
7 Weapon (3)
8 Check, restrain (4)
12 Applaud (7)
13 Japanese art of paper-folding (7)
17 Former coin of India and a girl's name (4)
19 Lowest point (5)
21 Chicken ___ masala, popular Indian dish (5)
23 Viral disease (3)
24 Noise made by a dove (3)

ACROSS

1 Architectural structure which tapers to a point (5)
4 Daughter's husband (3-2-3)
11 Peevishness (9)
12 Icy covering in a freezer (5)
13 Muslim religious leader (4)
14 Straw hat (6)
16 As ___, in accordance with (3)
18 Sheltered side (3)
19 Nefarious (6)
22 Annoyance (4)
24 Personal servant (5)
26 Made shiny (9)
27 Lacking altitude (3-5)
28 Root vegetable (5)

DOWN

2 Term of address expressing affection (3,4)
3 Brook (4)
5 Plain, open (5)
6 Doddery (6)
7 18th-century gambling card game (3)
8 Fun swimming-pool apparatus (5,5)
9 Having the oven and hob in separate units (5-5)
10 Release (a knot) (4)
15 Short-winged coastal bird (3)
16 Took (game) illegally (7)
17 Excessively studious (6)
20 Hut (5)
21 Spikes (of corn) (4)
23 Survey (4)
25 Edict (3)

The black squares have to be filled in as well as the words. For a start, four black squares and four numbers have been inserted. The black squares form a symmetrical pattern.

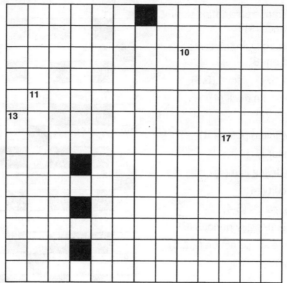

ACROSS

1 Spoil the appearance of
4 Motionless
9 Waterproofing material
10 Damp
11 Jump
12 Species of goose
14 Kings and queens
16 Sign of the zodiac
19 Wrestling hold
21 Large bucket
23 Arctic dwelling
24 Hiker
25 Bingo's 'top of the shop'
26 Upward slope

DOWN

1 Food item or course
2 Honestly
3 Restrict, inhibit
5 Egg-yolk painting medium
6 Budgie's warble
7 Specific type
8 Pretentious
13 Genesis
15 Observation post
17 Crumple
18 Glide across ice
20 Large juicy fruit
21 Push hard
22 Rattle, bother

ACROSS

1 Authentic (5)
4 Ruminant's chewed food (3)
6 Substance emanating during a seance (9)
7 Frightening character to children (8)
9 Hard spicy biscuit (6,3)
10 Part of the neck (4)
12 Region (4)
14 Unsolicited post (4,4)
17 Regularity (8)
19 Hop-drying kiln (4)
21 Difficulty (4)
23 Nazi march (5-4)
25 Parliamentary periods (8)
27 By one single action (2,1,6)
28 Draw (3)
29 Follow on (5)

DOWN

1 Change direction (4)
2 Disappointment (3-4)
3 Diminished (stocks) (8)
4 Pitman? (9)
5 In a way that can be verified (12)
8 ___ aunt, problem page columnist (5)
11 Big feather (5)
13 Black and white smelly animal (5)
15 Incendiary offence (5)
16 Cold remedy (12)
18 Excited, eager (5)

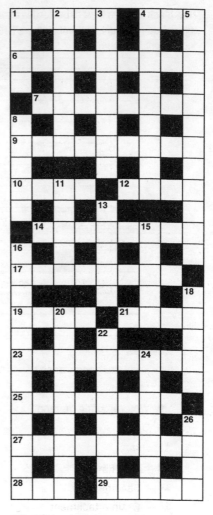

20 Wintertime countryside picture (9)
22 Denigrate (8)
24 Questionable (7)
26 Only (4)

First block in some squares in a symmetrical pattern to make a crossword. Next number the squares crossword-fashion, allowing for words ACROSS and DOWN. Finally, put the correct numbers against the jumbled clues below.

S	E	T	U	T	O	P	L	I	M	P
O	L	O	N	A	P	E	E	N	O	A
W	I	N	D	C	H	E	A	T	E	R
E	N	S	I	T	A	P	R	E	T	O
T	W	I	G	E	M	O	B	R	I	E
U	R	L	E	I	S	U	R	E	R	R
B	I	L	L	S	T	R	A	S	I	A
O	T	I	E	T	E	A	P	T	O	T
B	U	T	T	E	R	F	L	I	E	S
I	R	I	S	A	G	A	E	N	R	A
B	U	S	A	M	A	R	A	G	A	G

ACROSS

- — Hot drink
- — Soft cheese
- — Anorak
- — Little devil
- — Payment demand
- — Spoil
- — Free time
- — Become solid
- — Basin attachment
- — Brightly-coloured insects
- — Part of a tree
- — Public vehicle
- — Highest part
- — Large continent
- — Silence

DOWN

- — State of equality
- — In the distance
- — Throat infection
- — Barrel
- — Droop
- — Take a quick look
- — Hair-styling product
- — Scatter seeds
- — Pet rodent
- — Item of underwear
- — Sporting side
- — Engaging the attention
- — Baby's clothes protector
- — Diplomacy
- — Historical age

238 *CROSSWORD*

ACROSS

5 Evil (8)

7 Worthless horse (3)

8 Strongly flavoured dark brown coffee (5)

9 Undomesticated water bird (4,4)

11 Darts player's starting point (4)

12 Kick (4)

14 Parch (3,2)

15 Possess (3)

16 Unfavourable (7)

20 Tiny fairy (3)

21 Bad-tempered (5)

23 Dutch cheese (4)

24 Read quickly (4)

26 Eternal ___, three-sided love entanglement (8)

28 Location of an event (5)

29 Josh (3)

30 Instigator (8)

DOWN

1 Sheep-like (5)

2 Lethargically (10)

3 Artificial (3-4)

4 Without moral principles (12)

6 Art of selling (9)

10 Timbers (5)

13 In large amounts (7)

17 Causing a reduction in prices and earnings (12)

18 Sensitive, open (9)

19 Perishing (5)

22 Removal of religious influence from politics (10)

25 Messy (7)

27 Call off (a mission) prematurely (5)

All the Across clues are jumbled-up types of drink. The Down clues and answers are normal.

ACROSS

- 8 ADEM
- 9 CINOT
- 10 AELGR
- 12 NIEW
- 13 OPRT
- 14 ACDILOR
- 16 BEIRTT
- 18 CEKO
- 19 DILM
- 21 FPIL
- 23 CHNPU
- 24 GLNOOO
- 25 ACENRT
- 27 BEOOZ
- 28 AEKS
- 30 BREE
- 31 ADOS
- 32 ADHNSY
- 35 LEZTSER
- 37 FZZI
- 38 CHOK
- 41 OSTTU
- 42 AGHNO
- 43 AIST

DOWN

- 1 Abominable snowman
- 2 Arrival
- 3 Daze
- 4 Inactive
- 5 High playing card
- 6 Pop group
- 7 Occurred
- 11 Cavity for extricating water or oil
- 15 Male's youth
- 17 Unwell
- 19 Measures of 1,760 yards
- 20 Unspecified person
- 22 Dwindle away
- 23 Died
- 26 Component parts
- 29 Young goat
- 32 Sorting by dimension
- 33 Hearth receptacle (3-3)
- 34 Crest
- 36 Tightly drawn
- 39 Quote
- 40 Timid

240 *CROSSWORD*

ACROSS

9 Hostile (12)
11 Male red deer (4)
12 Wet flat land (3)
13 Demanding (4)
14 Swing round (5)
15 Plump, large (6)
16 Packs up and leaves (7)
18 Any sleep-inducing drug (8)
20 Imitated (4)
22 Collects (7)
24 Snowballed (4)
25 Dark-haired woman (8)
26 Notify, inform (6)
28 Cereal (3)
30 Echoes (8)
32 Maritime colour? (4,4)
33 Artificially high voice (8)
35 Downing tools (2,6)
36 Person who drives away evil spirits (8)
37 Thieves of game from private land (8)
40 Large area of salt water (3)
41 Dinner jacket, in America (6)
43 Divisions (8)
46 Functions (4)
47 Couches (7)
48 Has to (4)
49 Summarily terminate (5,3)
52 Amending proofs (7)
55 Ignores (rules) (6)
56 Burglary (5)
59 Mats (4)
60 Motor (3)
61 Erstwhile (4)
62 Protest rather than negotiation (6,6)

DOWN

1 Not yet created (6)
2 Useful ancillary person or thing (10)
3 Roof space (4)
4 Note in music (5)
5 Authoritarian communist (9)
6 Goal-getter (6)
7 Slum district (6)
8 Eccentricity (10)
10 Recently discovered (3)
17 Open, four-wheeled, horse-drawn carriage (7)
19 Windsurfing, aquaplaning, eg (5,6)
21 Woman's wallet (5)
23 Deprives (of heat or food) (7)
24 Have young (4,5)
27 Cricket teams (7)
29 Surrounded (11)
30 Mull over (7)
31 Audience (9)
34 Garment makers (7)
38 Blamed (7)
39 Bellows (5)
42 Alarming (10)
44 Lack of experience (10)
45 Legal (9)
50 Name for a cat that catches mice (6)
51 Legitimately placed to score (6)
53 Contemptible (2-4)
54 Military survey (5)
57 Oily substance (3)
58 Bus on rails (4)

ACROSS

1 A strong concoction going bad of meat cooked in a sour cream sauce (10)
6 Greek character getting in the way of the soot (4)
9 Guest finds it hidden in mask (7)
10 Concerning American girl, one with a royal insignia (7)
12 Begins after having convulsions but has only spasmodic bursts of activity (4,3,6)
14 Deodorant to come quickly (4-2)
15 Matches a variety of outlines (8)
17 Rum Bella splashed on collapsible canopy (8)
19 Cubist Roland hid bar (6)
22 Violent struggle on the campsite? (7,6)
24 Goddess had a first course that's incomplete (7)
25 X that can be defended (7)
26 Man located former pupil within limits of territory (4)
27 Men with agent eg rearranging appointment (10)

DOWN

1 But Eva's on the up (4)
2 Still in the forest fully clothed (7)
3 Achieve one's full potential – a small informal meeting about it (3,2,8)
4 Rule over an ancient Scandinavian (6)
5 Dock free movement of part of ship (8)
7 Disease, French complaint needing a change of air (7)
8 Language expert ran last over rocky height (10)
11 Last to the end of a boxing-match, or a race? (2,3,8)
13 Win, worker celebrating (10)
16 Coerce into using heavy club (8)
18 Sponger may be in hot water using this (7)
20 Shake three times going round helpless maid (7)
21 Lady found market bit of a laugh (6)
23 Early race warm up (4)

CROSSWORD 242

ACROSS

- **1** Children's game (8,5)
- **9** Quick (6)
- **10** Woodland flower (8)
- **11** Three players (4)
- **12** Table used in a religious service (5)
- **13** Get here (4)
- **14** Male relation (3)
- **15** Fire's end-product? (3)
- **16** Hit smartly (4)
- **18** Wide-mouthed fishing net (5)
- **20** Relax (4)
- **22** Woven together (8)
- **24** French liqueur (6)
- **25** Change to suit new circumstances (4,4,5)

DOWN

- **2** Possessor (5)
- **3** Supreme (7)
- **4** No matter which (3)
- **5** Wooden-soled shoe (5)
- **6** Impartial (7)
- **7** Strong sturdy horse (3)
- **8** Scallop (4)
- **12** Word opposite in meaning to another (7)
- **13** ___ bun, sticky cake (7)
- **17** Decrease in size (4)
- **19** Relating to sound (5)
- **21** Motionless up to now (5)
- **23** Major armed conflict (3)
- **24** Norm, standard (3)

243 CROSSWORD

ACROSS

1 Proclamation (5)
5 Win (4)
6 Proportion accepting an offer (6)
7 Lug (4)
8 Capable cat (6)
9 Encompassing many things (5-3)
12 'Cemetery' for old vehicles? (9)
15 Charged atomic particle (3)
16 Very angry (5)
17 Inebriated (5)
18 However (3)
19 Theatre entrance (5,4)
21 Animal that will devour humans (3-5)
24 Astral (6)
25 Big surplus (4)
26 Plenty (6)
27 Ill-mannered person (4)
28 In reserve (5)

DOWN

2 Document conferring honour (7)
3 Masterly (7)
4 Plait of hair (7)
5 Prepare (3,5)
9 Interstellar matter (6,4)
10 Large venomous spider (9)
11 Person seeking excitement (10)
13 Thorn (7)

14 By whatever means necessary (2,3,4)
20 Member of a lawless mob (8)
21 First seven-figure number (7)
22 In legend, famous female warriors (7)
23 Angry (7)

The black squares have to be filled in as well as the words. For a start, four black squares and four numbers have been inserted. The black squares form a symmetrical pattern.

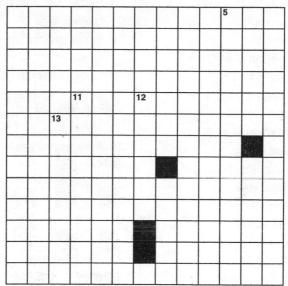

ACROSS

1 Not adjusted optically
5 ___ chi, system of exercises
7 Accomplish
8 Format
9 Do needlework
10 Revealed
12 Brand-name vermouth
13 Angkor ___, temple complex
14 Aversion
18 ___ G, comic TV character
20 Not in any place
23 Ape
24 *The Tale of Mr* ___, Beatrix Potter story
25 Silvery-white metallic element
26 Derek ___, British actor
27 East Anglian cathedral town
28 Birmingham's cricket ground

DOWN

1 Dated
2 Left untilled
3 Red wine of Tuscany
4 Badly ___ Boy, musician whose real name is Damon Gough
5 Dylan ___, writer
6 Examining of your own mental processes
8 Romanian currency units
9 Reproved
11 Bankroll
15 Capital of Uganda
16 Old Testament prophet
17 Pertaining to a standard English typing keyboard
19 Bring goods in
21 Composition for one instrument
22 Gypsy man

245 *CROSSWORD*

ACROSS

1 Gently burning (5)
4 Tumble (4,4)
11 Imagine (9)
12 Damn! (5)
13 Eye membrane (4)
14 Ready to fire (6)
16 Golf expert (3)
18 Frozen confection (3)
19 With enthusiasm (6)
22 Rouse (4)
24 Distinguishing quality (5)
26 Under a spell (9)
27 Abandoning (8)
28 Black card (5)

DOWN

2 Real (7)
3 Ellipse (4)
5 Leading (5)
6 Sexual impulse (6)
7 By way of (3)
8 Going backwards (10)
9 Became attached (to an organisation) (10)
10 Metric equivalent of 2.2lb (4)
15 Seek out the target (3)
16 Cast (7)
17 On/off control (6)
20 Popular garden bird (5)
21 Garden grass (4)
23 Cease (4)
25 Nautically astern (3)

The answer to each clue is a word which has a link with each of the three words listed. This word may come at the end (eg Head linked with Beach, Big and Hammer), at the beginning (eg Black linked with Beauty, Board and Jack) or a mixture of the two (eg Stone linked with Hail, Lime and Wall).

ACROSS

7 Bar, Knuckle, Toasted (8)
8 Billy, Nanny, Scape (4)
9 Compact, Drive, Slipped (4)
10 Dad's, Issue, Salvation (4)
11 Informed, Mannered, Wind (3)
13 Clenched, False, Front (5)
14 Pitch, Word, World (7)
16 Controlled, Counter, Low (7)
18 Back, Mark, Park (5)
21 Ground, League, Poison (3)
22 Pepper, Stone, Wheel (4)
23 Biting, Finger, Varnish (4)
25 Drop, Rain, Test (4)
26 Growth, Plan, Sanctions (8)

DOWN

1 American, Go, Speaker (6)
2 Further, Higher, Primary (9)
3 Demand, Grand, Offer (5)
4 Ante, Maid, Torture (7)
5 Boiled, Flip, Shell (3)
6 Mushroom, Pearl, Press (6)
12 Good, Nap, Tea (9)
15 Kane, Senior, Ship (7)
17 Column, Note, Seek (6)
19 Management, Point, Suez (6)
20 Bad, Donor, Money (5)
24 Ball, Job, Number (3)

The arrows show the direction in which the answer to each clue should be placed.

Mountain pasture	Boot-tie	▼	Spot or blot	▼	Roald ___, author of *Matilda*	▼	Surname of Man Friday's master
►	▼		Insubstantial ___ EA ___, US author	►			
River in Coleridge's *K bla Khan* ►			▼		___ Garner, jazz pianist		Poison
Most relaxed ►					▼		▼
►				AA Milne character ►			
Yield germ, we hear	German war vessels (1-5)		Separate from the sediment	___ Harrison, *My Fair Lady* actor ►			
►	▼		▼	Showed the way		Quits?	
Taken to court	Dame ___ Terry, early actress ►			▼		▼	
►				___ Wallace, author of *Ben-H r*		John ___, Arctic explorer	
Head	Larry ___, harmonica virtuoso ►			▼		▼	
►			___ Sharples, ex-*Street* character ►				
___ Laurel, early comedy actor	Leather chastisement strap ►						

ACROSS

4 Slump (3)
8 In the correct manner (8)
9 Roving (6)
10 Fly that transmits sleeping sickness (6)
11 Including (8)
13 Cut socially (4)
15 Drilled (5)
16 Wild drunken party (4)
18 Male sharpshooter (8)
20 Merry (6)
22 Part of the eye (6)
23 Too junior (5-3)
24 Absolutely! (3)

DOWN

1 Penitentiary (6)
2 Exact replica (4)
3 Elm, for example (4)
4 Coincidental (11)
5 Latin verb form (6)
6 Artificial cave (6)
7 Without delay (4)
12 Tent's rope (3)
13 ___ Browne, military officer's belt (3)
14 Sweltering (6)
15 ___ duck, fish dish (6)
17 Lasting resentment (6)
19 ___ bomb, nuclear device (4)
20 Green ornamental stone (4)
21 Tale (4)

249 CROSSWORD

ACROSS

9 Idiosyncrasies (6)
10 Laments (5)
11 Fighting fit (4)
12 Provide (for) (4)
13 Ship's facelift (5)
14 Implants (6)
15 Achievement of aims (7)
17 However (8)
19 Penultimate match in a tournament (4)
21 Elected assembly (7)
23 Most important fuel before the advent of nuclear power (4)
24 Letter cut-outs (8)
25 Baffle (6)
27 Common bird of several varieties (3)
29 Bright handkerchief (8)
31 Relating to a series of events (8)
32 Demented (8)
34 Begins afresh (8)
35 Rear entrance to a house (4,4)
36 Aimed (at) (8)
39 Stage pair (3)
40 Disorderly crowd (6)
42 Spins round (8)
45 Giant-sized (4)
46 Up-and-down movements (7)
47 Acquires by purchase (4)
48 Christmas decoration (8)
51 Second-hand vehicle (4,3)
54 Dregs (6)
55 Measure (5)
57 Small corner (4)
58 Hit a golf ball into the hole (4)
59 Devourer (5)
60 Switches from one track to another (6)

DOWN

1 Department (6)
2 Augury (10)
3 Old Russian emperor (4)
4 Prompt (5)
5 Accompaniment to lamb (4,5)
6 Garment (1-5)
7 Club's masseur, familiarly (6)
8 Material used in shop windows and doors (5,5)
16 Part (7)
18 Low-grade (11)
20 Additional (5)
22 Antechambers (7)
23 Reach adult status (4,2,3)
26 Forgiven (7)
28 Defending a habitat (of an animal) (11)
29 Weep copiously (7)
30 Fit to consume (of water) (9)
33 Behaves abjectly (7)
37 Amends (7)
38 Without exception (5)
41 Unfaithful (spouse) (10)
43 Promiscuous (10)
44 Single out (9)
49 Rejoices (6)
50 Congregates (6)
52 Cancels (6)
53 Cat noises (5)
56 Simplicity (4)

250 CROSSWORD

ACROSS

1 Destructive weapon (1-4)
4 Purge (3)
6 Mark on an envelope indicating time of posting (4,5)
7 Incoherent talker (8)
9 False name used by a writer (9)
10 Notch (4)
12 Seabird related to the gull family (4)
14 Particles of fine wheat used for puddings (8)
17 Casting out of spirits (8)
19 Way of acting (4)
21 House with a party wall (4)
23 Bitter (9)
25 Garden plant (5,3)
27 Of training, aimed at existing employees (2-7)
28 Clot, wally (3)
29 Nocturnal imagining (5)

DOWN

1 Secrete (4)
2 Mood following a scandal or shocking event (7)
3 Meddling nosey person (8)
4 Change around (9)
5 Relating to a section of an organisation (12)
8 Thorny, troublesome (5)
11 Set of principles (5)
13 Shell (5)
15 Moot point (5)
16 Second or later edition of a book (12)
18 Public telephone shelter (5)
20 Matching crockery (6,3)
22 Plagued (8)
24 Former (3-4)
26 Judge (4)

ACROSS

5 Correspondence (8)

7 Hardwood (3)

8 Gambol (5)

9 Establish the truth of (5,3)

11 Rake, profligate (4)

12 Butterfly-like creature (4)

14 Periods of seven days (5)

15 Adverse, harmful (3)

16 Gift, knack (7)

20 Impair (3)

21 In good time (5)

23 Repetition (4)

24 Twirl (4)

26 Gnarled, weather-beaten (skin) (8)

28 Lazy ___, revolving tray on a table (5)

29 Road-surfacing material (3)

30 Very calm body of water (8)

DOWN

1 Famous racecourse (5)

2 Shed or room for curing food (10)

3 Bird with a strutting walk (7)

4 Person who writes and solves codes (12)

6 One-time (9)

10 Brags (5)

13 Book of devotional songs (7)

17 In your ___, naked (8,4)

18 Enhance with ornaments (9)

19 Telling whoppers (5)

22 Atonement (10)

25 Pebbles found on beaches (7)

27 Tasteless, coarse (5)

The black squares have to be filled in as well as the words. For a start, four black squares and four numbers have been inserted. The black squares form a symmetrical pattern.

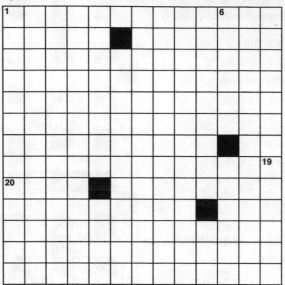

ACROSS

1 Disgusting
4 Pure
8 Loch north of Glasgow
10 Flood
11 Journal
12 ___ Bristow, darts star
14 Almost fall
15 Deceitfulness
17 David ___, of TV's *Bargain Hunt*
20 Robin ___, outlaw
21 Book of the New Testament
22 Work (flour) into dough
24 Sending for
25 Sounds
26 Sidestepped
27 Moroccan port

DOWN

1 **More replete**
2 Clear
3 Posterior
5 ___ Lewis, pop singer
6 Mulder's partner in *The X-Files*
7 Free (from)
9 Taking exception to
10 Severe (laws)
13 **Love deity**
14 Low seat
16 Contoured
17 Stubborn
18 Tended
19 Hirer
22 Part of the leg
23 Vietnamese monetary unit

ACROSS

1 Appropriate (9)
9 Score for the opponents (3,4)
10 Outward motion of the tide (3)
11 Harris cloth (5)
12 Pleasantly mild (5)
14 Will (5)
16 Piece of live coal (5)
18 Even number (3)
19 Fur scarf (3)
21 Aberdeen ___, breed of cattle reared for beef (5)
22 Seed of an oak (5)
23 Medieval tournament (5)
25 Striped mammal of the giraffe family (5)
26 ___ up, recap (3)
27 Paired with a similar foreign town (7)
28 Very much required (9)

DOWN

1 Make a clean ___ of it, confess (6)
2 Favouring democratic socialism (6)
3 Sexually arousing (11)
4 Variety of crispy lettuce (7)
5 Supreme being (3)
6 Intoxicated state (11)
7 Poultry (4)
8 Sicken with an excess of sweetness (4)
13 Dock (4)
15 Man of the hour (4)
17 Travel voucher given to senior citizens or disabled people (3,4)
19 Japanese art of dwarf-tree growing (6)
20 Creature (6)
23 Aeroplanes (4)
24 Single thing (4)
25 Lyric poem (3)

The arrows show the direction in which the answer to each clue should be placed.

Releases eggs (of a fish) ▼		__ Abbott, 1940s comedian ▼		Rich		▼ Alternative to a floppy (1,1,3)	Shuttle HQ (inits)
				▼			▼
▶ Old Shanghai drugs joint? (5,3)		Kind of dung beetle ▶				Brand-name cream 'sherry'	
			Votes against ▶			▼	
Dialect 'anything'		Dark red insect resin	__ Hamilton, Nelson's mistress ▶				
▶		▼			Spouter is a bloke, we hear		Tweaked
Jura's neighbour	Latvia's capital		Peter __, UK actor ▶		▼		▼
▶	▼					Certain air	
Covered walk		Scottish word for a scratch	Spanish cry of triumph	High-pitched bark ▶		▼	
Matures (5,2) ▶		▼	▼				
			Before, poetically ▶				
Prison	Group of four ▶						

All the Across clues are jumbled-up jewellery terms. All the Down clues are straightforward.

ACROSS

7 CENOORT

8 ADEELMR

10 ABBELU

11 MNETDAIA

12 ACEMO

14 ADEEELPRS (4-5)

18 DOPR

20 BELRY

21 ADRS

22 EEEJLLRWY

24 AAIRT

27 DEHILOOR

30 ADDEIM

32 ADDIMNO

33 ACHIJNT

DOWN

1 Roman robe

2 Old paving stone

3 Waste pipe

4 Jane Austen novel

5 Fantasisers

6 Even

9 Unemployed

13 Concur

15 Toy human

16 More scarce

17 Cain's brother (Bible)

19 Pay bonuses

23 _____ Bremner, comedy impressionist

25 Sloping script

26 Perfect

28 Prepare for publication

29 Buckle

31 Devours

256 CROSSWORD

ACROSS

4 Apples and ___, stairs in rhyming slang (5)
9 Proceed (from a source) (7)
10 Aircraft (5)
11 Mineral water resort (3)
12 Wino (3)
13 Equipment (3)
14 Triumph (7)
15 Lack of porousness (15)
19 Season of the Pentecost (7)
20 Animal used for truffle hunting (3)
21 Underwired garment (3)
22 Two performers (3)
23 Australian wild dog (5)
24 Swimmer's breathing tube (7)
25 Protection for a front door (5)

DOWN

1 Watersport vehicle (3,3)
2 Deer (4)
3 Conversing about business at a social event (7,4)
4 Troublesome or annoying person or thing (4)
5 Flowering shrub (6)
6 Conical child's plaything (8,3)
7 Tall slender hunting dog (6)
8 Deep anxiety (4)
16 Bending easily (6)
17 Fire-lighting material (6)
18 Annual (6)
19 Move through water (4)
20 Very smart (4)
21 Form of transport with pedals (4)

In each of these clues, one letter has been printed incorrectly or left out entirely. Can you work out what the clues should be and solve the puzzle? 8 Across, for example, should read 'One of a kind', which is UNIQUE.

ACROSS

7 Hard hit
8 One of a king
9 Cork product
10 Lead sculpture
11 Stained
12 Box-like
14 Noble pet
17 Oil
19 Dive on
20 Queerly
22 Aesop's tall
24 Ask for elms
26 Partly oxen
28 Lone garment
29 Vessel for asses
30 Sharpness of mint
31 Arm gone

DOWN

1 Extreme pettiness
2 Live out
3 Oral overview
4 Easily started
5 Heave at the altar
6 Sunny moth
13 Small lip
15 Flat dish
16 Noting
17 Spite
18 Apply fiction
21 Thin
23 Demanding wok
24 Plan-spoken
25 Literary kid
27 Cup of meat
28 All-mannered

ACROSS

1 In a sinking direction (9)
6 Land unit (4)
10 Scold (4,3)
11 Brighter (7)
13 Pig fat prepared for use in cooking (4)
14 Athletics field event (6,4)
16 Go aboard ship (6)
18 Desktop container for work pending (2-4)
21 Decorative shoot of water (8)
22 Sluggish (5)
24 Deficient (10)
26 Wooden shoe (4)
29 Position of a building (4)
30 Large edible crustacean (5,5)
32 View diminishing towards the horizon (5)
34 Bolster from below (8)
36 Comprehend (6)
37 Mark of shame (6)
40 River which drives grinding equipment (10)
41 Chinwags (4)
44 Betray your principles for the lure of money (4,3)
45 Relating to external stimulation (7)
46 Decorative skirting (4)
47 Excessively flattering (9)

DOWN

2 Come to mind (5)
3 Midday (4)
4 Ratify (6)
5 Ruse (9)
7 Mingle at a party (9)
8 Fascinated (6)
9 Stealthy hunter (7)
12 Charged with emotion (8)
15 Suntanned (7)
17 Tending to rise (7)
19 Lapis ___, decorative stone (6)
20 Presenting (7)
23 Communication (7)
25 Made of a rough woollen cloth (6)
27 Inclination (7)
28 Work (7)
31 Assertive manliness (8)
33 Person who works with horses (6,3)
34 Not deserved (9)
35 Light stud (4-3)
38 Caused laughter (6)
39 Based on effect (6)
42 Love in France (5)
43 Small stinging insect (4)

259 *JOLLY MIXTURES*

In this puzzle, each clue is simply an anagram of the answer – but watch out!
There might be more than one possible solution to each clue. For instance, the
clue 'TALE' might lead to the answer 'LATE' or 'TEAL'. You'll have to look at how the
answers fit into the grid to find out which alternative is correct.

ACROSS

7	BRIDES
8	HEADER
9	PAL
10	VIED
11	MEAN
12	ART
14	NORSE
17	FINER
19	BRAID
20	CAROB
22	LONER
24	RAM
26	LIED
28	HEAT
29	RAP
30	ANIMAL
31	CORDON

DOWN

1	DEIGNS
2	REEF
3	STILE
4	RECAP
5	MASH
6	CANTER
13	BREAM
15	ROB
16	ARE
17	DIE
18	FRO
21	RELOAD
23	POTION
24	PAPAL
25	CHARM
27	VILE
28	THIN

ACROSS

1 Howl (6)
5 Mastermind (6)
9 Reverence (3)
11 Chums (7)
12 Cooking apparatus (7)
13 Disinclined (4)
15 Be expecting (5)
16 Web, warren (4)
17 Extremely disgusting (4)
19 Deciding game in sports (5)
20 Erode (4)
24 Straighten (7)
25 Badly brought up (3-4)
26 Self-importance (3)
27 Jammed (6)
28 Groom (6)

DOWN

2 Remove (from the premises) (5)
3 Track (4)
4 Very narrow around the middle (garment) (4-7)
5 Process of starting to grow (11)
6 Mean with money (4)
7 Extremely (5)
8 Unpleasant exhalation (9)
10 Ideal espoused by economic liberals (4,9)
14 Garden tool (3)
16 Cat's cry (3)
18 Release (3,2)
21 Eagle's nest (5)
22 Flower similar to the carnation (4)
23 Supplication (4)

261 _CROSSWORD_

ACROSS

1 Including (3)

8 Amoral (12)

9 Fate, destiny (3)

11 Early life (5)

12 One who distributes relief to the poor (7)

14 Popular tinned fish (4)

15 Loan shark (6)

18 Substance used against Boris Karloff in his horror films (6)

20 Trees bearing acorns (4)

23 Dear to the heart (7)

25 Humorous ape (5)

27 Source of minerals (3)

28 Writer of a saint's life story (12)

29 Tool that works a lock (3)

DOWN

1 Butter-fingered (3,6)

2 Obligation (4)

3 Fir tree (6)

4 May (5)

5 Large area of water (5)

6 Canned meat product (4)

7 Dill-like aromatic plant (6)

10 On the dot (9)

13 Fail to keep pace (3)

16 Disburden (6)

17 Small species of deer (3)

19 On fire (6)

21 Old saying (5)

22 Clear off! (5)

24 Nullify (4)

26 Flesh of a pig used as meat (4)

The black squares have to be filled in as well as the words. For a start, four black squares and four numbers have been inserted. The black squares form a symmetrical pattern.

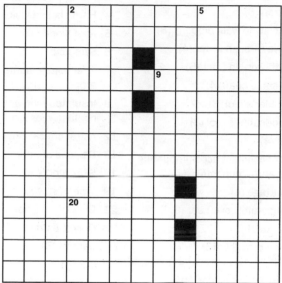

ACROSS

7 Bird expert
8 Fishes with a rod and line
9 Capital of Poland
10 Popular sweets
11 Rich fabric
14 Scolding
16 ___ *Up Mother Brown*, song
19 Drool
21 Fainting fits
22 A main division of Christianity

DOWN

1 Rich south-east Asian sultanate
2 Boned (fish)
3 Selected
4 Stares fiercely
5 ___ Stravinsky, composer
6 Lee Harvey ___, alleged assassin of JFK
12 Keeps company (with)
13 Disrobe
15 ___ Benn, Labour MP
17 ___ Borgnine, US actor
18 Muslim world
20 Investigates

263 CROSSWORD

ACROSS

1 Person occupying a premises (7,6)
9 Patron (6)
10 Inability to walk properly (8)
11 Move through water (4)
12 Cloth worn in front (5)
13 Versatile bean (4)
14 Cobbler's tool (3)
15 Woodcutter's tool (3)
16 Kid (4)
18 Establishment accommodating car and occupants (5)
20 Shortage (4)
22 Deliberately overhear (6,2)
24 Jeering (6)
25 Deep thought (13)

DOWN

2 Relation by marriage (2-3)
3 Rising current of hot air (7)
4 Hard-shelled fruit (3)
5 Roof worker (5)
6 Symbolic (7)
7 Affectionate name for grandma (3)
8 Insulated food and drink container for picnics (4)
12 Astronomical calendar (7)
13 Dispose of entirely (4,3)
17 Skip, ignore (4)
19 Type of saw (5)
21 Division of a poem (5)
23 Only even prime number (3)
24 Saloon (3)

First block in some squares in a symmetrical pattern to make a crossword. Next number the squares crossword-fashion, allowing for words ACROSS and DOWN. Finally, put the correct numbers against the jumbled clues below.

ACROSS

- — Extremely
- — Mineral source
- — One who drives a float
- — Shoot
- — Paper fastener
- — Wipe out
- — Peel
- — Nudge
- — Sword
- — Wide awake
- — Ancient Celtic priest
- — Short sleep
- — Time period
- — Consumed
- — Heath plant
- — Everyone
- — Oarsperson
- — Overseer
- — For

DOWN

- — Madame Tussaud model
- — Absorbent cloth
- — Cried like a cat
- — Small garden bird
- — Arid
- — Black-eyed ___, showy plant
- — Snake
- — Watercourse
- — Yemeni port
- — ___ Sharif, actor
- — Mohammed ___, ex-boxer
- — Quiz team
- — Make joyful
- — Elector
- — Detection system
- — Before
- — Send
- — Be incorrect
- — Scheme
- — Frozen water
- — Jump

A	S	S	T	A	P	L	E	R	U	M
D	R	U	I	D	E	E	R	A	S	E
D	U	S	T	E	W	A	R	D	E	W
E	R	A	I	N	A	P	E	A	T	E
R	I	N	D	A	X	E	P	R	O	D
E	V	O	R	O	W	E	R	A	W	E
V	E	R	Y	E	O	L	E	P	E	E
O	R	E	F	P	R	O	V	A	L	L
T	O	M	I	L	K	M	A	N	U	A
E	R	I	C	A	I	A	L	E	R	T
R	O	T	E	N	D	R	I	L	E	E

ACROSS

6 Deep, wide, artificial waterway (4,5)

7 Revise (for an exam) (3,2)

8 Blockhead (3)

9 Circular movement of water (4)

10 Predatory freshwater fish (4)

12 Small handbag (8)

15 Luggage carrier on the top of a car (4,4)

17 Distinguished, well-known (9)

18 Doctrinaire (8)

20 Lacking in allegiance (8)

23 Ostentatiously creative (4)

24 Wide-beamed sailing dinghy (4)

27 Tooth on a wheel (3)

28 Instinctive notion (5)

29 Device for honing pencils (9)

DOWN

1 Irregularity (9)

2 Slightly burnt (6)

3 Latitude (5)

4 Preferring one's own company (8)

5 Con man (7)

11 Environmentally harmless (3-8)

13 Double (7)

14 Stage parody (4)

16 Pleasant feature (7)

17 Nautical whistle (4)

19 Graphic representation of a complex process (4,5)

21 Essential (part) (8)

22 Corpse (7)

25 Beating with a rod (6)

26 Counters (5)

All the letters needed for the answers in each row and column are given – cross-referencing coupled with anagram skills will ensure the correct solution. To get started, locate the rarer letters first.

ACROSS

1 AACGGIRS
2 AAGGILOO
3 ABLNOOP
4 AEINPQTU
5 ORSUY
6 EEIMNNTV
7 ADEPRRY
8 IILLNNOO
9 ACELORTU

DOWN

1 BCEEGIIP
2 AAGLLMOS
3 ADEILLPS
4 AINOO
5 CENOOQRRU
6 INNRU
7 AAGILORT
8 AGNOOUYY
9 AENPRTTV

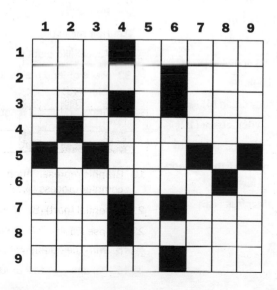

267 *CROSSWORD*

ACROSS

1 Earnings from investments etc rather than work (7,6)
10 Mass, sermon (7)
11 Unavoidably (7)
12 Ship's funnel (10)
14 Sign of some future event (4)
16 Nearer the front (of the body) (8)
18 Silly people, dolts (5)
21 Complete list (9)
22 Great in size (5)
23 Sound of an object being thrown into water (6)
25 Wonder (8)
28 Branch of the armed services (3,5)
29 Plastic tumbler (6)
31 Spiky flower (5)
33 Wet weather (9)
35 Bite with a snap (5)
36 Make smaller (8)
40 Upper body organ (4)
41 Soldier on horseback (10)
44 Sentimental in a sickly way (7)
45 Iron bar with a flattened end used as a lever (7)
46 Small citrus fruit (7,6)

DOWN

2 Quotient (5)
3 Of the backbone (9)
4 Object of play (3)
5 Corrupt (6)
6 Conurbation (4)
7 Distance gauge (9)
8 Baked ___, pudding with ice cream and meringue (6)
9 Expiring (5)
13 Low point (6)
15 Cave in (8)
17 In name only (7)
19 'Evening star' planet (5)
20 Brain (8)
21 In an easy manner (8)
24 Lack of haste (8)
26 Boring (7)
27 Hair-raising (5)
30 Acacia-like plant (6)
32 Piece of land that is almost an island (9)
34 Star undergoing a catastrophic explosion (9)
37 Watchman (6)
38 Nom de ___, pen-name (5)
39 Double-size bottle (6)
42 Name commonly given to a movie gangsters' boss (2,3)
43 With the addition of (4)
45 Bill and ___, talk amorously (3)

268 CROSSWORD

ACROSS

1 Sprightliness (7)

7 Place (inside) (5)

8 ___ trip, self-gratifying experience (3)

9 On-course betting system (4)

10 Applaud (4)

12 Grace, refinement (8)

14 Point out errors (4,5)

15 Quarantined (8)

18 Prosthetic orb (5,3)

21 Essential (9)

23 Show (8)

25 Bursts (4)

26 Penchant, predilection (4)

28 T'ai ___, martial art (3)

29 Smartens (up) (5)

30 Fail to satisfy, disappoint (3,4)

DOWN

2 Middleman (2-7)

3 Genteel woman (4)

4 Your native land (3,3,7)

5 Scuttle away (6,3)

6 Military unit (5)

11 Bold (6)

13 Carefully look at (5)

16 Horse's odds (8,5)

17 Another time (5)

19 Disposition (6)

20 Laboratory worker (9)

22 Crops protector (9)

24 Arrange gaps (5)

27 Potato (4)

ACROSS

1 Inactive medicine used as a control (7)
7 Forward (money) (5)
8 Solidify (3)
9 Affectation of superiority (4)
10 Hospital dormitory (4)
12 Gardening accessory (4-4)
14 Tennis infringement (4,5)
15 Statue maker (8)
18 Base to land a chopper (8)
21 Doubtful (9)
23 Exactly (8)
25 Claret, for instance (4)
26 Gradient (4)
28 Ball (3)
29 Colour for 'Go!' (5)
30 Put into words (7)

DOWN

2 Type of Italian 25 Across (9)
3 Dainty (4)
4 Blood-sports enthusiast in Africa (3-4,6)
5 Moralise tediously (9)
6 Effortless movement (5)
11 Sly (6)
13 Bird reputed to bring babies (5)
16 Charity's money tin (10,3)
17 Supposed spirit appearing after death (5)
19 Argot (6)

20 Temporarily acquiesce (4,5)
22 Backbiting (9)
24 Rush (5)
27 Jelly made from seaweed, used in glue making (4)

270 CROSSWORD

ACROSS

4 That lady (3)
8 Breezy (8)
9 In uniform fashion (6)
10 Shun (6)
11 Harsh criticism (8)
13 Changed the colour of (4)
15 Clear in the mind (5)
16 Fan (4)
18 Beginner (8)
20 Soft brightness of a smooth or shiny surface (6)
22 Quartz, chalcedony etc (6)
23 Be heavier than (8)
24 Smuggle (3)

DOWN

1 Brittle (6)
2 Opulent (4)
3 Unfreeze (4)
4 Petroleum, eg (11)
5 View (6)
6 Confer (6)
7 Tart, quiche (4)
12 Clean (fish) (3)
13 Brownish horse colour (3)
14 Subterfuge (6)
15 Lower spine region (6)
17 Cattle feed (6)
19 Radiate (4)
20 Plenty (4)
21 Plant's unit of reproduction (4)

The black squares have to be filled in as well as the words. For a start, four black squares and four numbers have been inserted. The black squares form a symmetrical pattern.

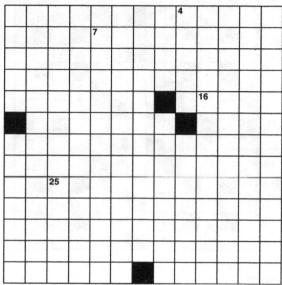

ACROSS

1 Variety of firework
4 Information on a book cover
7 Junior to
9 Jewish leader
10 ___ days, the past
11 Variety of bingo
12 Any planet
15 Lightness of temper
18 Watch chain
20 Appeal to
21 Crest
22 Intense desire
24 Condiment stand
27 ___ or tails
30 Girl's name or heather
31 Autumn zodiac sign
32 Of the countryside
33 Shout of approval
34 Easy task
35 **Bread** raising agent

DOWN

1 Small rodent
2 Dark-brown pigment
3 Physique
4 Yellow-flowering shrub
5 Cow's milk bag
6 Work table
8 The same
13 Sequence
14 Bloodsucking insect
16 Suffuse
17 Fashion, general mode
18 Affected, whimsical
19 Any Scottish mountain
23 Very select
24 Abdominal pain
25 Of a town or city
26 Instruct
27 Torment
28 Major artery
29 Forced apart

Two straightforward crosswords – but their clues have been mixed up. You have to decide which clue belongs to which pattern, but two words have been entered to give you a start.

ACROSS

1 Hamper	1 Digest
5 Semi-darkness	5 Painter
9 Stage of development	9 Gangway
10 Damage	10 Niche
11 Spring festival	11 Bible strong man
12 Lid	12 Guest-house
14 Indian dress	14 Empty space
17 Intelligence	17 Louse egg
18 Fog	18 Highest point
20 Tendency	20 Subject
22 Communion table	22 Nip
23 Sunshade	23 Put back
24 Devil	24 Leap about
26 Forces chaplain	26 Mistake
29 Object of worship	29 Spoken test
30 Fruit seed	30 Fragment
32 Tinned fish	32 Require
33 Go over	33 Trite
35 Sausage (colloq)	35 Agree
36 Quality of sound	36 Bemoan
37 Pale yellow	37 Pile up
38 Hostility	38 Lace-hole
39 Bee's food	39 Unbelief

DOWN

1	Run in	1	Clever
2	Lithe	2	Make safe
3	Reckless	3	Large-scale
4	Buffalo	4	Fling
5	Advantage	5	Mixture of snow and rain
6	Cure	6	Bring up
7	Creepy-crawly	7	Keep back
8	Gentle	8	Heat
13	Huge	13	Baddie
15	In front	15	Tidiness
16	Join up	16	Urge forward
18	City of northern Italy	18	Watchful
19	Stone worker	19	Get a goal
21	Listening organ	21	Study room
22	Soft drink	22	Expert
24	Ring	24	Spitting image
25	Two-quart bottle	25	Leap on
27	Trickery	27	Brick debris
28	Chief journalist	28	Seldom
30	Knees-up	30	Flat, woollen hat
31	Claw	31	Eye-shield
33	Finest	33	Govern
34	Enjoy	34	Window glass

273 CROSSWORD

ACROSS

1 Female aristocrat (8)
6 Advantage, right (9)
7 Once round a racetrack (3)
8 Telephone kiosk (5)
9 Teacher (8)
12 Vein of metal ore (4)
13 Facts or information used as a basis for reckoning (4)
16 Chicory with purplish leaves (9)
18 Highly contagious viral infection (9)
19 Conservative (4)
20 Portray favourably (4)
23 Hackneyed (8)
26 Large African animal (5)
27 To the point (3)
28 Health, comfort (4-5)
29 Solidified (8)

DOWN

1 Type of furnace (6)
2 Not hindered (9)
3 Long traffic queue (8)
4 Hunt for (4,3)
5 Network (4)
10 Quite, pretty (10)
11 Philanthropic (10)
14 Pale (5)
15 Search around (5)
17 Yield (to authority) (5)
21 Calling forth (9)
22 Totally occupied (8)
24 Minute bump on the skin (7)
25 Manipulated (6)
26 Bird of prey (4)

CROSSWORD 274

ACROSS

1 Emissary (5)
4 Fission explosive (4,4)
11 Mould-killer (9)
12 Private's weapon (5)
13 Pork joint (4)
14 Cheerful and self-confident (6)
16 Rile, needle (3)
18 Cheat (3)
19 Consume (6)
22 Second-brightest star in a constellation (4)
24 Creek, small bay (5)
26 Reversion to an earlier ancestral characteristic (9)
27 Trivial but annoying (8)
28 Follow a winding course (5)

DOWN

2 ___ violet, antiseptic (7)
3 Panel pin (4)
5 Agree (with) (3,2)
6 Murdered saint (6)
7 Out of connection (3)
8 Fail to remain in line (of soldiers) (5,5)
9 State of severe distress (10)
10 Travel permit (4)
15 Consume (3)
16 Chilled first-aid accessory (3,4)
17 Pertaining to teeth (6)
20 Clothe yourself in (3,2)
21 Usual, average (4)
23 Long-necked river bird (4)
25 Unhewn timber chunk (3)

275 CROSSWORD

ACROSS

9 Comedy (6)
10 Heroic tales (5)
11 Lean upon, border (4)
12 Dance movement (4)
13 Finely chopped meat (5)
14 Personify (6)
15 Very important (7)
17 Rotor (8)
19 Cab (4)
21 Hat with a turned-up brim (7)
23 Hitched (4)
24 Dismal expression (4,4)
25 Persistently annoy (6)
27 Bug (a telephone line) (3)
29 Family member who lived before you (8)
31 Member of staff (8)
32 Impressive (8)
34 Gun that fires pellets (3,5)
35 Lens of a microscope (8)
36 Post-World War I decade (8)
39 1440 minutes! (3)
40 Piece of music written for a solo instrument (6)
42 Cosmonaut (8)
45 Vague (4)
46 Robber who watches for police approaching (7)
47 Performs in a film (4)
48 Stagger and fall (4,4)
51 Prepare for printing (7)
54 Cricket analysis official (6)
55 Instruct, enlighten (5)
57 Use your teeth (4)
58 Immediately, at once (4)
59 Reference book item (5)
60 Gives moisture to (plants) (6)

DOWN

1 Scissor user? (6)
2 Harvesting beer ingredients! (3-7)
3 Stuff full (4)
4 Female donkey (5)
5 Rescuer (9)
6 Value (6)
7 Gossip, chat (6)
8 Lacking direction (10)
16 Lure (7)
18 Deflected (11)
20 Oak's fruit (5)
22 Unsuccessful person (2-5)
23 Bomber (9)
26 Hunters (7)
28 Place where a footballer stands to have a free shot at the goal (7,4)
29 Without an object (7)
30 Fit for imitation (9)
33 Part of foot, sometimes varnished (7)
37 Correctly (7)
38 Honour highly (5)
41 Prismatic (10)
43 Make worse (10)
44 Small vegetable marrow (9)
49 Organ containing the vocal cords (6)
50 Whirlpool (6)
52 Intact (6)
53 Kitchen flooring material (5)
56 Involuntary reaction to tiredness (4)

ACROSS

- **1** Scatterbrained (7)
- **7** Of birth (5)
- **8** Blood relatives (3)
- **9** Equal (4)
- **10** Accustomed (4)
- **12** Narrative of misfortunes (3,5)
- **14** Calculate, reckon (6,3)
- **15** Having no accommodation (8)
- **18** Visual imagination (5,3)
- **21** Deliver an oration (9)
- **23** Toxic heat-resistant mineral (8)
- **25** Experience (4)
- **26** Thimbleful (4)
- **28** Conifer (3)
- **29** Warn (5)
- **30** Fanatics (7)

DOWN

- **2** Leaver of rubbish (9)
- **3** ___ the lily, improve what is already beautiful (4)
- **4** Regard as important (4,9)
- **5** Become more pronounced (9)
- **6** Derogatory in an insinuating way (5)
- **11** Record or CD player with two speakers (6)
- **13** Analysis (5)
- **16** Absurd poems (8,5)
- **17** Collect a great deal (5)
- **19** Become ill (6)
- **20** Nocturnal winged insect (5,4)
- **22** Exclaim (9)
- **24** Rub (5)
- **27** Weary (4)

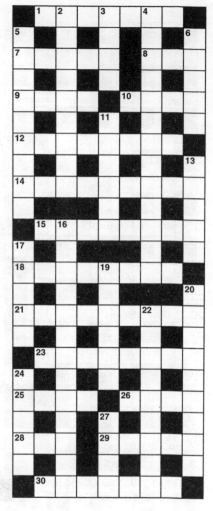

ACROSS

1 Harridan (8)
6 Huge land mass (9)
7 Which zodiac sign is represented by a lion? (3)
8 Leading lay person (5)
9 Knowledgeable (8)
12 Remark upon (4)
13 Composition (4)
16 Complicated and embarrassing state of affairs (9)
18 Pain-relief medication (9)
19 In a sluggish manner (4)
20 Move house stealthily to avoid creditors (4)
23 Visor (8)
26 Grey matter (5)
27 Knight's title (3)
28 Of very small bore (9)
29 Guard (8)

DOWN

1 Inconstant (6)
2 Summer hat for a child (3,6)
3 Radiantly warm (5-3)
4 Organisation controlled by a dominant person (7)
5 Top performer (4)
10 Faithlessness (10)
11 Serving as a sign (of) (10)
14 Rods (5)
15 ___ paddle, early swimming movement (5)
17 Bar-room fight (5)

21 Servant who aids her mistress (5,4)
22 Velvet-like material (8)
24 Instance (7)
25 Fervent request (6)
26 Mountain stream (4)

ACROSS

4 Trashy trivial entertainment (3)
8 Spend the night (4,4)
9 Handsome young man (6)
10 Add (6)
11 Festive month? (8)
13 Disturb (4)
15 Rough (ride) (5)
16 Wise old man (4)
18 Fiscal practice (8)
20 Knight's sleeveless coat (6)
22 Popular name for poor-quality whisky (3-3)
23 Period of active retirement (5,3)
24 Pass away (3)

DOWN

1 Ideal country (6)
2 Genus (4)
3 Very keen (4)
4 Be the strongest element (11)
5 Irregular (6)
6 Universe (6)
7 Heap, mound (4)
12 Mediterranean shrub (3)
13 Plump (3)
14 Happy (6)
15 Overheated (6)
17 Building where vehicles are housed (6)
19 Triangle's top (4)
20 Work (4)
21 Trunk (4)

ACROSS

1 Personify as a god (5)
5 Coat peg (4)
6 Salad food (6)
7 Leading (4)
8 ___ *Bells*, Christmas song (6)
9 Relating to the chest (8)
12 Subject to intense indoctrination (9)
15 Rock bottom (3)
16 Dirty mark (5)
17 Object (5)
18 Drone (3)
19 Sole one (9)
21 Raving (8)
24 Originator (6)
25 Tongue-lashing (4)
26 Thick alcoholic drink (3-3)
27 Acrid (4)
28 Acute apprehension (5)

DOWN

2 Sentimental (7)
3 Filled (with danger) (7)
4 Funnel-shaped (7)
5 Self-made alcoholic drink (4,4)
9 External-wall coating (6-4)
10 Cleaning lady (9)
11 Outstanding (10)
13 Hole to breathe through (7)
14 Uninterested (9)

20 Modern armourer (8)
21 Computer file for storing electronic messages (7)
22 Immune-system stimulator (7)
23 In loving mood (7)

ACROSS

5 Herring-like fish (8)

7 Red, inflamed (3)

8 Proverbial centre (5)

9 Former (8)

11 Virtually black (4)

12 Front of the lower jaw (4)

14 Fringe benefits (5)

15 Miss the mark (3)

16 Speech (7)

20 Butt (3)

21 Esprit de ___, feeling of solidarity (5)

23 Exercise electoral privilege (4)

24 Computer's set of binary digits (4)

26 Drastically (8)

28 Spirits dispenser (5)

29 Rough-leaved tall tree (3)

30 Trilling singer (8)

DOWN

1 Treat mercifully (5)

2 Electric casserole dish (4,6)

3 Volcanic vent (7)

4 Slight saltiness, as in a river estuary (12)

6 Spectacle (9)

10 Quick (5)

13 Largest bird in the world (7)

17 Loss of a driving force (12)

18 Supply (9)

19 Sea-girt pieces of land (5)

22 Bee secretion used in health products (5,5)

25 Thin crisp biscuit (7)

27 Board for filing nails (5)

ACROSS

8 Vulgar streak on the court (8)
9 Begrudged having to compete in final (6)
10 Idiot left in bed (4)
11 The result of a cameraman's snap decision (10)
12 Like a small company and many a story (10)
14 Successful strikes (4)
15 Many set to get general pardon (7)
16 Importance of sculpture outside, right? (7)
20 Some in Paris leased little bit of land (4)
22 Wipe down an unusual piece of glass (10)
23 The arms of fierce females (6-4)
24 Nothing in tennis to adore (4)
25 Aircraft goes to top of the heavenly body (6)
26 Study something banal and feel guilty about it (8)

DOWN

1 Sweep round complete dance area (8)
2 Fingered soft material (4)
3 I'd return with gin, perhaps, to make you downhearted (8)
4 Once again have suspicions about the small fort (7)
5 Alternatively, put bad beef outside earlier (6)
6 Exaggeration about the spinning toy (4,3,3)
7 Post Ed destroyed for tyrant (6)
13 Quietly taking offence about making an introduction (10)
17 Grand hand-outs distributed (8)
18 Tear oven to pieces and restore to a good condition (8)
19 Nice tax arrangement – it's not right (7)
21 Building firm (6)
22 Garland from the war removed (6)
24 The French way to get fat (4)

ACROSS

4 Policeman, in short (3)
8 Electric grass cutter (8)
9 Paradoxical (6)
10 Prejudiced against the old (6)
11 Hit repeatedly with gunshot (8)
13 Horse's neck hair (4)
15 Descendant, offshoot (5)
16 Harsh grating sound (4)
18 Delusions of persecution (8)
20 Outer edge (6)
22 Admire (6)
23 Examine (4,4)
24 Secular (3)

DOWN

1 Scar (6)
2 Flightless bird found in New Zealand (4)
3 Dirty mark (4)
4 Obscurely (11)
5 Variety of dessert apple (6)
6 Peeping Tom (6)
7 Store away in order (4)
12 Creamy snack food (3)
13 Chart, diagram (3)
14 School rubber (6)
15 Spade-like tool (6)
17 Work avoider (6)
19 Prayer-ending word? (4)
20 Earth's closest neighbour in space (4)
21 Swindle (4)

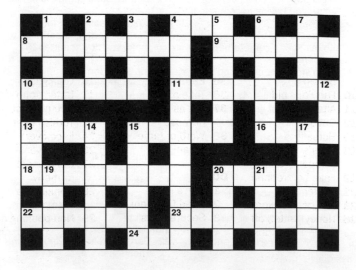

In each of these clues, one letter has been printed incorrectly or left out entirely. Can you work out what the clues should be and solve the puzzle? 1 Across, for instance, should read 'Cutting tool', which is HACKSAW.

¹H	²A	³C	K	⁴S	A	⁵W	⁶	⁷	⁸

(Crossword grid with numbered squares: 1 H A C K S A W, 5, 6, 7, 8, 9, 10, 11, 12, 13, 14, 15, 16, 17, 18, 19, 20, 21, 22, 23, 24, 25, 26, 27, 28, 29, 30, 31, 32, 33, 34, 35, 36, 37, 38)

ACROSS
1 Putting tool
5 'The Scottish pray'
9 Receive by pretending
10 Fabulous bid
11 Alter to fat
12 Got sauce
15 Horse fool
18 River's compartment
19 Fake beforehand
21 Of clan
23 In a perfect word
25 Honey written off as unrecoverable (3,4)
26 Tearful respect
27 Protective year for cyclists
30 But right
34 Rang
35 Battle cry
36 Take a zip
37 Sat aside for a purpose
38 Word of tame meaning

DOWN
1 Nun's role
2 Bead fragment
3 Secure laces
4 Manic man
5 Tidy organism
6 Nautical cap
7 Fill with soy
8 In
13 Shorten next
14 Raise
16 Gullfighter
17 Bitter, soup
20 Live product
22 Turkish chef
24 Face over
25 Falls over
27 Gory leader, formerly
28 Donkleylike mammal
29 Non-peaking actor
31 Christmas bind
32 Invested
33 Measure of meat

ACROSS

9 Deep round bowl for desserts (7,5)
11 Spacious (4)
12 Main point (3)
13 Bargain (4)
14 Show contempt (5)
15 Surrender, yield (4,2)
16 Dreamy (7)
18 Car flank by the kerb (8)
20 Indian gown (4)
22 Under normal circumstances (2,1,4)
24 Makes an exit (4)
25 Dejected (8)
26 Treat badly (3-3)
28 Except, save (3)
30 Anyone with an income, fiscally (8)
32 Appearing from concealment (8)
33 Trespass (on) (8)
35 Domestic servant (8)
36 Magnanimous spirit (8)
37 Tense uncertainty (8)
40 Cart track, groove (3)
41 Long outburst (6)
43 Extremely hot (8)
46 Fully flavoured (4)
47 Stand clear (3,4)
48 Encrusted with sugar (4)
49 Unwanted post (4,4)
52 Fishing spear (7)
55 Water channel (6)
56 Put out (a candle) (5)
59 Aquatic plant (4)
60 View, look at (3)
61 Children's game (4)
62 Complete wiping out (12)

DOWN

1 ___ pig, rodent (6)
2 Process of becoming accustomed (10)
3 Hostelries (4)
4 Monastery (5)
5 Space traveller (9)
6 Puzzling riddle (6)
7 Coarse sail cloth (6)
8 Without evidence (10)
10 Pistol (3)
17 College (7)
19 Nuclear reactor (4,7)
21 Pleasant cooking smell (5)
23 Obvious (7)
24 Powerful explosive (9)
27 Fill to excess (7)
29 Growing on the land (11)
30 One of three at a multiple birth (7)
31 Section of prose (9)
34 Savings in reserve (4,3)
38 Celebrity tracker (7)
39 Be aware of (5)
42 Immoral (behaviour) (10)
44 Variety of insurance cover (5,5)
45 In a natty way (9)
50 Warning hooter (6)
51 Film director's command (6)
53 Useless (2-4)
54 Stale-smelling (5)
57 Price charged for a service (3)
58 Fronded plant (4)

285 *JOLLY MIXTURES*

In this puzzle, each clue is simply an anagram of the answer – but watch out! There might be more than one possible solution to each clue. For instance, the clue 'TALE' might lead to the answer 'LATE' or 'TEAL'. You'll have to look at how the answers fit into the grid to find out which alternative is correct.

ACROSS

7 LEARNT

8 BOSSES

9 ARE

10 LEFT

11 VEER

12 DON

14 TACIT

17 ADOBE

19 LATER

20 ROMAN

22 TAXER

24 GUN

26 MUST

28 TEAL

29 RAT

30 INBRED

31 UMPIRE

DOWN

1 FINEST

2 LIFT

3 GENRE

4 BROAD

5 LIES

6 DANCES

13 CANOE

15 ANT

16 ARC

17 TEA

18 TOP

21 IMPART

23 ROTTER

24 LAGER

25 UNITE

27 DIET

28 POLE

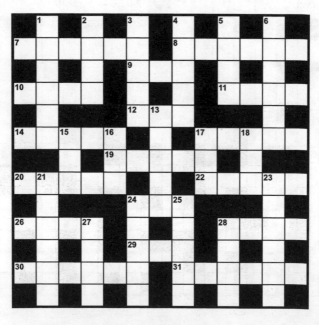

ACROSS

1 Beneficial (9)
9 Difficult to find (7)
10 Affectedly shy (3)
11 Demand as a right (5)
12 North Africans (5)
14 Group of bees (5)
16 Draw as a conclusion (5)
18 Speak (3)
19 Food soaked in liquid (3)
21 Straight-backed (5)
22 Speak (5)
23 Ermine (5)
25 Noise of a sheep (5)
26 Species of snake (3)
27 Diamond shape or medicated sweet (7)
28 Computer's device for floppies (4,5)

DOWN

1 Nook (6)
2 Stop in passing (6)
3 Turf event (4,7)
4 Suppose (7)
5 Jewel (3)
6 Covered with a sweet substance (5-6)
7 Famous female singer (4)
8 Private stables (4)
13 Welly (4)
15 Covet (4)
17 Suitability (7)
19 African wildlife tour (6)
20 Human beings (6)
23 Price reduction event (4)
24 Flow gently (4)
25 Bottom (of the sea) (3)

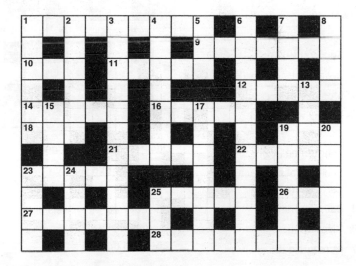

287 CROSSWORD

ACROSS

1 Flexible water tube (8)

6 Item of no consequence (5,4)

7 Enter into a record book (3)

8 Set (5)

9 Advocate, sponsor (8)

12 Minute opening in the surface of the skin (4)

13 Phase (4)

16 Identifying wrongly (9)

18 Long thin cigar (9)

19 Variety of chalcedony (4)

20 After-bath powder (4)

23 American word for a lift (8)

26 Sleeveless garments (5)

27 Sheep (3)

28 Defending player (9)

29 Unfair or partial (3-5)

DOWN

1 Push roughly (6)

2 Show-off (9)

3 Religious travellers (8)

4 Moulded beforehand (7)

5 Photograph of your insides (1-3)

10 Abhorrence (10)

11 Rocket that can escape the Earth's atmosphere (5,5)

14 Court hearing (5)

15 Gives up (5)

17 Nursemaid (5)

21 Previously mentioned (9)

22 Dangerous vapour (5,3)

24 Make clear (7)

25 Covered with jewels or sequins (6)

26 Wish (for) (4)

The black squares have to be filled in as well as the words. For a start, four black squares and four numbers have been inserted. The black squares form a symmetrical pattern.

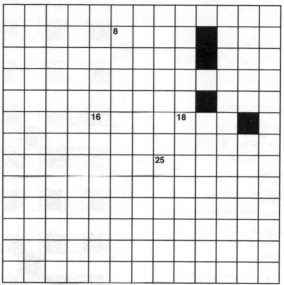

ACROSS

1 Incorporate
5 Competent
8 Knock from power
9 Glad
11 Silence
12 Beginning of a baby
13 Cut with a toothed blade
15 Metal container
16 Formed cavities in
19 Brand name of mints
20 Mischievous
23 Packed in a carton
27 Haul
29 Mode of holding
30 Sun worshipper
31 Place showing animals
32 Any of two
34 Detect sound
35 Passes away
36 Barked shrilly

DOWN

1 Reset
2 Sneaky
3 Spanish dance
4 Handy
6 Intolerant person
7 ___ on, goading
10 Follower
14 Which person?
16 Cooking surface
17 Loose
18 Mum's partner
21 Worthless dog
22 Burned brightly
24 Believes
25 Dining place
26 Parted with voluntarily
28 Dwarf
29 Became
33 Fruit of the dog rose

289 CROSSWORD

ACROSS

1 Native American religious pole (5)
4 Slashed (3)
6 Marine fish (9)
7 Vessel with a high mast (4,4)
9 Inflammation of the nasal cavities (9)
10 Desire (4)
12 Harmful microbe (4)
14 Protector (8)
17 Dull (weather) (8)
19 Hard dry biscuit (4)
21 Broth (4)
23 Whisky cocktail (9)
25 Wet-weather protection (8)
27 Showing the lining by mistake (6,3)
28 Cover (3)
29 Become demented (2,3)

DOWN

1 ___ jug, beer mug in the form of a man in a hat (4)
2 Ground (7)
3 As a vegetarian diet, for example (8)
4 Sleeping-berth (9)
5 Member of a silent religious order (8,4)
8 Consume (3,2)
11 Force out with your thumb (5)
13 Wire fitted to straighten teeth (5)
15 Added photo (5)
16 Military trial (5,7)
18 Birds with long slender necks (5)
20 Lightly tanned (3-6)
22 Monitoring organisation (8)
24 Genteel cafe (3,4)
26 Horse-breeding establishment (4)

First block in some squares in a symmetrical pattern to make a crossword. Next number the squares crossword-fashion, allowing for words ACROSS and DOWN. Finally, put the correct numbers against the jumbled clues below.

S	T	E	P	O	S	T	R	A	N	D
A	L	L	E	A	T	H	E	R	B	U
V	I	S	A	T	Y	R	V	I	N	E
E	L	E	C	T	E	A	U	D	I	T
A	L	B	E	A	G	L	E	E	G	G
B	E	T	C	L	O	T	T	W	E	E
E	G	O	L	O	C	A	L	F	R	Y
S	A	T	I	N	O	R	I	G	I	D
P	L	U	M	P	S	O	B	R	A	Y
A	E	R	I	V	I	E	R	A	U	K
M	I	N	T	E	X	E	A	B	L	E

ACROSS

- In the neighbourhood
- Humbug
- Bird of prey
- S African currency
- Tiny
- Proficient
- Stiff
- Accounts check
- Grape plant
- Pace
- Passport endorsement
- Cowskin
- Donkey's noise
- Stone fruit
- Wager
- Choose by vote
- Shiny fabric
- French Mediterranean coast

DOWN

- Rotate
- Satirical stage show
- Communion table
- Spiced ham
- Half a dozen
- Rescue
- Pigpen
- Zodiac's scales
- Seize
- Offa's earthwork
- Claw
- Otherwise
- Unlawful
- W African republic
- Dried up
- Extremity
- Tranquillity
- Song for two

ACROSS

1 Not justified (9)
9 Have recourse to (7)
10 Raincoat (3)
11 Put into words (5)
12 Piece of prose (5)
14 Sound of bagpipes (5)
16 Large-scale, overall (5)
18 Range of knowledge (3)
19 Dotty (3)
21 Clothes-drying machine (5)
22 Sky colour (5)
23 Parcel out (5)
25 Pleated frilling (5)
26 Common dog command (3)
27 Starchy milk pudding (7)
28 Irreverence (9)

DOWN

1 Denounce (6)
2 Help (with) (4,2)
3 Act of deciding the price again (11)
4 Parer (7)
5 About to arrive (3)
6 Moving-image recorder (5,6)
7 Fruit seeds (4)
8 Repudiate (4)
13 Just open (4)
15 Part of a ship (4)
17 Liqueur that is often blue (7)
19 Dish of nuts, cereals and fruit (6)
20 Adroitly (6)
23 Industrious insects (4)
24 Run in slow strides (4)
25 Strike hard (3)

All the letters needed for the answers in each row and column are given – cross-referencing coupled with anagram skills will ensure the correct solution. To get started, locate the rarer letters first.

ACROSS

1 FILOPPRU
2 DENOOORU
3 EENPSTU
4 AENRSSTW
5 ACCEE
6 EFGLMNOR
7 AEIILOP
8 ABCEERSU
9 DEEEGLNW

DOWN

1 AFLMNOTU
2 CDEEOOPS
3 ADEENORT
4 AGGNU
5 BCEEIPRRS
6 EERUW
7 AELNOOPP
8 CEEIINRU
9 EEFLLSSW

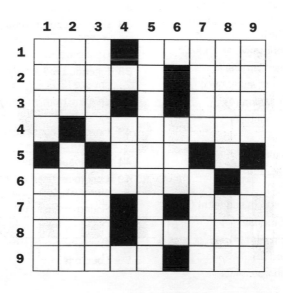

ACROSS

9 Lowest surfaces of rooms (6)
10 Wavy, bendy (5)
11 Grape plant (4)
12 Domain (4)
13 Angered (5)
14 Reduces (6)
15 Starts to chill out (7)
17 High award or honour (8)
19 Flightless bird from New Zealand (4)
21 Train wagon (7)
23 Speed of walking (4)
24 Hitting hard (8)
25 Plant fertiliser (6)
27 Be wrong (3)
29 Earner (8)
31 Improving the mind (8)
32 The best medicine? (8)
34 Doorway (8)
35 Indisputable (alibi) (4-4)
36 Deep shaft dug to locate water (8)
39 Item of neckwear (3)
40 Disease-carrying fly (6)
42 Source of vegetable oil (8)
45 Tightly fasten (4)
46 Going round (7)
47 Moist (4)
48 Boys' jumper (8)
51 Shepherded (7)
54 Helix (6)
55 Chokes with sediment (5)
57 Is appropriate (4)
58 Human joint (4)
59 Roused (5)
60 Corroborate (4,2)

DOWN

1 One who prepares leather (6)
2 White topping for a Christmas cake (5,5)
3 Questions (4)
4 Search (for talent) (5)
5 Condition of expecting a baby (9)
6 Arranged in regular sequences (6)
7 Positive declaration (6)
8 Establishes (10)
16 Made filthy (7)
18 Suspect's dab? (11)
20 Lounger (5)
22 Apply new emulsion to (7)
23 Company's store of money for small items (5,4)
26 Sanitation (7)
28 Echo (11)
29 Relative of the weasel (7)
30 Was inactive (9)
33 Cigar-shaped submarine weapon (7)
37 Gentle waves (7)
38 Extended Saturday morning snooze (3-2)
41 Leaping from a snowy slope (3-7)
43 Unwanted consequence (of a drug) (4,6)
44 Unpleasantly noticeable (9)
49 Cool room used as a meat store (6)
50 Sound intensity (6)
52 Dine in a restaurant (3,3)
53 Lumbers, drags (5)
56 Loud cries (4)

CROSSWORD

ACROSS

1 Beat favourite runner? (7)
9 Woman one took from port (9)
10 Impose too great a strain on open tool, reportedly (7)
11 Strong liquor used by the brigade to put out the conflagration? (9)
12 Ginger's remarkable expression of amusement (7)
13 Take food? Some of it repeats (3)
14 Initially a fellow with the story was friendly (7)
16 Land collapsed into sea (7)
20 Release a Parisian before tea has arrived (7)
24 Girl's suit said to be shaggy (7)
25 I say nothing (3)
26 Madman put money before lady with twitch (7)
27 Sung good wishes, happened to have gone by sea (9)
28 Ramp for pram, for example (7)
29 Doubtful place, it's moving around to be included (9)
30 A certain Edward conceals the skin (7)

DOWN

2 Enjoying oneself in possession of most of the money (6,3)
3 Soldier found diagram under section of writing (9)
4 Fear Tex is exempt from duty (3-4)
5 'E erects another hide (7)
6 Unusually grow in vermin, but produce a plant (7)
7 Impression made in the publishing world (7)
8 I park crookedly after father to obtain some pepper (7)
15 The French before one garland (3)
17 Runner appearing twice in luxurious kidskin! (3)
18 Attack on guffaw in the street (9)
19 Involved in the eighth trick, say (9)
20 Unwind during a French dance (7)
21 Storage box queen takes to English town (7)
22 Greek maiden dropped second article in American city (7)
23 Be remiss, though somehow gentle with one hundred (7)
24 A comprehensive case (7)

ACROSS

4 Large white bear (5)
9 Someone else (7)
10 Make joyful (5)
11 Nest-making insect (3)
12 Append, attach (3)
13 Salty oriental sauce (3)
14 Imposing structure (7)
15 Bland, uninspiring and safe (6,2,3,4)
19 Delicacy (7)
20 Film props and scenery (3)
21 Each one (3)
22 Shred (3)
23 Slogan (5)
24 Alligator pear (7)
25 Person who settles up (5)

DOWN

1 Muslim salutation (6)
2 Go into receivership (4)
3 Having frequent pauses to deliver election speeches (7-4)
4 Entreat (4)
5 Undeveloped (6)
6 Act of sending post to your new address (11)
7 Gambling place (6)
8 ___ out, dispense (4)
16 Give, contribute (eg money to charity) (6)
17 To an excessive degree (6)
18 Large blob (6)
19 Eminence (4)
20 Deck beam (4)
21 Swift graceful horse (4)

ACROSS

1 Heavenly winged creature with a human face (6)
5 Feudal farm building (6)
9 High card (3)
11 Lost one's ___, popular expression meaning 'gone quite mad' (7)
12 Flattened utensil used for spreading and smoothing (7)
13 Welsh national vegetable (4)
15 Fundamental principle (5)
16 Early harp (4)
17 Be inclined (4)
19 Nasal cavity (5)
20 Barrages (4)
24 Gin and vermouth mixture (7)
25 Give up completely (7)
26 Feline (3)
27 Accidental (6)
28 Absorbed (6)

DOWN

2 Multitude (5)
3 Decree (4)
4 Long-grain cereal used in Indian cooking (7,4)
5 Hand-signal (11)
6 On holiday (4)
7 Filmy (5)
8 Minor (5-4)
10 Embracing (9)
14 Child (3)
16 Young man (3)
18 Direction of the Arctic Circle (5)
21 Do a sum (3,2)
22 Animal native to Africa (4)
23 Set of matching shoes (4)

ACROSS

- **1** Female seal (3)
- **8** Lack of a fixed abode (12)
- **9** Grain from which whisky can be made (3)
- **11** Luggage box (5)
- **12** Ruler of a wide dominion (7)
- **14** Widely used coin (4)
- **15** Aromatic kernel (6)
- **18** Money case (6)
- **20** ___ Sally, fairground game (4)
- **23** Corpulence (7)
- **25** Narcotic from the poppy (5)
- **27** Evergreen climber (3)
- **28** Alien spacecraft (6,6)
- **29** Day before (3)

DOWN

- **1** Seal (an area) (6,3)
- **2** Stimulate (the appetite) (4)
- **3** Ascribe (6)
- **4** Happy accident (5)
- **5** Someone who escorts people to their seats (5)
- **6** Good buy (4)
- **7** Starry (6)
- **10** Original model (9)
- **13** Cut (grass) with a scythe (3)
- **16** Idle chatter (6)
- **17** Diffuse substance (3)
- **19** Each (6)
- **21** Long-term custom (5)
- **22** Yellowish gemstone (5)
- **24** Morally bad (4)
- **26** Slimy soil (4)

298 CROSSWORD

ACROSS

5 Publication appearing in instalments (8)

7 Renegade (3)

8 Wimp (5)

9 Pale-yellow flower (8)

11 Rain in ice pellets (4)

12 Solo vocal piece (4)

14 Conjecture (5)

15 Towing boat (3)

16 Beset (7)

20 Behold (3)

21 Young ___, revolutionaries (5)

23 Bad-mannered (4)

24 Urge on (4)

26 Finish a race exactly level (4-4)

28 Cowboy's rope (5)

29 Piece of legislation (3)

30 Unique (8)

DOWN

1 Glowing particle thrown out from a fire (5)

2 Keep company (with) (10)

3 Pair (7)

4 Noble (12)

6 Driver's measuring device (4,5)

10 Upper part of the leg (5)

13 Place apart (7)

17 Psychological lapse (8,4)

18 With the legs on each side of (9)

19 Moneylending (5)

22 Fit to be quoted (10)

25 By means of (7)

27 Set off (5)

The answer to each clue is a word which has a link with each of the three words listed. This word may come at the end (eg Head linked with Beach, Big and Hammer), at the beginning (eg Black linked with Beauty, Board and Jack) or a mixture of the two (eg Stone linked with Hail, Lime and Wall).

ACROSS

1 Bannister, Black, Moore (5)
3 Alec, Stanley, William (7)
6 Jeremy, Simon, Sinclair (5)
8 Alan, Elizabeth, Walsh (7)
9 Baker, Dexter, Firth (5)
11 Botham, Gallagher, Neeson (4)
13 Baker, Jones, Stoppard (3)
15 Diaz, Mackintosh, Rhona (7)
17 Gabor, Peron, Pope (3)
18 Diamond, Morrissey, Sedaka (4)
19 Cushing, Davison, Sallis (5)
22 Harding, Melissa, O'sullivan (7)
24 Fielding, Shapiro, Worth (5)
25 Manning, Matthews, Youens (7)
26 Fonda, Lenny, Winkler (5)

DOWN

1 Dale, Fyfe, James ___ Justice (9)
2 Jennifer, Owl, Zane (4)
3 Holness, Monkhouse, The Builder (3)
4 Edward, King, Norman (4)
5 Bruce, Hall, Ted (6)
7 Dylan, Hardy, Leslie (6)
10 Dunne, Handl, Sutcliffe (5)
12 Linda, Paul, Stella (9)
14 Cotten, Lesley, Stalin (6)
16 Arthur, Glenn, Jonathan (6)
20 Brittain, Duckworth, Lynn (4)
21 Bates, Bennett, Ladd (4)
23 Danson, Hughs, Ray (3)

300 CROSSWORD

The arrows show the direction in which the answer to each clue should be placed.

Fillets for the hair ▼		Island north-west of Rhodes ▼		Illegal action		Sufficient	Pond amphibian
				▼			▼
Strange		Tiny drink ▶				Encourage to do wrong	
			Cabbage salad ▶			▼	
▶ __ Absolom, Al Large in *Doc Martin*		Nigerian language	Amount owed ▶				
▶		▼			Items of value		Strength, power
Flip of a pop single (1-4)	*Mona* __, painting		Has a meal ▶		▼		▼
▶	▼					Jacob's hirsute brother	
Spates		American form of 'Ltd' (abbr)	__ Edmondson, *Comic Strip* actor	South-east Asian coin of small value ▶		▼	
Native of old Thailand ▶		▼	▼				
				Barnstaple's river ▶			
▶ Pale yellow coastal particles	Official population count ▶						

CROSSWORD 301

ACROSS

1 Person easily moved to tears (3-4)
7 Piles of hay (5)
8 Edge of a container (3)
9 Sombre colour (4)
10 Brand (4)
12 Entreating (8)
14 Scourer (4,5)
15 Emphasised (8)
18 Sweat, drip (8)
21 Prevent from having an effect (4,2,3)
23 Informed guess (8)
25 Person next in line (4)
26 Any aromatic plant used in cooking (4)
28 Effete dandy (3)
29 Angler's basket (5)
30 Avow (7)

DOWN

2 Bandit, crook (9)
3 Foot (4)
4 Shopper looking for the best deals (7-6)
5 Eggs of a common amphibian (9)
6 Fine particles produced in burning (5)
11 Fit for eating (6)
13 Partial darkness (5)
16 Indoor footwear item (6,7)
17 Sharply pointed (5)
19 Calm, peaceful (6)
20 Literary exaggeration (9)
22 Free of guilt (9)
24 Budge (5)
27 Floating waste matter (4)

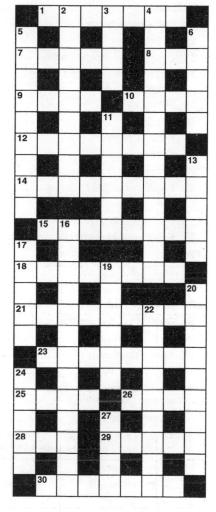

ACROSS

9 Critical and harsh (5-7)
11 Pleat (4)
12 Be under an obligation (3)
13 Metallic element used in galvanising (4)
14 Clearly evident (5)
15 Arrogant (6)
16 Proof of payment (7)
18 Estimations (8)
20 Cigarette butt (4)
22 Highly polished (7)
24 Recompensed (4)
25 Feeling guilty (8)
26 Exact retribution for (6)
28 Gearwheel (3)
30 Well-built (8)
32 Quip (3-5)
33 Heavy rainfall (8)
35 Dealing with, attending to (8)
36 Rescue craft (8)
37 Senior politicians (8)
40 Day before a notable event (3)
41 Mammals related to the weasel (6)
43 Stand, abide (8)
46 Entomb (4)
47 Receptacles for plugs (7)
48 Move suddenly (4)
49 Sluggishness (8)
52 Having ESP (7)
55 Carve a raised decoration (6)
56 Fastens by cable (5)
59 Anger, annoy (4)
60 Came across (3)
61 Crack (4)
62 State of unhappiness with people in authority (12)

DOWN

1 Alternative (6)
2 Sports item made from willow wood (7,3)
3 Come to a halt (4)
4 Move stealthily or furtively (5)
5 Cavy (6,3)
6 Cite (as proof) (6)
7 Imaginary paradise (6)
8 Dispersing (10)
10 Nocturnal bird (3)
17 Savoury turnovers (7)
19 Section of a government department (11)
21 Molar, eg (5)
23 Alluring look (4,3)
24 Foresaw (9)
27 Maddens (7)
29 Collected (3,8)
30 Walks uncertainly (7)
31 Celebration of one hundred years (9)
34 Orchestral musicians (7)
38 Books of maps (7)
39 Devourer (5)
42 Competition (10)
44 Freshen up (a house) (10)
45 Long-term finance expert (9)
50 Munches noisily (6)
51 Within (6)
53 Ice houses (6)
54 Snug (5)
57 Wembley match whistler (3)
58 Cook slowly in liquid (4)

303 CROSSWORD

ACROSS

6 Cash reserve kept for dishonest use (5,4)

7 Violently explode (5)

8 Male domestic cat (3)

9 On any occasion (4)

10 Granary (4)

12 Youngster approaching adulthood (8)

15 Show to be wrong (8)

17 Overcharge (9)

18 Listen in (8)

20 Force into a small space (8)

23 Plant also known as ladies' fingers (4)

24 Variant of the card game whist (4)

27 Fester (3)

28 Bunch of twigs for sweeping (5)

29 Obstinate, stubborn (3-6)

DOWN

1 Cinema torch-bearer (9)

2 Tomorrow? (6)

3 Trough (5)

4 Piece of luggage (8)

5 Part of a broken set (7)

11 Job involving illuminating gas mantles in the street (11)

13 Abridged essence (7)

14 Precious (4)

16 Herb of the marjoram family (7)

17 Holiday hotel feature (4)

19 Bother (9)

21 Country's history (8)

22 Depraved (7)

25 Legitimately placed to score (6)

26 Community of monks or nuns (5)

ACROSS

1 Scaling of the scalp (8)
6 Greyish verdant colour (4-5)
7 Become (3)
8 Desert haven (5)
9 Name applied to a great Indian prince (8)
12 Jump in figure skating (4)
13 Cagily observed (4)
16 Present voucher? (4,5)
18 Jot, whit (9)
19 Prolonged pain (4)
20 Measurement of land (4)
23 Much stressed (8)
26 Arrive by plane (3,2)
27 Young male (3)
28 Maximum volume or power (4,5)
29 Body organ that is sometimes taken out (8)

DOWN

1 Medical measure (6)
2 Cope with successfully (9)
3 Pertaining to a certain area (8)
4 Fragrant flower (7)
5 Emphasis of responsibility (4)
10 Help (a criminal) (3,3,4)
11 Extensive (5-5)
14 Rustic person (5)
15 Assert (5)
17 Complete trust and unquestioning confidence (5)

21 Petty official's portable pad (9)
22 Accursed (8)
24 Notification of earnings (7)
25 Grammatical arrangement of words (6)
26 Small flute (4)

The black squares have to be filled in as well as the words. For a start, four black squares and four numbers have been inserted. The black squares form a symmetrical pattern.

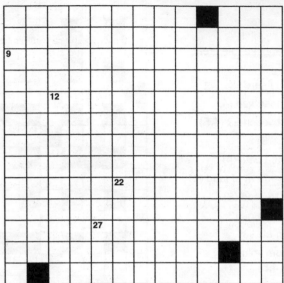

ACROSS

1 Person in control of secret agents
8 Smile
9 Deadly
10 Long story
13 Indian social group
16 First-class mark
17 Old language
18 Ballroom dance
19 Aggressively male
20 Fresh, original
21 Facial growth
24 Crossbar on a ladder
27 Pertaining to colour
28 Smelling organ
29 Sharp sense

DOWN

2 After part of a ship
3 Greatest
4 ___ Claus, present-giver
5 Triumph
6 Taking control
7 In a weird way
11 Heavy defeat
12 Hot taste
13 Substitute for chocolate
14 Ballroom dance
15 South African elk
22 Moral principle
23 Collection of birds not in flight
25 Alert
26 Mince ___, Christmas fare

ACROSS

1 Open palm (4,2,3,4)
9 Photographer's aid (6)
10 Power of determining (8)
11 Floor-length coat (4)
12 Cubed (5)
13 Aristocratic title (4)
14 Colourant (3)
15 Duration of life (3)
16 Whet (4)
18 Embalmed body (5)
20 Prepare (a gun) for firing (4)
22 Seven-sided figure (8)
24 Animal feed (6)
25 Acting graciously to inferiors (13)

DOWN

2 Insect's maggot stage (5)
3 Good quality cut of beef (7)
4 Transient craze (3)
5 Widespread destruction and great disorder (5)
6 Vacation (7)
7 Word expressing denial (3)
8 Abbot (4)
12 Minor deity (7)
13 Resolved (7)
17 Left remaining (4)
19 Great ___ think alike, saying (5)
21 Free from dirt and impurities (5)
23 Also, as well (3)
24 Opponent (3)

307 *CROSSWORD*

ACROSS

1 Quick-moving (5)
4 Brown sugar (8)
11 Daydreamer (9)
12 Unblocked (5)
13 Gain by merit (4)
14 Go to bed late (4,2)
16 Hold back (prices) (3)
18 Point (3)
19 Part of a nun's dress (6)
22 State of deep unconsciousness (4)
24 Arrow (5)
26 Depository (9)
27 Circus animal (8)
28 Young horses (5)

DOWN

2 Powerful snare for catching wildlife (3,4)
3 Great deal (4)
5 List of competitors (5)
6 Omit (6)
7 (They) exist (3)
8 Letter conveyed by plane (10)
9 Flavour that develops after swallowing (10)
10 Handle of a sword (4)
15 Electrical unit (3)
16 College head (7)
17 Spasmodic jerk (6)
20 Builder in stone (5)
21 Appear menacingly close (4)
23 Office chit (4)
25 Drink made from fermented malt (3)

CROSSWORD 308

ACROSS

4 Fuel (3)
8 Old paper size (8)
9 ___ bomb, nuclear explosive (6)
10 Snub (6)
11 Resident (8)
13 Rouse (4)
15 Performer in a play (5)
16 Restive (4)
18 Free gift (8)
20 Upset, annoyed (3,3)
22 Uncover (6)
23 Study of religion (8)
24 Needing water (3)

DOWN

1 Open arcade (6)
2 Male voice range (4)
3 Apex (4)
4 Specific chance (11)
5 Cavalry soldier (6)
6 Body (6)
7 Ploy (4)
12 Flatfish (3)
13 Tie the knot (3)
14 Hard coating of teeth (6)
15 Further ___, at a more distant location (6)
17 Messy, dirty (6)
19 Domestic furnace (4)
20 Writer of odes (4)
21 Fee for using a bridge (4)

Two straightforward crosswords – but their clues have been mixed up. You have to decide which clue belongs to which pattern, but two words have been entered to give you a start.

The grid contains the entered letters spelling **ALLIES** reading down from square 7.

ACROSS

1 Thread
5 Plot
9 Squabble
10 Make an accusation
11 European capital city
12 Sore
15 Trafalgar Square bird
17 Nevertheless
18 Sorcery
19 Notice, spot
20 Grow old
22 From that time on
24 Scoundrel
26 Ran away
27 Provide a feast, give pleasure
28 Rectangle
30 Weapon (3-3)
31 Channel port
32 More orderly
33 Citrus fruit

1 Make a tape
5 Heaven of Norse mythology
9 Financial check
10 Settlement
11 Pass (of time)
12 Senior journalist
15 Most peculiar
17 Bind
18 Shop where milk, cheese and butter are sold
19 Work with a spade
20 Objective
22 Hang in the air
24 Woman making her first society appearance (abbrev)
26 Signal fire
27 Stylist's creation
28 False
30 Food made from fermented milk
31 Roam freely
32 Loathe
33 Malodorous

DOWN

1 Noise, din
2 Long-haired dog
3 Scolded
4 Lacking moisture
5 Take to court
6 Solidly-built
7 Caught sight of
8 Indicate by a sign
13 Creepy
14 Fast
15 Command
16 Lubricated
20 Kidnap
21 Overjoyed
22 Hunting dogs
23 Less complicated
24 Informal
25 In a skilful way
29 Obtained
30 In the past

1 Meagre
2 Become less severe
3 In no particular order
4 Owing
5 Assist
6 Scottish football team
7 Friendly nations joined by treaty
8 Looking over
13 Australian wild dog
14 Radioactive gas
15 Football playing area
16 Part of a flower
20 Overseas
21 Wooden hammer
22 Safe
23 Make better
24 Mythical beast
25 Rebound
29 Organ of hearing
30 Word of agreement

ACROSS

9 Abuse, cruelty (3-9)
11 Eternally (4)
12 Exclamation of mild disapproval (3)
13 Costly Chinese porcelain (4)
14 Avoid (5)
15 Valve in a musical instrument (6)
16 Brief but comprehensive in expression (7)
18 In the front row at a prize fight (8)
20 Old Icelandic epic (4)
22 Drive insane (7)
24 Vault (4)
25 Refuse to talk about (feelings) (6,2)
26 Monstrous woman (6)
28 Soak (up) (3)
30 Suggestive (of) (8)
32 Item left out (8)
33 Prison block for those awaiting execution (5,3)
35 Australian animal (8)
36 Produce (8)
37 Unstable by being overloaded above (3-5)
40 Dark, badly lit (3)
41 Bishop's chair (6)
43 Tenant (8)
46 Aid to discovery (4)
47 Free from pretence (7)
48 Acorn-bearing plants (4)
49 Keep in an unchanged condition (8)
52 Stun, amaze (7)
55 Spirited (6)
56 Cavity in the skull connected to the nose (5)
59 Current (4)
60 Plural of 'is' (3)
61 Chinese dog (4)
62 Actor or actress supplying the romantic element in a film (4,8)

DOWN

1 Animal with white hair and pink eyes (6)
2 Putting on of plays (10)
3 Powerful engines (4)
4 Upper storey (5)
5 Blustering (9)
6 Act as mediator (4,2)
7 Playing against (6)
8 Within a ship (5,5)
10 Great ___, extinct bird (3)
17 Crush (into a confined space) (7)
19 Person elected by workers to represent them (4,7)
21 Isolated (5)
23 Eating away (7)
24 Aviation technology (9)
27 Relating to sight or touch, for example (7)
29 Cash from Mum or Dad? (6,5)
30 Food such as beef and lamb (3,4)
31 Out of work (2,3,4)
34 Compensation (7)
38 Stowers (7)
39 Style of sweater (1-4)
42 Person behaving outrageously (10)
44 Headland (10)
45 Concentrated (9)
50 Job ___, unemployed person (6)
51 Kings or queens (6)
53 Practice of not wearing clothes (6)
54 Slow mover (5)
57 Large rounded vase (3)
58 Badger's burrow (4)

311 *JOLLY MIXTURES*

In this puzzle, each clue is simply an anagram of the answer – but watch out!
There might be more than one possible solution to each clue. For instance, the
clue 'TALE' might lead to the answer 'LATE' or 'TEAL'. You'll have to look at how the
answers fit into the grid to find out which alternative is correct.

ACROSS

7 ANEMIC
8 LENSES
9 ODE
10 MOAT
11 REAL
12 NIT
14 STONE
17 CHORE
19 CRUEL

20 GLANS
22 BEAST
24 CAR
26 RASP
28 SIFT
29 BAR
30 BALEEN
31 ERECTS

DOWN

1 TINSEL
2 MARE
3 ACTED
4 ANGLE
5 LIES
6 REREAD
13 RUNIC
15 SAP
16 GUT

17 **ROB**
18 ASH
21 LINE-UP
23 STEALS
24 BREAM
25 ACHES
27 BURY
28 CAFE

ACROSS

1 Worrying (9)
9 Idealistic reformer (7)
10 Traffic hold-up (3)
11 Unit of domestic power (5)
12 Shoulder, bear (5)
14 Play for time (5)
16 Flooded (5)
18 Brewer's vat (3)
19 Storage vessel (3)
21 Map book (5)
22 South American beast of burden (5)
23 Gemstone's surface (5)
25 Large milk container (5)
26 Weird (3)
27 Two-handled jar for holding liquids (7)
28 Colourful insect (9)

DOWN

1 One-sided (6)
2 Chinese boat (6)
3 Arousal of excitement (11)
4 Frozen cataract (7)
5 Sticky substance exuded by plants, especially the eucalyptus (3)
6 Devil-may-care attitude (11)
7 Deceitful person (4)
8 Exclusively (4)
13 Scope (4)
15 Large low-pitched brass instrument (4)
17 Legal term for a violent physical attack (7)
19 Denouement (3-3)
20 Garish (6)
23 Deed of extraordinary achievement (4)
24 Just about manage (4)
25 Lorry driver's compartment (3)

ACROSS

4 Ornament (5)
9 Pacific shellfish (7)
10 Express sentiment (5)
11 Tin (3)
12 Angling item (3)
13 Shaggy beast of burden (3)
14 Strive to equal (7)
15 Argumentative (15)
19 Cutting (7)
20 Small lump (of butter) (3)
21 Paper sack (3)
22 Afternoon meal (3)
23 Cereal (5)
24 Highly infectious disease (7)
25 Pig out (5)

DOWN

1 Cloth (6)
2 Baton (4)
3 Compiling publicity material (11)
4 Adorn festively (4)
5 Picture house (6)
6 Disavowal (11)
7 Realm (6)
8 Pug-nosed dog (4)
16 Sugar confection (6)
17 Drink of the gods (6)
18 Congestion of events (6)
19 Place for confining a beast (4)
20 Step (4)
21 Root vegetable used in sugar making (4)

ACROSS

1 Pope's envoy (6)
5 Time-honoured (3-3)
9 Small goods vehicle (3)
11 Nice to touch (7)
12 Person who snares animals for their fur (7)
13 Part of the face (4)
15 Anything beyond the Earth's atmosphere (5)
16 Additional factor (4)
17 Cut down (4)
19 Hang without a trial (5)
20 Front of a ship (4)
24 Row of houses (7)
25 Occasion of public visiting (4,3)
26 Holy lady (3)
27 Display (3,3)
28 One who is paid in return for work (6)

DOWN

2 Open (a bottle) (5)
3 Invent (a phrase) (4)
4 Excess financial outlay (11)
5 Calm fine weather (11)
6 Flair, dash (4)
7 Extended collar of a coat (5)
8 Impasse (9)
10 Transversely (9)
14 Earth's closest star (3)
16 Vigour (3)
18 More severe (5)
21 Horizontal line of a rooftop (5)
22 Saintly ring of light (4)
23 Carry (4)

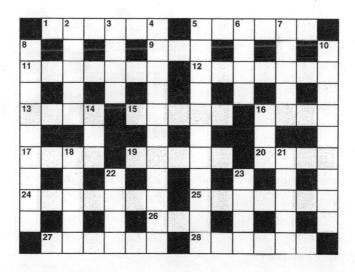

315 CROSSWORD

ACROSS

1 Wrong (5)

5 Gas used in fluorescent tubes (4)

6 Quicker than allegro (6)

7 Colossal (4)

8 Rub causing friction (6)

9 Climbing up (8)

12 Allure (9)

15 Moray ___, fish (3)

16 Implicit (5)

17 Gain access to (5)

18 Costume, outfit (3)

19 Form of camping shelter (5,4)

21 Ominous (8)

24 Facilitate (6)

25 Lash mark (4)

26 Sudden (6)

27 Quarter pint (4)

28 Chirrup (5)

DOWN

2 Fine flexible leather (7)

3 Keep alive (7)

4 Alerting (7)

5 Author (8)

9 *The Three ___*, 1948 Gene Kelly film (10)

10 Went up and down (9)

11 Someone who starts trouble (10)

13 Exclusive group (7)

14 Mistaken (9)

20 Dark bluish-grey colour (8)

21 Fruity liqueur (4,3)

22 Finch-like flyer (7)

23 Regular oval (7)

First block in some squares in a symmetrical pattern to make a crossword. Next number the squares crossword-fashion, allowing for words ACROSS and DOWN. Finally, put the correct numbers against the jumbled clues below.

S	A	M	B	A	L	L	E	A	N	T
A	L	O	E	L	E	E	T	D	O	H
W	O	R	S	T	A	S	H	O	R	E
E	N	S	P	O	N	S	O	R	A	M
D	E	E	R	O	O	T	S	E	R	E
A	W	N	I	D	I	O	T	A	U	L
D	E	A	N	D	S	O	I	T	E	M
E	S	S	T	E	E	P	L	Y	S	O
B	O	S	S	Y	A	L	E	P	E	R
U	L	E	U	E	G	O	N	E	R	A
T	O	T	E	D	O	T	O	D	A	Y

ACROSS
- Bruce ___, kung fu expert
- Patron
- The self
- Coastline
- With extreme gradient
- Dry and withered
- One suffering from a skin disease
- Fool
- Inclined
- Most dire
- The present
- High-ranking university official
- Domineering
- Carried
- Latin American dance
- Antlered ruminant
- Article

DOWN
- Sound
- Scheme
- Subject
- Female sheep
- Wrote mechanically
- Regret
- Runs fast
- Dot-and-dash code
- Cut wood
- Looked at
- Marine eel
- Showing enmity
- First appearance
- Worthwhile possession
- Highest male voice
- Not as much
- Worship

317 _CROSSWORD_

ACROSS

1 Hoard (5)
4 Actor's signal (3)
6 Resolved (6,3)
7 Brought low (8)
9 Large container for mixing a hot alcoholic drink (9)
10 Exaggeratedly effeminate (4)
12 Brush the surface (4)
14 Operate (8)
17 Will administrator (8)
19 Cavort (4)
21 Song of thanksgiving (4)
23 Ornamental shrub with bright berries (9)
25 Quack medicine (5,3)
27 Encouraging (9)
28 Clear spirit (3)
29 Avidity (5)

DOWN

1 Cut (with shears) (4)
2 Toasted bread cube served with soup (7)
3 Ability to see (8)
4 Like ___, running smoothly (9)
5 Complex relationship (12)
8 Piquant, hot (5)
11 Purplish-red colour (5)
13 Clean with abrasive (5)
15 Tusk stuff (5)
16 Angling for gems? (5,7)
18 Stupid (5)
20 Grievous wrong (6,3)
22 Guidance device (8)
24 Mouth-like opening (7)
26 Matured (4)

All the letters needed for the answers in each row and column are given – cross-referencing coupled with anagram skills will ensure the correct solution. To get started, locate the rarer letters first.

ACROSS

1 ADEEINSW
2 AEGINNOO
3 ADDEHOS
4 EEELMNNT
5 AEFRT
6 ADGINPRW
7 AEORTTU
8 EEEINRTT
9 AADENSTT

DOWN

1 DNNOOOST
2 EDFINRTU
3 AADEEIRW
4 ALNOW
5 DEEHIINRT
6 DEMNN
7 AAEEEGST
8 AAEEGNTT
9 AEEPRSTT

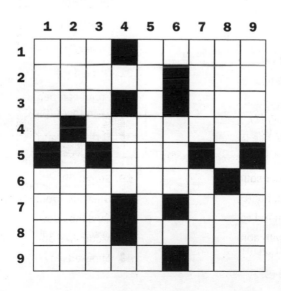

ACROSS

1 Nutritious (9)

6 Cut, splice (4)

10 Light saddle (7)

11 Berry-like fruit (7)

13 Christmas season (4)

14 Finish (3,2,3,2)

16 Scottish girl (6)

18 Workplace site of incoming mail (2-4)

21 For each (8)

22 Corundum (5)

24 Car's protective framework (6,4)

26 Identical partner (4)

29 Accustomed (4)

30 Ingenuity (10)

32 Follow (5)

34 Intrepid (8)

36 Hurried (6)

37 Dialect (6)

40 Source, fount (10)

41 Bounced sound (4)

44 Portico (7)

45 Assortment (7)

46 Projection (4)

47 Praise (9)

DOWN

2 Divide exactly (5)

3 Planned (4)

4 Iniquitous (6)

5 Certainty of death (9)

7 Remove moisture from (9)

8 Height of excellence (3-3)

9 Glittering (7)

12 Garden flower (5,3)

15 Place (7)

17 Egg dish (7)

19 Cut into thin pieces (6)

20 Indoor athlete (7)

23 Undertook (7)

25 All-inclusive (6)

27 Oozing (7)

28 Endless (7)

31 Discard (8)

33 Caribbean percussion instrument (5,4)

34 Furtive (9)

35 Opposite-meaning word (7)

38 Turn on a point (6)

39 Cry (6)

42 System of belief (5)

43 Show anxiety (4)

CROSSWORD

The Across clues consist of jumbled-up names of aircraft. The Down clues are straightforward.

ACROSS

- 7 ABEILNP
- 8 EHLSTTU
- 10 DEGILR
- 11 AAEILNPR
- 12 ACELM
- 14 BDEGIIILR
- 18 AMPU
- 20 ACITV
- 21 DNOR
- 22 AAEELNOPR
- 24 EIPPR
- 27 EFIIPRST
- 30 ABDEGR
- 32 AEIJLNV
- 33 ACHMNOR

DOWN

- 1 Medicinal tablet
- 2 Sleigh
- 3 Inactive
- 4 Scorch
- 5 Male horse
- 6 Scottish valley
- 9 Cab
- 13 Sharp
- 15 Modern Persia
- 16 Big
- 17 Elliptical
- 19 Christ's followers
- 23 Require
- 25 Of a certain Asian country
- 26 Religious head
- 28 Ask earnestly
- 29 Coloured eye part
- 31 Every one

ACROSS

1 Floor-cleaning implement (3)
8 Noisy and unruly (12)
9 Durable cloth (3)
11 Cunningly escape from (5)
12 Shoe repairer (7)
14 Fight between two (4)
15 Metal alloy for beer tankards (6)
18 Make moist (6)
20 State (4)
23 Put into a certain pattern (7)
25 Egg-producing organ (5)
27 Took food (3)
28 Official snapper? (12)
29 Racket (3)

DOWN

1 Any pouched mammal (9)
2 Head of the Roman Catholic Church (4)
3 Undertake (6)
4 Sweltered (5)
5 Zest (5)
6 Clutch (4)
7 Sit with your arms and legs close to your body (4,2)
10 Copper's cosh (9)
13 Former (3)
16 Reputable (6)
17 Worn piece of cloth (3)
19 Indifference (6)
21 Grass road-edging (5)
22 Belonging to a king or queen (5)
24 After deductions (4)
26 Place where work is done, especially near a farm or dock (4)

ACROSS

1 Tooth doctor's tool (8,5)
9 Cleanly (6)
10 Country with an elected head of state (8)
11 Prohibit (4)
12 Search for water (5)
13 Move extremely slowly (4)
14 Wildebeest (3)
15 Brown (3)
16 Soft, impressionable (4)
18 Gatekeeper's cottage (5)
20 Identical (4)
22 Grouse (8)
24 System of electrical flex (6)
25 Having a kind and gentle nature (6-7)

DOWN

2 Merge (5)
3 Three-book set (7)
4 Upper atmosphere (3)
5 Scatter (5)
6 Satisfied (7)
7 High tennis shot (3)
8 Metallic element used in galvanising (4)
12 Stupid person (7)
13 Underwriter (7)
17 Eagerly excited (4)
19 American version of a cafe (5)
21 Skin disease in hairy and woolly animals (5)
23 Shepherd's ___, dish of meat and mashed potatoes (3)
24 Grief (3)

In each of these clues, one letter has been printed incorrectly or left out entirely. Can you work out what the clues should be and solve the puzzle? 31 Across, for instance, should read 'Pours forth', which is SPILLS.

Across

7 Hold lack (6)
8 Guarantee against boss (6)
9 Use a suade (3)
10 US skate (6)
11 Pork station (4)
12 Tony insect (3)
14 Striked animal (5)
17 Ford used in an apology (5)
19 Crookery (5)
20 Braker (5)
22 Tench (5)
24 Sake (3)
26 Verse for (4)
28 Snow respect towards (6)
30 Fermented drunk (3)
31 Pours fort (6)
32 Code (6)

Down

1 Public sneaking (6)
2 Faces given (4)
3 Asian ration (5)
4 Rightness (5)
5 Scond-hand (4)
6 Ribber (6)
13 Sound of any king (5)
15 Money-producing insect (3)
16 Section of clay (3)
17 Unsappy (3)
18 Common tyre of rodent (3)
21 Blings together (6)
23 Lacking race in movement (6)
24 Exposion (5)
25 In hat place (5)
27 Molest (4)
29 Decant (4)

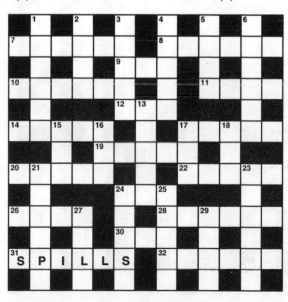

324 CROSSWORD

ACROSS

1 Female performer (7)
7 In Scotland, a landed proprietor (5)
8 Coniferous tree (3)
9 Undiluted (alcoholic drink) (4)
10 Casserole (4)
12 Height (8)
14 Culinary lining material (4,5)
15 Hired killer (8)
18 Importance (8)
21 Chemical lethal to rodents (3,6)
23 Too young (5-3)
25 Toga (4)
26 Emend (a journalist's work) (4)
28 Going through (3)
29 Queen's favourite dog (5)
30 Postpone (a court case) (7)

DOWN

2 Most exciting (9)
3 Travelled (4)
4 Strongroom (6,7)
5 Highlander's cap (9)
6 Large black birds (5)
11 Ideal land (6)
13 Old woman (5)
16 Room's wainscoting (8-5)
17 Tyre in the boot (5)
19 Member of an unruly mob (6)
20 Doubtful (9)
22 Malicious speaker (9)
24 Valiant (5)
27 Reflected sound (4)

The answer to each clue is a word which has a link with each of the three words listed. This word may come at the end (eg Head linked with Beach, Big and Hammer), at the beginning (eg Black linked with Beauty, Board and Jack) or a mixture of the two (eg Stone linked with Hail, Lime and Wall).

ACROSS

7 Button, Cloud, Field (8)
8 Apple, Horse, Wheel (4)
9 Billy, Compulsive, Dice (4)
10 Cabin, Cut, Neck (4)
11 Cup, Flip, Shell (3)
13 Birth, Mat, Take (5)
14 Part, Secretary, Two's (7)
16 Chest, Compartment, Fridge (7)
18 Estate, Secret, Special (5)
21 Butter, Green, Paper (3)
22 Sea, Song, Whooper (4)
23 All, Big, Cloth (4)
25 Box, Landing, Stick (4)
26 Broadcast, General, Local (8)

DOWN

1 Chamber, Ground, Mound (6)
2 Actor, Assassination, Reference (9)
3 Party, Stage, Trip (5)
4 Moth, Penguin, Purple (7)
5 Coconut, Cream, Dry (3)
6 Komodo, Root, Snap (6)
12 Bolognese, Junction, Western (9)
15 Friends, Go, Times (7)
17 Blind, Coaster, Steam (6)
19 Boat, Escape, Minded (6)
20 Arrest, Cover, Garment (5)
24 Chair, Fore, Yard (3)

The arrows show the direction in which the answer to each clue should be placed.

	▼	_ Mesmer, creator of Felix the Cat	▼	Someone who plays unfairly	▼	Son of Abraham	▼
Official language of Pakistan							
▶ Miserable people		Large flightless bird		_Brave New World_ drug		Closes one eye	
		▼		▼		▼	
Akira ___, Japanese film director	Chinese Mafia		Of the ear ▶				
Side, squad ▶	▼				String of events		Tempos
▶			Puts questions to ▶		▼		▼
George Gershwin's brother		Parts of pens	Socially inept person	Clairvoyance (inits) ▶			
Rage given sausage, but no starter ▶		▼	▼			Boy's name in Wales	
▶				Orfe ▶		▼	
Kate ___, British news reporter	Execute ▶						
Scottish river ▶				Official name of MI6 (inits) ▶			

ACROSS

1 Transparent film (7)

7 Get rid of people thought to be undesirable (5)

8 Large vase (3)

9 Chink (4)

10 False god (4)

12 First showing (8)

14 Indubitable (9)

15 Self-determination (4,4)

18 Take part in speedboat-towed sport (5-3)

21 Having bishops (9)

23 Like a comet in brilliance (8)

25 Line behind which darts players stand (4)

26 Any flying vertebrate (4)

28 Count among your possessions (3)

29 Coffer (5)

30 Hide away (7)

DOWN

2 Area of crop-growing land (9)

3 Drew (4)

4 Rendered speechless (13)

5 Engine ignition device (5,4)

6 Aspect (5)

11 1440th of a day (6)

13 Snake (5)

16 Remote possibility (7,6)

17 Dessert (5)

19 Illegal enterprise (6)

20 Throw light upon (9)

22 Germane (9)

24 Connect with a computer system (3,2)

27 Ornamental maple shrub (4)

328 *CROSSWORD*

ACROSS

9 Root vegetable (6)
10 French pancake (5)
11 Partner in war (4)
12 One-sidedness (4)
13 Cast feathers (5)
14 Serve a prison sentence (2,4)
15 Computer-readable strip on a supermarket product (3,4)
17 Acrobatics (8)
19 Inactive (4)
21 Boastful threat (7)
23 Wreck (4)
24 Be proud (4,4)
25 ___ cake, pastry (6)
27 Dutch ___ disease, tree ailment (3)
29 Ordinary (3-2-3)
31 Obscure, arcane (8)
32 Any delicious food (8)
34 Unequal (contest) (3-5)
35 Total idiot (8)
36 Point of death (4,4)
39 Feel sorry (3)
40 Singers (6)
42 Ascribe, attribute (8)
45 Front (4)
46 Provide with a new home (7)
47 Chat, gossip (4)
48 Someone deputed to watch proceedings (8)
51 Bubbly (7)
54 Affirms (6)
55 Sister's daughter (5)
57 Conservative (4)
58 Biting insect (4)
59 Involving danger (5)
60 Imperturbably (6)

DOWN

1 Mooring yard (6)
2 Verify using an alternative source (5-5)
3 Basic particle (4)
4 Look high and low (5)
5 Dangerously unsafe structure (5,4)
6 Infrequently (6)
7 Price-fixers' ring (6)
8 Small citrus fruit (10)
16 Virtuoso, adept (3,4)
18 Soft drink made with water and a grain (6,5)
20 Serious play (5)
22 Supervise (7)
23 Happening again (9)
26 Go faster (5,2)
28 Highest-ranking sports teams (5,6)
29 Chronicler (7)
30 Proverbially, a crowd (9)
33 Cut with a two-bladed implement (7)
37 Ooze (7)
38 Bagpipes sound (5)
41 Beyond the usual limits (10)
43 Withdrawal (10)
44 Lack of stature (9)
49 Being (6)
50 Church changing room (6)
52 In an unnerving way (6)
53 Blue-green gem (5)
56 Every one (4)

329 CROSSWORD

ACROSS

5 Most committed group members (4,4)

7 Stale (3)

8 Allotted vocation (5)

9 Rapid and continuous beating (4,4)

11 Fleshy part of the ear (4)

12 Rough attempt (4)

14 Periods of time (5)

15 Abate (3)

16 Alms (7)

20 Sturdy oil-fired cooker (3)

21 Blackboard support, perhaps (5)

23 Flying frame (4)

24 Tinned meat product (4)

26 Theatre advertisement (8)

28 Hairdressing tools (5)

29 In what way? (3)

30 Narrowly focused (of a mind) (3-5)

DOWN

1 Disorganisation (5)

2 Better, more apt (10)

3 Saving (7)

4 Halloween option? (5,2,5)

6 Childlike sweet? (5,4)

10 Airy (5)

13 Expropriator (7)

17 Uplifting (5-7)

18 Move a cursor to an earlier point (9)

19 Hold liable (5)

22 Tomb-like (10)

25 Condition of gross overweight (7)

27 Open-eyed (5)

ACROSS

1 Slot for a broadcast (7)
7 Ongoing function (5)
8 Blot, stain (3)
9 Alike (4)
10 Be informed (4)
12 Online communication place (4,4)
14 Stop that! (5,2,2)
15 Space through which light passes (8)
18 Late afternoon (8)
21 Ecstatic (9)
23 Person who tells lies (8)
25 Skein of yarn (4)
26 Beetle, scoot (4)
28 Try to win the affection of (3)
29 Set of principles (5)
30 Develop in the mind over a long period (7)

DOWN

2 Dead (9)
3 Be crowded (with) (4)
4 Make or break (6,2,5)
5 Sweet lump for tea and coffee (5,4)
6 Carrion birds (5)
11 Shares dealer (6)
13 Swiftness (5)
16 Unearned allowance (7,6)
17 Fixed hard look (5)
19 Conforming (2,4)

20 Augmentation (9)
22 Reckless mischief (9)
24 Flamboyant (5)
27 Short tail of some animals including the deer and rabbit (4)

The black squares have to be filled in as well as the words. For a start, four black squares and four numbers have been inserted. The black squares form a symmetrical pattern.

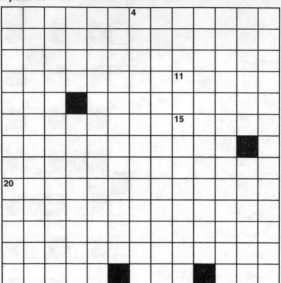

ACROSS

8 Scottish island group
9 Brian ___, singer who left Roxy Music in 1973
10 Without a weapon
11 Constellation containing Betelgeuse
12 Sinbad's giant bird
14 Joyce ___, St Trinian's actress
17 ___ Nabokov, author of *Lolita*
19 Sir Laurens Van ___ Post, author
21 Bill ___, guitarist
23 ___ Hellman, writer of *The Little Foxes*
26 ___ *Grant*, former newsroom drama
27 ___ of Aragon, royal husband of Isabella of Castile

DOWN

1 Men's monthly glossy mag
2 Star in the constellation Lyra
3 Hovel
4 Bill Fraser's character in *The Army Game*
5 Major fuel company
6 Put more in
7 WE ___, creator of Biggles
13 Explorer who 'found' America
14 ___ about, gallivant
15 Pelt
16 Caribbean island
18 ___ *Towers*, novel by Enid Blyton
20 Drink greedily
22 German oven manufacturer
24 ___ Lane, Superman's 'girl'
25 ___ The Terrible, Russian tsar

ACROSS

4 Biblical meaning of 'trespass' (3)
8 Mark down (8)
9 Currently receiving attention (2,4)
10 Thick alcoholic drink (3-3)
11 Equestrian sport (8)
13 Hold on to (4)
15 Disorderly (5)
16 Peace treaty (4)
18 Work rate (8)
20 Pessimistic, depressing (6)
22 Peeping Tom (6)
23 Imagine (8)
24 Sense organ (3)

DOWN

1 Sandy, reddish (6)
2 Glance through (4)
3 Drooped (4)
4 Person who casts metal in a factory (11)
5 Satisfactorily (6)
6 Enclosed – be quiet! (4,2)
7 Without delay (4)
12 Part of the digestive system responsible for processing food (3)
13 Precious or semi-precious stone (3)
14 Fastening (6)
15 Supply with new electrical cables (6)
17 Sticky (6)
19 Assert (4)
20 Change residence (4)
21 Scramble (4)

333 *CROSSWORD*

ACROSS

1 Society (9)
9 Into parts (7)
10 Under the weather (3)
11 Increase the running speed of a car's engine (3,2)
12 British coin (5)
14 Place to air ideas (5)
16 One who jumps head first (5)
18 Divot (3)
19 Thick head of hair (3)
21 Trunk (5)
22 Sweat box? (5)
23 Large meal (5)
25 Proof of whereabouts at the time of a crime (5)
26 Habitual drunkard (3)
27 Word meaning the same (7)
28 Prospective (9)

DOWN

1 High steep rock faces (6)
2 Judge's form of address (2,4)
3 Ceaseless (11)
4 Violator (7)
5 Puppy's cry (3)
6 Conquering (11)
7 First garden (4)
8 Cry of a donkey (4)
13 Rare gaseous element (4)
15 Slimy mud (4)
17 Stringed instrument player (7)
19 Breakfast dish (6)
20 Soft shade (6)
23 Closed or clenched hand (4)
24 ___ Sally, fairground game (4)
25 Unit of current (3)

ACROSS

8 Defer tea break for union (8)
9 Join egghead first and make an appearance (6)
10 Some Arab leaders are talented (4)
11 Carriage to drive mad round harbour (10)
12 Picture-house? (3,7)
14 Pole to practise boxing (4)
15 European has a point that's relevant (7)
16 Person put forward to reorganise one mine (7)
20 Boast about the bird (4)
22 Offer head affection (10)
23 It shows the running total when a number embark (10)
24 Employs American naval vessel round east (4)
25 Rip off a woollen coat (6)
26 It's clear board is hiding poor gin (8)

DOWN

1 Carried in the main (8)
2 Very dry, prophet said (4)
3 Damn lion mauled instrument (8)
4 Parts of head churches (7)
5 Barney breaks out close at hand (6)
6 Get authority for agent to go back on duty (10)
7 Girl has inside knowledge of the meeting list (6)
13 Manager we'd ordered to run nature reserve (4,6)
17 Twice finished food cooked for too long (8)
18 Direction of the wind that blows daisy in cathedral city (8)
19 Discover one in France on the ground (7)
21 Remember to phone again (6)
22 Mad battle to get stone slab (6)
24 One form of trust (4)

335 CROSSWORD

ACROSS

6 Fences of stakes (9)

7 Young of the eel (5)

8 Ill-bred dog (3)

9 Spike of a fork (4)

10 Wound with a knife (4)

12 Large South American snake (8)

15 Obliterate (8)

17 Respectability (9)

18 Well-built, strong (8)

20 Unfair sporting tactics (4,4)

23 Zenith (4)

24 Plays a role (4)

27 ___ by mouth, hospital instruction (3)

28 Variety of wheat grown in spring (5)

29 Cause to be at a disadvantage (5-4)

DOWN

1 Police velocity check (5,4)

2 Cleft (6)

3 Practice of lending money (5)

4 Well-taught (8)

5 Attribute (7)

11 Vividly (11)

13 Strong women (7)

14 Ever so (4)

16 Deep crevasse in a glacier (7)

17 Light shoe (4)

19 Nocturnal winged insect (5,4)

21 Forget (8)

22 Night bird (4,3)

25 Transporter for dangerous chemicals (6)

26 Byword (5)

In each of these clues, one letter has been printed incorrectly or left out entirely. Can you work out what the clues should be and solve the puzzle? 1 Across, for instance, should read 'Rush', which is DASH.

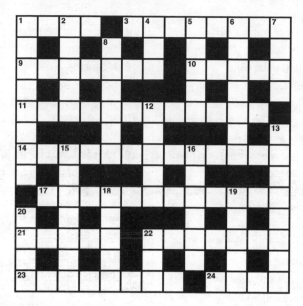

ACROSS

1 Dill pain (4)
3 Had on lean (8)
9 Setting room (7)
10 Convivial gatering (5)
11 Wave out (12)
14 Reference wok (13)
17 Dow (12)
21 Oly fruit (5)
22 Land of fifty spates (7)
23 Locked at (8)
24 At hat time? (4)

DOWN

1 Came into might (8)
2 Muslim omen's quarters (5)
4 Puddle for a boat (3)
5 Indian join (5)
6 Explosive port of a missile (7)
7 Divisions of the leek (4)
8 Type of bandy (6)
12 Flint (5)
13 Keep in a certain skate (8)
15 Preparing fod (7)
16 Filed with surprise (6)
18 Gloamy (5)
19 Native to Eise (5)
20 Period of tome (4)
22 Feeling of winder (3)

337 CROSSWORD

ACROSS

9 Unclear utterance (12)
11 At a distance (4)
12 Sister (3)
13 Beast of burden (4)
14 Male duck (5)
15 Superfluous (6)
16 Feel delight, make merry (7)
18 Bright weather (8)
20 Corrosive liquid substance (4)
22 Have as a golf handicap (4,3)
24 Meaningless repetition (4)
25 Panic-monger (8)
26 Springtime Christian festival (6)
28 Fishing implement (3)
30 Particular case (8)
32 Long-lasting (8)
33 Limping (8)
35 With raised level walks (8)
36 Change in an opposite direction (8)
37 Sympathetically (8)
40 Large antelope from Africa (3)
41 Think over (6)
43 Strategic (8)
46 Resist boldly (4)
47 Search out (7)
48 Masticate (4)
49 Plane (8)
52 Extremely stupid (7)
55 Exuberant strength of body (6)
56 ___ of, in addition to (2,3)
59 Vermin (4)
60 Scull or sweep (3)
61 Performing insect (4)
62 Sterilisation (12)

DOWN

1 Insecure (6)
2 Owner of property (10)
3 Back (4)
4 Caused by the moon (5)
5 Benefit from (4,3,2)
6 Mogul (6)
7 Social outcast (6)
8 Style of dwelling (10)
10 Scoundrel (3)
17 Inscribed legend (7)
19 Woman's restaurant job (11)
21 Double-dot punctuation mark (5)
23 Ball retriever (7)
24 Turn up again (9)
27 Staunchly (7)
29 Utter poverty (11)
30 Badly raised (3-4)
31 Disloyalty (9)
34 Letter, as in the Bible (7)
38 Kernel (7)
39 Abandon (5)
42 Out of the running (10)
44 Destroy by fire (10)
45 Cook over an open fire (4-5)
50 Of singing groups (6)
51 Erode (6)
53 Thought (6)
54 Throw rocks at (5)
57 Lummox (3)
58 Intended victim (4)

338 *JOLLY MIXTURES*

In this puzzle, each clue is simply an anagram of the answer – but watch out!
There might be more than one possible solution to each clue. For instance, the
clue 'TALE' might lead to the answer 'LATE' or 'TEAL'. You'll have to look at how the
answers fit into the grid to find out which alternative is correct.

ACROSS

1	HAM NET	20	RED LID
4	MASHED	23	PALEST
7	SNUG	26	LIE
9	LAW	27	LAKE
10	VASE	28	OSLO
11	A DOG	30	SILT
12	NO UP	31	ACT
13	POT	32	VEIL
14	DO WASH	33	ANGERS
17	RESEAT	34	SUN ROD

DOWN

1	GLEANS	18	TAN
2	GNAT	19	APT
3	AM OWED	20	ERRS IN
4	US TALE	21	DART
5	NAME	22	SELECT
6	RETIED	23	RESIST
8	OLDS	24	BALE
10	BOSS	25	EEL GAS
15	DAN	27	LINK
16	LOW	29	VENO

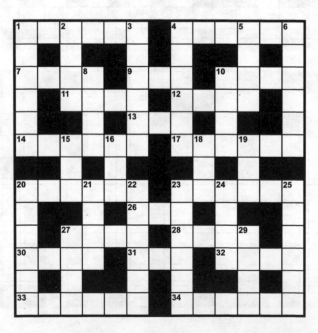

The arrows show the direction in which the answer to each clue should be placed.

Cartoon character, wife of Eb	Helen of Troy's mother	▼	___ Mustard, Cluedo suspect	▼	River in Thailand	▼	Happily occupied
►	▼		Feeble person ――― Look secretly	►			
Born Free lioness	►		▼		Throws out		Stumbles
Most stupid ►					▼		▼
►				Mal de ___, seasickness ►			
Crazy	Pertaining to sight		Shaggy yarn	___ Amin, Ugandan dictator ►			
►	▼		▼	Cash giver (inits)		Slender shoots	
Ann ___, *I Am David* author		Hop-drying kilns ►		▼		▼	
►					Tight coil of hair		Article
Anything		Confines ►			▼		▼
►				Cry of disgust ►			
Former French Sudan		Wash out in clean water ►					

340 CROSSWORD

ACROSS

1 Mushiness (8)
6 Bankrupt (9)
7 Examine and pass as sound or correct (3)
8 Show to be the case (5)
9 Emphatic boxing victory (8)
12 Rich bean (4)
13 Bean curd (4)
16 ___ yourself, bite off more than you can chew (9)
18 Telling of a story (9)
19 Decorated (a cake) (4)
20 Swamplands (4)
23 Relating to star systems (8)
26 Fine quality coffee bean (5)
27 Pub, hotel (3)
28 Graphic representation of a complex process (4,5)
29 Excellently (4,4)

DOWN

1 Menial servant (6)
2 Doubt (9)
3 What is another name for pimento, said to contain the flavours of cinnamon, nutmeg and cloves? (8)
4 Vibrating effect in music (7)
5 Small inflamed swelling at the edge of the eyelid (4)
10 Irascibility (10)
11 Amazing (10)
14 Animal related to the giraffe (5)
15 Noise of a frog (5)
17 Eagle's nest (5)
21 Remove or exclude from consideration (9)
22 Having a rough irritating texture (8)
24 Constituent of milk (7)
25 Implant (6)
26 Bungle (4)

ACROSS

4 South African elk (5)
9 Unclear, hazy (7)
10 Principle (5)
11 Female antelope (3)
12 Mature acorn (3)
13 Hawthorn (3)
14 Leave untended (7)
15 Escalator (6,9)
19 Great ape (7)
20 South African antelope (3)
21 Collection of animals (3)
22 Round vegetable (3)
23 Source (5)
24 Soothing song (7)
25 Alpine trill (5)

DOWN

1 In full flower (6)
2 Rusty old ship (4)
3 Delinquency (11)
4 Gently swirl (4)
5 Items of business (6)
6 In a way involving risk (11)
7 Place for watching films (6)
8 Lewd humour (4)
16 Against (6)
17 Developed (6)
18 Any item whose name derives from a person (6)
19 Natural talent (4)
20 Make annoyed (4)
21 Enthusiasm (4)

342 *CROSSWORD*

ACROSS

1. Wig, hairpiece (6)
5. Suddenly back out (3,3)
9. Time past (3)
11. Big axe (7)
12. Toy (3,4)
13. Associated with us (4)
15. Pare (5)
16. Insincere talk (4)
17. Stride easily (4)
19. Bind (5)
20. Style of jazz singing (4)
24. Lowest form of wit? (7)
25. One with a lot of experience (3,4)
26. Personal (3)
27. Line drawn on a weather map (6)
28. Trap in a net (6)

DOWN

2. Aroma, smell (5)
3. Smoker's briar (4)
4. Small quake (5,6)
5. Pivot (11)
6. Eastern system of exercise (4)
7. Plant life (5)
8. Substance emanating during a seance (9)
10. Overworked phrase (9)
14. Bring an action against (3)
16. Salad vegetable also known as Manchester lettuce (3)
18. ___ up, feels brighter (5)
21. Tactless, insensitive (5)
22. Dress (4)
23. Dutch cheese with a red coating (4)

First block in some squares in a symmetrical pattern to make a crossword. Next number the squares crossword-fashion, allowing for words ACROSS and DOWN. Finally, put the correct numbers against the jumbled clues below.

ACROSS
- Biting insect
- Kimono sash
- Tall building
- Enjoyment of health
- Untruth
- Primate
- Fuss
- Pungent vegetable
- Chairperson's hammer
- Strong soap
- Football result
- Was acquainted
- Ovum
- Poem
- Go by plane
- Honey insect
- Sea eagle
- Gulp
- Pair
- Hero
- Wildly wave arms about

DOWN
- Artless
- Part of the ear
- Marine gem
- Region
- Pub counter
- Newt
- Heavenly being
- Kind, type
- Nation
- Radiant
- Single
- Sense
- Marry
- Type of exercise
- Brandish
- Squeeze out water
- Planet
- Harnessed
- Farm fowl
- Wrath
- Faint

S	O	S	W	A	L	L	O	W	H	A
T	O	W	E	R	A	O	N	I	O	N
A	B	O	D	E	B	B	E	E	L	G
T	W	O	G	A	P	E	D	L	Y	E
E	R	N	E	Y	E	L	I	D	O	L
T	I	F	F	L	A	I	L	I	K	E
G	N	A	T	Y	R	E	K	N	E	W
E	G	G	I	F	L	Y	B	A	D	O
E	A	L	I	E	E	O	B	I	E	R
S	C	O	R	E	A	G	A	V	E	L
E	E	W	E	L	F	A	R	E	E	D

344 CROSSWORD

ACROSS

1 Expanse of water (3)
8 Apparently attractive but with no value or integrity (12)
9 Away from the wind (3)
11 Upright staircase post (5)
12 Containing vapour (7)
14 At any time (4)
15 Bundle (6)
18 Photographing device (6)
20 Component of a list (4)
23 Circular building (7)
25 Sign on (5)
27 Knack (3)
28 Piece of equipment for playing recorded music (8,4)
29 Make a mistake (3)

DOWN

1 Opening in a fortification for the passage of troops (5,4)
2 Prayer's conclusion (4)
3 Surf the internet (6)
4 Set of steps for climbing over a wall or fence (5)
5 Drunken revel (5)
6 Fail to catch (4)
7 General commotion (6)
10 Automatic moving staircase (9)
13 Curve (3)
16 Ceremonial custom (6)
17 Jar cover (3)
19 Inflatable mattress, used by campers (3,3)
21 Scruffy (5)
22 Device recording fuel consumption (5)
24 Headland (4)
26 Large area of fresh water (4)

All the letters needed for the answers in each row and column are given – cross-referencing coupled with anagram skills will ensure the correct solution. To get started, locate the rarer letters first.

ACROSS

1 AAADRRSY
2 AEEORRTW
3 CCEGGIY
4 CMOOPSTU
5 AEOPR
6 CDEHNORW
7 EEGILPY
8 AABCEELL
9 ACEENPPT

DOWN

1 ACILMPSW
2 ACCEIPRR
3 ENOOOPYY
4 CCOTW
5 ACEEGLNRT
6 AAEOR
7 BDDEEEPT
8 AAEEGRUY
9 AEGHLPRS

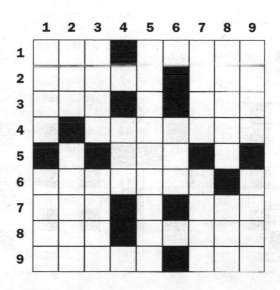

ACROSS

9 Muddy hollow (6)
10 Supposes (5)
11 Top covering of a house (4)
12 Did the crawl (4)
13 Swarm (5)
14 Off-guard (6)
15 In fury (7)
17 Visor (8)
19 Skirt length (4)
21 Swathes (5,2)
23 Puddle (4)
24 Simpleton (8)
25 Decomposed (6)
27 Naughty sprite (3)
29 Judges the value of (8)
31 Submissively fond of your wife (8)
32 Plump for (6,2)
34 Quiet, unspoilt (8)
35 Displays (8)
36 Constraining influences (8)
39 Make legal claim (3)
40 Roving in search of adventure (6)
42 Forcing (open) (8)
45 Eyelid infection (4)
46 Clothes (7)
47 Postal system (4)
48 More voracious (8)
51 Apart (7)
54 False accusations (6)
55 Yawned (5)
57 Small European duck (4)
58 Sheepshank, for instance (4)
59 Praise (5)
60 Sends out (a liquid) (6)

DOWN

1 Brought by air (4,2)
2 Hottest time of year (10)
3 Former ruler of Iran (4)
4 Idolise (5)
5 Show (a film) in cinemas again (2-7)
6 Presuppose (6)
7 Expansion (6)
8 Hot central belt of the Earth (6,4)
16 Disorderly (7)
18 Rowdy macho behaviour (11)
20 Smooths (5)
22 Social facade (7)
23 State of being brief and to the point (9)
26 Curls up (7)
28 Done with no aim (11)
29 Stark, sombre (7)
30 Withdraw (9)
33 Thrown out of accommodation (7)
37 Changes (7)
38 Feeling of boredom (5)
41 Seclusion (10)
43 Deep thought (10)
44 Set apart, seclude (9)
49 Compels payment of (6)
50 Foot part (6)
52 Glorifies (6)
53 Upset (a liquid) (5)
56 Measured quantity of medicine (4)

ACROSS

8 Stark appearance of exposed headland (8)
9 Returning story to editor makes one thrilled (6)
10 Propensity to be dishonest (4)
11 The demon drink? (4,6)
12 Strong belief every prisoner has (10)
14 Pain of little account to man (4)
15 After midday his gun went off, causing great suffering (7)
16 Shorten a spanner (7)
20 Gap left in gardening tool (4)
22 Sent mad about dial vandalism (10)
23 Consider it to be carefully thought out (10)
24 Shot despicable presenter (4)
25 Smoother wave? (6)
26 Check reportedly valuable animal (8)

DOWN

1 New car or wreck, stressed (8)
2 Felt wrong, not right (4)
3 Protection of French boundaries (8)
4 Nasty pain, sir? Take this! (7)
5 Instruction for saving electricity (6)
6 Private enterprise claims a tip for development (10)
7 Thief's strange charm (6)
13 Poorly valued live entertainment (10)
17 Germs from bad crab I ate (8)
18 Stagger drunkenly about noon to find criminal (8)
19 Romantic concerns? (7)
21 Fairy king gives order to little Ronald (6)
22 Gloomy feature in arid surroundings (6)
24 Don't expose the skin (4)

ACROSS

1 Absent (3)
8 Preservation (in law) (12)
9 Central calm area of a cyclone (3)
11 Crisis (5)
12 Land for the benefit of the people (7)
14 Heroic act (4)
15 Took an opinion survey (6)
18 Thrive (2,4)
20 Encourage (4)
23 Fast erotic dance (7)
25 Muslims' God (5)
27 Turkish commander (3)
28 Major financial institution (8,4)
29 Sheep (3)

DOWN

1 Excess population (9)
2 Make a meal for (4)
3 Land surrounding a great house (6)
4 Far-reaching (5)
5 Temporarily shelved (2,3)
6 Mosque leader (4)
7 Witticism understood only by a few (2-4)
10 Level space (9)
13 Weird, strange (3)
16 Weakly (6)
17 Male relation (3)
19 Lubrication tin (6)
21 Cornerstone (5)
22 String-like bikini briefs (5)
24 Absent (4)
26 Cod-like fish (4)

349 *CROSSWORD*

ACROSS

1 Independent means (7,6)
9 Sycophantic (6)
10 Womaniser (8)
11 Car for hire (4)
12 Hooded fur coat (5)
13 Public houses (4)
14 Health resort (3)
15 Small goods vehicle (3)
16 Essence (4)
18 Syncopated ballroom dance (5)
20 Request (4)
22 Recently appointed person eager to make changes (3,5)
24 Simplified English (6)
25 Quality of being individual (13)

DOWN

2 Lively dance (5)
3 Enamel (7)
4 Miniature (3)
5 Become liable to (5)
6 Source of tapioca (7)
7 Guy (3)
8 Enclosed compartment for heating or cooking food (4)
12 Finish military training (4,3)
13 ___ trading, illegal stock-market dealings (7)
17 Mountain goat (4)
19 Impressionist (5)
21 Survive (5)
23 Underwired garment (3)
24 Friend, mate (3)

The black squares have to be filled in as well as the words. For a start, four black squares and four numbers have been inserted. The black squares form a symmetrical pattern.

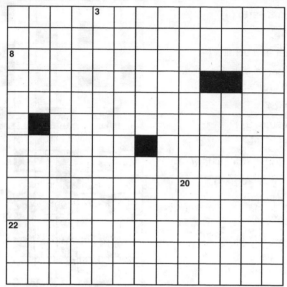

ACROSS

1 Aggressively confident
5 Die-like
8 Shadow
9 Impartial judge
10 Male parents
12 Come clean
14 Formally
16 Cow that has not yet calved
18 ___ to, should
19 Glowing
22 Eliminate from the body as waste
24 Boredom
26 Tiny
27 Route

DOWN

1 Pretence
2 Research workshop
3 Visual representation
4 Vehicle for conveying a coffin
5 Kale, for instance
6 Excluding
7 Museum head
11 Object
13 Civilian dress
14 Carry on
15 Matter of chance
17 Dormant
20 Dormant
21 Cheerfully
23 Fish-shop fish!
25 Immediately

351 *CROSSWORD*

ACROSS

1 Meshed tool for separating the lumps out of powder (5)

5 Badger's earth (4)

6 Loll (6)

7 Partner in a conflict (4)

8 Wine bottle with the capacity of two ordinary bottles (6)

9 Fetch (8)

12 Disclosure (9)

15 For (3)

16 Duck sought for its down (5)

17 Astrological ram (5)

18 Zodiac lion (3)

19 Austerity (9)

21 Without deception (8)

24 Timber used in cabinet-making (6)

25 Placard (4)

26 Convert into cipher (6)

27 Heavily printed (4)

28 Place of access (5)

DOWN

2 Place in quarantine (7)

3 Seller of wines (7)

4 Make elaborate (7)

5 Smooth (8)

9 Consider again (10)

10 Delay (9)

11 To a very great extent (10)

13 Cowboy hat (7)

14 Tolerant (9)

20 Eminent (8)

21 Limit of vision in any direction (7)

22 ___ chip, electronic component (7)

23 Wash (clothes) (7)

The arrows show the direction in which the answer to each clue should be placed.

School work done outside lessons ▼	Refugees	▼	Ran quickly	Persian inn	▼ Volcano in Sicily
Concerning the historical feast ▶	▼			▼	Waste matter from ore
West Country river ▶			Measurements used in printing ▶		▼
▶					
Spinal anaesthesia	Bug a phone	Rebukes	Be full to the point of overflowing	Originally called	
Hempen fabric ▶	▼	▼	▼	▼	
▶				Giggle	Augurs
More learned	Irritates ▶		▼		▼
Restore after marking for deletion	Shola ___, UK soul singer ▶			Chris ___, Auberge singer	
▶			Midge ___, singer with Ultravox ▶	▼	
Health resorts	The ___ Sanction, 1975 film ▶				
▶			Possesses ▶		

353 MISSING LINKS

The answer to each clue is a word which has a link with each of the three words listed. This word may come at the end (eg Head linked with Beach, Big and Hammer), at the beginning (eg Black linked with Beauty, Board and Jack) or a mixture of the two (eg Stone linked with Hail, Lime and Wall).

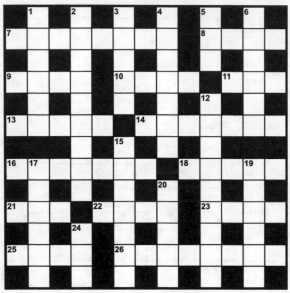

ACROSS

7 Clock, Railway, Under (8)
8 Gold, Let, Mould (4)
9 Ahead, Ground, Open (4)
10 Doctor, Dry, Off (4)
11 Berry, Drop, Lap (3)
13 Goat, Land, Sea (5)
14 City, Letter, Punishment (7)
16 Hawk, Hedge, House (7)
18 Duty, Top, Weight (5)
21 Baby, Battle, Wolf (3)
22 Father, Ladder, Quick (4)
23 Rock, Swimming, Table (4)
25 Cap, Deep, Knock (4)
26 Blade, Cold, Pad (8)

DOWN

1 Bread, Press, Wild (6)
2 Cafe, Public, System (9)
3 Be, Common, Way (5)
4 Base, Currency, Point (7)
5 Age, Hand, Hat (3)
6 On, Shy, Video (6)
12 Chunks, Juice, Weed (9)
15 Ant, Beauty, No (7)
17 Company, Grand, Single (6)
19 African, Shrinking, Ultra (6)
20 Bill, Silver, Wooden (5)
24 It, Room, Work (3)

ACROSS

1 Sharp point (5)
4 Secure (4,4)
11 Brief romance (9)
12 ___ pants, tapered cropped women's trousers (5)
13 Motivate (4)
14 Document holder (6)
16 Deep vessel for stir-frying (3)
18 Large cask (3)
19 Frostily (6)
22 Huge smile (4)
24 Drum held between the knees (5)
26 Spell out (3,6)
27 Dark purple vegetable (8)
28 Not easily bent (5)

DOWN

2 Angular figure (7)
3 Wrinkle (of eyebrows) (4)
5 Alter, make improvements to (5)
6 Again! (6)
7 Venomous serpent (3)
8 Complicated nature (10)
9 Permitting small alterations or movements (10)
10 Strongly against (4)
15 Sign of agreement (3)
16 Avert (4,3)
17 Ornamental spiral (6)
20 Blue flower (5)
21 Overdue (4)
23 Person from Glasgow, for instance (4)
25 Worn-out horse (3)

355 *CROSSWORD*

ACROSS

9 Bedlam (6)
10 Snap (your fingers) (5)
11 Lopsided (4)
12 Excessive supply (4)
13 Colour of jet (5)
14 Plan (6)
15 Put in code (7)
17 King's killer (8)
19 Folklore monster (4)
21 Comical (7)
23 Plant embryo (4)
24 Garment to wear in a
   downpour (8)
25 Make unwanted advances
   towards (6)
27 Woodcutting tool (3)
29 Keeper of a bird of prey (8)
31 Machine for destroying
   documents (8)
32 Well-to-do (8)
34 Sufficient (8)
35 Person who travels to and from
   work (8)
36 Full of triumph (8)
39 Bare rocky hill (3)
40 Split (6)
42 Have greater authority than (8)
45 Obscene discourse (4)
46 Imaginary line that circles the
   Earth (7)
47 Variety (4)
48 Growling (8)
51 On view (7)
54 Stilettos (6)
55 Central pillar of a winding
   staircase (5)
57 Heading (4)
58 Scottish family group (4)
59 One getting up (5)
60 Dog with thick curly hair (6)

DOWN

1 Red-backed sandpiper (6)
2 Large flat white legume (6-4)
3 Pierce with a knife (4)
4 Get lost! (5)
5 Early-morning rail vehicle (4,5)
6 Engaging in a winter sport (6)
7 Derived from milk (6)
8 Soldiers (10)
16 Group of soldiers (7)
18 Small pastry case filled with an
   egg and milk mixture (7,4)
20 South American fruit (5)
22 Eucalyptus (3,4)
23 Lack of personal
   confidence (4-5)
26 Gush (7)
28 Way out (6,5)
29 Drooping (7)
30 Feature writer (9)
33 Furthest limit (7)
37 Discover (7)
38 Bottom point (5)
41 (Due to happen) at any
   moment (10)
43 Circular pane resembling a
   flower (4,6)
44 State of being fat (9)
49 Irrational (6)
50 Underwrite (6)
52 Briskly (6)
53 Weapon with a long blade (5)
56 Part of the face (4)

356 _CROSSWORD_

ACROSS

1 Picture puzzle (5)

4 Adhesive substance (3)

6 Topsy-turvy (9)

7 Villainous main character (4-4)

9 Her Majesty's postal service (5,4)

10 Small carpets (4)

12 Wave the hair by using chemicals (4)

14 Plough back (profits) (8)

17 Too many pills? (8)

19 Pulsate (4)

21 Begging request (4)

23 Definitely (9)

25 Ultimate (8)

27 Suitable for cooking immediately (4-5)

28 Outfit (3)

29 Milky juice from plants (5)

DOWN

1 Flushed, pink (4)

2 Whimsical flattery (7)

3 On-screen translation (8)

4 Halcyon days (6,3)

5 Weather of a very small area (12)

8 Picture edging (5)

11 At that place (5)

13 Mean (5)

15 Artist's support (5)

16 Jargon (12)

18 Lecherous woodland being (5)

20 Now, currently (2,7)

22 Relating to the chest (8)

24 Adhesive compound (7)

26 North American wild cat (4)

ACROSS

5 Cotton pile fabric with ribs (8)

7 Feel sorrow (3)

8 Set belief (5)

9 Mixed (8)

11 Athletic breed of horse from the Middle East (4)

12 Be aware (4)

14 Meres (5)

15 Extreme annoyance (3)

16 Deem, decide (7)

20 Dull stupid fellow (3)

21 Happen consequentially (5)

23 ___ vera, health juice (4)

24 Cut down (4)

26 Closely sealed (8)

28 Aberdeen ___, cattle breed (5)

29 Choose (3)

30 Mad (8)

DOWN

1 Steep hillside (5)

2 Large sandpiper (10)

3 Fond of the open air (7)

4 Established (4-8)

6 Country squire (9)

10 Brick partitions (5)

13 Took upon oneself (7)

17 Demoralising (12)

18 Boat with two hulls (9)

19 Spas (5)

22 Transparent (3-7)

25 Leather made from the coat of a swine (7)

27 Examine (5)

ACROSS

4 Teacher's title (3)
8 Common rodent (5,3)
9 Sarcastic in a literary way (6)
10 Forge (6)
11 Handling (questions) skilfully (8)
13 Manipulated (4)
15 Coils (of yarn) (5)
16 Novice reporters (4)
18 Drug (8)
20 Unfold (3,3)
22 Writing-table with drawers (6)
23 Dig up (8)
24 Detrimental (3)

DOWN

1 Portable cooking stove (6)
2 Hit smartly (4)
3 Ale cart (4)
4 Haughty, stubborn (5-6)
5 Watercourses (6)
6 Scandinavian (6)
7 King of the jungle (4)
12 Airy matter (3)
13 Large container (3)
14 Port worker (6)
15 Jacuzzi (3,3)
17 Reward (6)
19 Have a common boundary with (4)
20 Front of the head (4)
21 Central block of a wheel (4)

ACROSS

1 Come ashore (9)
9 Say again (7)
10 Small loop (3)
11 Enter data (3,2)
12 Seek votes (5)
14 Ethic (5)
16 Large drain (5)
18 Flow out (3)
19 Undergo (an examination) (3)
21 Pastimes (5)
22 Copy (5)
23 Condemn without a proper trial (5)
25 Plain clothes (5)
26 Small seed (3)
27 Covered walk (7)
28 Conscientiousness (9)

DOWN

1 Pass a spell in jail (2,4)
2 Residential area (6)
3 Treat as unimportant (4,5,2)
4 Rock-garden plant (7)
5 All family members (3)
6 Outrageous behaviour (11)
7 Cutting remark (4)
8 Cock a snook at (4)
13 Ship's prison (4)
15 Adhere to (4)
17 Eager (7)
19 Oriental skiff often with sails (6)
20 Place of worship (6)
23 Feature of the face (4)
24 Standard or customary behaviour (4)
25 Demented (3)

360 CROSSWORD

ACROSS

4 Reason (5)
9 Godlessness (7)
10 Young bird of prey (5)
11 Fish spawn (3)
12 Youngster (3)
13 Purpose (3)
14 Pundit (7)
15 Only just gain first place (in a horse race) (3,2,1,5,4)
19 Speculate, risk (7)
20 Cannabis (3)
21 Sadness, heartache (3)
22 Twosome (3)
23 Just over a yard (5)
24 Comics' straight men (7)
25 Cruel (5)

DOWN

1 Bulge out in the wind (6)
2 Narrow-bladed spade (4)
3 Attractive contest winner (6,5)
4 Old stringed instrument (4)
5 Slum section (6)
6 Measurement, count (11)
7 Joyous (6)
8 Which word may mean 'to mix' or 'prison'? (4)
16 Five times eighteen (6)
17 Reddish turnips (6)
18 Fashion-conscious (6)
19 Seductive woman (4)
20 Nosegay (4)
21 Salary (4)

Complete the crossword and the circled letters will reveal the title of a book by Bill Bryson, in which he states: ' My first rule of travel is never to go to a place that sounds like a medical condition and Critz clearly was an incurable disease involving flaking skin.'

ACROSS

- **1** Scandalous
- **6** Jump with a rope
- **10** Secret hoard
- **11** Never giving up
- **12** Out of danger
- **13** Mark of a wound
- **14** No longer fresh
- **16** Salary, wages
- **17** Shopkeeper
- **19** Irritating thing
- **22** Boredom
- **25** Royal dog
- **26** Midday
- **27** Seabird
- **29** Complainant
- **30** Waterlily
- **31** Bird's home
- **32** Update a room

DOWN

- **1** Mania
- **2** Flow of vehicles
- **3** Pain
- **4** Lure
- **5** Make uneasy
- **7** Smart alec (4-3)
- **8** Glue
- **9** Torvill or Dean (3-6)
- **15** Not able to endure
- **17** Regret
- **18** Think back
- **20** Incursions
- **21** Plot with another
- **23** Lack of movement
- **24** Cappuccino
- **25** Male chicken
- **28** Singing voice

The arrows show the direction in which the answer to each clue should be placed.

Wattle ▼		Put out of sight ▼		Rendered more complex ▼		Covent Garden entertainment ▼	Money owing ▼
▶							
Penny-pinched		Expected any time now? ▶				(From) a distance ▼	
▶			Dismal ▶				
Law passed by parliament ▶		Manipulate	Mad ▶				
▶		▼			Norse heaven? ▼		One man deprived of a grave ▼
Citizen of Riyadh, eg	Garment labels ▼		Big ___, friend of Noddy ▶				
▶						Lake south of Huron ▼	
Spirited horses		Main export of Qatar	Dagger originating in Okinawa ▼	Hairstyle fixer ▶			
Become extremely angry (2,5) ▶		▼	▼				
▶				Glass edge ▶			
Vietnam's continent	Jennie ___, *Women in Love* actress ▶						

In each of these clues, one letter has been printed incorrectly or left out entirely. Can you work out what the clues should be and solve the puzzle? 1 Across, for instance, should read 'Filled with happiness', which is JOYFUL.

ACROSS

1 Filled with hippiness (6)
5 Every yar (6)
8 Consomer (4)
9 Povlsions (8)
10 Preject (5)
11 Make barge (7)
14 Go in starch of (6)
15 Pint to (6)
17 Sobtracts (7)
19 Assigned to a sation (5)
21 Frozen desert (3-5)
23 Openable harrier (4)
24 Mussing (6)
25 Expresses grutitude (6)

DOWN

2 Building used to dry hips (9)
3 Vary angry (7)
4 Misplate (4)
5 Clopping (8)
6 Synthetic fire (5)
7 Gut older (3)
12 Stricture containing something (9)
13 Protective strop in a car (4,4)
16 Dud's mother (7)
18 Mile relative (5)
20 Lave out (4)
22 Young bar or dog, for example (3)

ACROSS

1 Nomads (9)

6 Liquid measure (4)

10 Light-coloured bitter beer (4,3)

11 Vanquish (7)

13 Cape, headland (4)

14 So they say (10)

16 Portable computer (6)

18 Suffering (2,4)

21 Made with a needle and thread (4-4)

22 Stout rope (5)

24 Clandestine (10)

26 Thin part of a wine glass (4)

29 Male parent of a horse (4)

30 Occasion where all pay their way (5,5)

32 Short match (5)

34 Support from below (8)

36 Separate grain (from corn) (6)

37 Church attendant (6)

40 Add pictures to (10)

41 Nocturnal birds (4)

44 Gin and vermouth mixture (7)

45 Metal weightlifting rod (7)

46 Rise and fall repeatedly (2-2)

47 In a harmful way (9)

DOWN

2 Volume of maps (5)

3 Meter's face (4)

4 Species of monkey (6)

5 Quality of radio signals (9)

7 Quality of being circular (9)

8 One who suffers for his or her beliefs (6)

9 Long and leggy (7)

12 Prying (8)

15 Deity (7)

17 High-stepping horse (7)

19 Seen it before? (4,2)

20 Atmospheric conditions (7)

23 Shouting insults (7)

25 Flow back (6)

27 Abounding (7)

28 Beginner (7)

31 Take part in speedboat-towed sport (5-3)

33 Erudite (9)

34 Calm (9)

35 Alternative name for cartilage, especially if found in meat (7)

38 Perturb (6)

39 Firmly fixed (6)

42 Ferris ___, fairground ride (5)

43 Part of the eye (4)

365 *JOLLY MIXTURES*

In this puzzle, each clue is simply an anagram of the answer – but watch out! There might be more than one possible solution to each clue. For instance, the clue 'TALE' might lead to the answer 'LATE' or 'TEAL'. You'll have to look at how the answers fit into the grid to find out which alternative is correct.

ACROSS

1	LOPPER	20	LAPPED
4	US FRED	23	STREAK
7	SITE	26	PEA
9	ART	27	RASE
10	STUB	28	CATS
11	HUTS	30	METE
12	GORE	31	TEN
13	DEN	32	SATE
14	RETURN	33	UNTROD
17	HEIGHT	34	LEAPER

DOWN

1	PET ANT	18	KIN
2	DOSE	19	THO
3	RATTLE	20	COD ROT
4	DORSET	21	MOPE
5	FUEL	22	ENDEAR
6	THE CAD	23	CORSET
8	HUNS	24	PEAS
10	GRAB	25	ANTLER
15	PAR	27	TEAS
16	LEE	29	PEAT

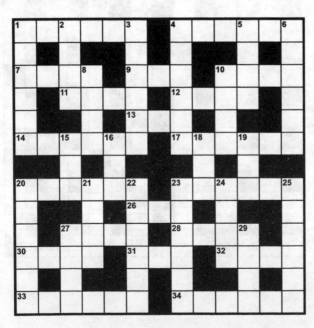

CROSSWORD **366**

ACROSS

1 Be quiet! (4,2)
5 Walk with a limp (6)
9 Day before (3)
11 Establisher (7)
12 Invigoration (7)
13 Quote as an example (4)
15 Poisonous substance (5)
16 Song of thanksgiving (4)
17 Release (4)
19 Final Greek letter (5)
20 Exam success (4)
24 Roasting joint (7)
25 Offer too much for (7)
26 Swindle (3)
27 Pledge (6)
28 Fertilised egg (6)

DOWN

2 Blow up (5)
3 Neat (4)
4 Dramatic production (11)
5 Fish skeleton (11)
6 Annoyance (4)
7 Undistinguished (5)
8 Away from the racetrack (3-6)
10 Close to (9)
14 One's inner self (3)
16 Leg joint (3)
18 Song of death (5)
21 Monastery building (5)
22 Game like hockey, played on horseback (4)
23 Pavement edge (4)

367 CROSSWORD

ACROSS

1 Bedding item (5)
4 Structure that holds a rocket before take-off (8)
11 Railway operated by cables (9)
12 Greek bread (5)
13 Compass direction (4)
14 Linger (6)
16 Make a hollow with the hands (3)
18 Swear (3)
19 Set, as a burden or task (6)
22 Aquatic plant (4)
24 Big old American saloon car (5)
26 Extremely wicked (9)
27 Tasteful grace (8)
28 Heavy shoes (5)

DOWN

2 Carpentry tool (7)
3 Bite into (4)
5 Made warm and dry (5)
6 Sibling's son (6)
7 Cap, bonnet (3)
8 Assess again (10)
9 Bubble (10)
10 Jumping insect (4)
15 Go a-courting (3)
16 Yell (4,3)
17 Bright showy flower (6)
20 Sudden terror (5)
21 Free from harm (4)
23 Gusto, zest (4)
25 Female deer (3)

ACROSS

1 Lending money at excessive interest rates (5)
4 Strongly marked (8)
11 Groom's all-male celebration (4,5)
12 Final Greek letter (5)
13 Bar, tablet (4)
14 Withdraw from a party or federation (6)
16 Deceive, swindle (3)
18 Strange (3)
19 Salt and ___, condiments (6)
22 Mosque official (4)
24 Central African mammal (5)
26 Place for visitors to write comments (5,4)
27 Christmas season (8)
28 Sudden increase (5)

DOWN

2 Followed (7)
3 Lasso cord (4)
5 Possibly (5)
6 Bent (6)
7 Dead heat (3)
8 Continually have a cigarette in your mouth (5-5)
9 Study of the mind (10)
10 Honest, sincere (4)
15 Outdo (3)
16 Acquit (yourself) (7)
17 Impaired (6)
20 Bleeped? (5)
21 Flat (4)
23 Desist (4)
25 Implement for boring small holes (3)

Two straightforward crosswords – but their clues have been mixed up. You have to decide which clue belongs to which pattern, but two words have been entered to give you a start.

The grid contains the entered words **EXTREME** (at 18) and **R** (at 19).

ACROSS

1 Bun	**1** Coarse file
6 Compact _____, music device	**6** Stronghold
9 Fashion designer	**9** Meet
10 Elderly	**10** Arch
12 Disorientated, off-course	**12** Merit
14 Soft	**14** Occupancy
16 Lots	**16** Army quarters
18 Drastic	**18** Withdraw
20 Brace oneself	**20** Jewelled headband
21 Practical joke	**21** Himalayan kingdom
22 Let in	**22** Serving spoon
23 Flat, woollen hat	**23** Dutch pottery
25 Squad	**25** Written composition
27 Pudding	**27** Tax department
30 Ridicule	**30** Decipher
32 Look	**32** Tooth coating
35 Greek love-god	**35** Section
36 Domesticated	**36** Finished
37 Building	**37** Awake
38 Compassion	**38** Jetty
39 Public school	**39** Stumble

DOWN

1 Corrode
2 Eager
3 Think about
4 Begin
5 Shoot at
6 Antenna
7 Press clothes
8 Large town
11 Boundary
13 Strengthen
15 Akin
17 Spur
19 Rome co-founder
24 Icy
26 News story
28 Meaning
29 Horrid
30 Rubbish tip
31 Risotto ingredient
33 Always
34 Tilt

1 Informal conversation
2 Scrutinise
3 Survive
4 Celestial object
5 Clan
6 Cross out
7 Of speech
8 Marquee
11 Males
13 Cunning plan
15 Lordly
17 Old lamp
19 Raised strip
24 Magazine boss
26 Figurine
28 Second planet from the sun
29 Weird
30 Profound
31 Expense
33 Ship's pole
34 Snare

370 CROSSWORD

ACROSS

1 Electrical-circuit component (8)
6 Verdancy (9)
7 Hot racing tip (3)
8 One who makes an effort with little success (5)
9 Curving street (8)
12 Marble-like agate (4)
13 Ankle-length coat (4)
16 Decorative fragrant petals (3-6)
18 Her Majesty's letters? (5,4)
19 Nocturnal flyers (4)
20 Skin growth (4)
23 Accent (8)
26 Articles of porcelain (5)
27 Large antelope (3)
28 Beautiful creative object (4,2,3)
29 Strainer (8)

DOWN

1 Judgment (6)
2 Groom's all-male celebration (4,5)
3 Unsteady (8)
4 Previous (3-4)
5 Old Russian emperor (4)
10 Insignificance (10)
11 Akin (to) (10)
14 Heart vessel (5)
15 Christmas plant (5)
17 Lovers' meeting (5)

21 Accessory for holding back the hair (5,4)
22 Curved line (8)
24 In advance of (5,2)
25 Person who performs on ice (6)
26 Large loose hood (4)

ACROSS

1 Make hazy (5)
4 Costing an ___ and a leg, exorbitant (3)
6 Argumentation (9)
7 Summary of the plot of a play (8)
9 Spicy sausage often used on pizzas (9)
10 Adoration (4)
12 Graven image (4)
14 Dazzling (8)
17 Without exception (8)
19 Leaving point (4)
21 Widely held but false notion (4)
23 Incorporating (9)
25 Beneficial (8)
27 Dictatorship (9)
28 Short-lived hobby (3)
29 Cotton yarn (5)

DOWN

1 Augur (4)
2 Cloth headgear item (4,3)
3 Fisherman's jumper of oiled wool (8)
4 Book's concluding section (9)
5 Branch of science dealing with minute organisms (12)
8 Slop over (5)
11 Officer's butler (5)
13 Entanglement (5)
15 Surface decoration (5)
16 Military aides (7,5)
18 Upper leg (5)
20 Electrically guarded (9)
22 Vital (8)
24 Penetration (7)
26 Letters used in printing (4)

ACROSS

5 Attraction resulting in sticking together (8)

7 Sewer rodent (3)

8 Staple Italian dish (5)

9 Prompt, cue (8)

11 Heavy shower (4)

12 Stage in a butterfly's development (4)

14 Revise (for an exam) (3,2)

15 Common beverage (3)

16 Apparition (7)

20 Little devil, wicked spirit (3)

21 Unpleasant (5)

23 Work-shy (4)

24 Accompanied vocal solo in a cantata (4)

26 Sailor's dance (8)

28 Loud in music (5)

29 Old card game (3)

30 Command (8)

DOWN

1 Keep a tally (5)

2 Temporary support for concrete work (10)

3 Free from germs (7)

4 Insurance agent (4,8)

6 Bear off (5,4)

10 Bread morsel (5)

13 Arranging intervals (7)

17 Party or coalition representing left-wing elements (7,5)

18 Complete (6,3)

19 Without question (2,3)

22 Painstaking (10)

25 In profusion (7)

27 Sturdy footwear (5)

The answer to each clue is a word which has a link with each of the three words listed. This word may come at the end (eg Head linked with Beach, Big and Hammer), at the beginning (eg Black linked with Beauty, Board and Jack) or a mixture of the two (eg Stone linked with Hail, Lime and Wall).

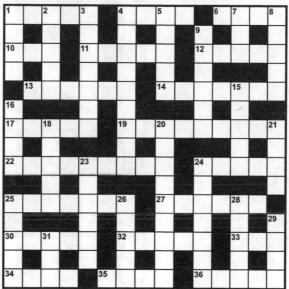

ACROSS

1 BURST, NINE, RAIN (5)
4 GLOVE, READY, WARE (4)
6 DOUBLE, STRAP, WAG (4)
10 FORE, RED, SAW (3)
11 CORN, MARSHAL, MOUSE (5)
12 CITY, EAR, TUBE (5)
13 BALL, FODDER, WATER (6)
14 JUDGEMENT, NATURE, PRICE (7)
17 BEHIND, FRENCH, UNSAID (5)
19 CRY, GROUND, SOCIAL (9)
22 DRIVE, PILOT, VENDING (9)
24 BLACK-EYED, HAMPSHIRE, LAZY (5)
25 CURRENCY, LEGION, OFFICE (7)
27 BOAT, ESCAPE, MINDED (6)
30 BOARD, GROUND, HEAVENS (5)
32 BACK, SLICER, STREAKY (5)
33 AWAY, FLUNG, SO (3)
34 FAMILY, HOUSE, MUG (4)
35 DUMB, HARE, JAR (4)
36 BIRD, RETIREMENT, RISER (5)

DOWN

1 AWAY, LIST, PLASTER (4)
2 COMIC, HOUSE, SOAP (5)
3 LAWYER, MECHANISM, SELF (7)
4 BAG, STAY, SUCCESS (9)
5 BERRY, COMMUNITY, FLOWER (5)
7 MOTHER, PEA, PECK (3)
8 MAID, SHARK, WET (5)
9 MUSCLE, PAPER, TYPE (6)
15 AGAINST, HAND, TOWEL (5)
16 BITTEN, CIRCUS, POWDER (4)
18 ALL, HOURS, NOON (5)
20 COLLEGE, DRAWING, FAULT (9)
21 BE, DOG, GOOSE (4)
23 AUNT, NAME, VOYAGE (6)
24 LAND, NESS, WAYS (7)
25 BEAN, DAY, MIDNIGHT (5)
26 ART, MAN, SAVAGE (5)
28 ON, SPECIAL, UP (5)
29 AREA, HOUND, MATTER (4)
31 OFF, SELF, SOME (3)

374 CROSSWORD

ACROSS

1 Stun with amazement (7)

7 Elliptic (5)

8 Fix (3)

9 Detriment (4)

10 Show approval (4)

12 Go away! (5,3)

14 Retailer of men's clothing (9)

15 Unripe (8)

18 Poisonous plant (8)

21 School friend (9)

23 Disgusting (8)

25 Ajar (4)

26 Fright (4)

28 Source mineral (3)

29 Bring about (havoc) (5)

30 ___ attention, soldier's stance (5,2)

DOWN

2 Page designed to be removed (4,5)

3 Rhyming verse (4)

4 Load-carrying vehicle (4-4,5)

5 Assembler of objects of interest (9)

6 Yawning (5)

11 Ointment for treating bruises (6)

13 Moisture extractor (5)

16 Personnel control (3-10)

17 Protective garment (5)

19 Spurn (temptation) (6)

20 Measure of typing speed (9)

22 Reparation (9)

24 Sign in to a computer system (3,2)

27 Long-necked waterbird (4)

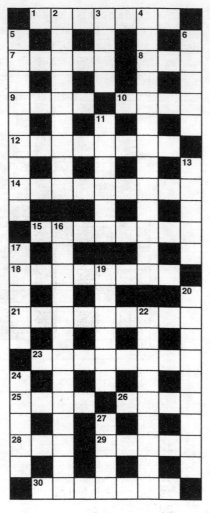

In each of these clues, one letter has been printed incorrectly or left out entirely. Can you work out what the clues should be and solve the puzzle? 22 Across, for instance, should read 'Coils', which is LOOPS.

ACROSS

7 Colourful flowering plank (6)
8 Pay weed (6)
9 Immortal bing (3)
10 Cell or hide (4)
11 Timings (4)
12 Swoop (3)
14 Wrungdoing (5)
17 Darning signal (5)
19 Exactly mutched (5)
20 Tatted up (5)
22 Boils (5)
24 Stange (3)
26 Unwielding (4)
28 Beams of sight (4)
29 Long period of tame (3)
30 Jilted (6)
31 Robbing a cloth over (6)

DOWN

1 Not as might (6)
2 Curse of action (4)
3 Honey received for work (5)
4 With great city (5)
5 Tender unconscious (4)
6 Volution (6)
13 Unit of height (5)
15 Get shop of (3)
16 Blight colour (3)
17 Each and very (3)
18 Tone by (3)
21 Devises (6)
23 Living money for (6)
24 Booking receptacles (5)
25 Picks (a curd) (5)
27 Member of the deerage (4)
28 Strong word (4)

ACROSS

9 Collared dress with buttons down the front (12)
11 Engrave on metal (4)
12 In days gone by (3)
13 Flat round plate (4)
14 Light modelling wood (5)
15 Ends prematurely (6)
16 Confrontation (4-3)
18 Lawn weed (8)
20 Area of a church (4)
22 Yarn maker (7)
24 Ballooned (4)
25 Replacement orb (5,3)
26 Like angles over 90° (6)
28 Hit sharply (3)
30 Afternoon snack (5,3)
32 By general agreement, without voting (2,3,3)
33 Nares (8)
35 Cross-border goods vendor (8)
36 Not tried and tested (8)
37 Listened to advice (4,4)
40 Bonfire effigy (3)
41 Tries (6)
43 Bright in the dark (8)
46 Hit, thump (4)
47 Darts (7)
48 Consumes food (4)
49 Loosening (shoes) (8)
52 Victorian madhouses (7)
55 Looked amused (6)
56 Tapestry (5)
59 Mugging weapon (4)
60 Poem often addressed to a person or object (3)
61 Very dark (4)
62 Expert on paintings (3,9)

DOWN

1 Australian word for a girl or young woman (6)
2 Bat-and-ball players (10)
3 Wash (the decks) (4)
4 String instrument (5)
5 Big and strong (9)
6 Groups of tarot cards (6)
7 Mutiny (6)
8 Absent-mindedness (10)
10 Turkish ruler (3)
17 Speediest (7)
19 Arson (4-7)
21 Lighter in colour (5)
23 Tiled high-point of a house (7)
24 Hide out (2,2,5)
27 Withstood (7)
29 Minimum income level needed to live (7,4)
30 ___ up, bring to the imagination (7)
31 Ensuing effect (9)
34 Besieges (7)
38 Liquid diffusion in plants (7)
39 Be jubilant (5)
42 Small marine sessile creature (3,7)
44 Fine ribbed fabric (10)
45 Big talkers (9)
50 Backstreets (6)
51 ___ summer, late burst of hot weather (6)
53 Lose (6)
54 Place where the legs join the abdomen (5)
57 Commercials (3)
58 Hardens (4)

377 *JOLLY MIXTURES*

In this puzzle, each clue is simply an anagram of the answer – but watch out!
There might be more than one possible solution to each clue. For Instance, the
clue 'TALE' might lead to the answer 'LATE' or 'TEAL'. You'll have to look at how the
answers fit into the grid to find out which alternative is correct.

ACROSS

1 BEATER	20 CAPERS
4 AT REAR	23 SNARED
7 APES	26 PAY
9 OPT	27 ONCE
10 SLOE	28 SEAT
11 LURE	30 MARE
12 NOPE	31 ALE
13 PAR	32 ACHE
14 DIG SET	33 EDITED
17 MRS EON	34 DENSER

DOWN

1 PAIRED	18 ARE
2 BRAE	19 DAM
3 PET REX	20 SCARED
4 STEP SO	21 MOAT
5 NO NA	22 DYE ELI
6 AN EXAM	23 PASSER
8 RUSE	24 TONE
10 EARS	25 HER ART
15 RAG	27 ACRE
16 SPA	29 DAIS

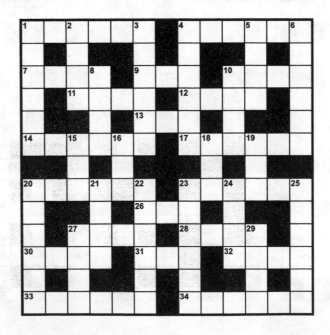

438|

ACROSS

1 Flaky part of the head? (5)
4 Widespread disease (8)
11 Lacking moral restraint (9)
12 Another name for the adder (5)
13 Forget to include (4)
14 ___ sugar, powdery variety (6)
16 T'ai ___, martial art (3)
18 Charged particle (3)
19 In continual discomfort (6)
22 Flax pod (4)
24 Deduce logically (5)
26 Cleared up (6,3)
27 Greatness of mind or character (8)
28 Enlighten (5)

DOWN

2 Hassock (7)
3 Plunder (4)
5 Watchful, wide awake (5)
6 Of varying types (6)
7 Area plan (3)
8 Warmth (10)
9 Rebuke, remonstrance (10)
10 Brass musical instrument (4)
15 Move on snow (3)
16 Reduce heat gradually (4,3)
17 Section of a scout troop (6)
20 Lifting machine (5)
21 Corner, narrow recess (4)
23 Distort to a curve (4)
25 Half-truth (3)

379 CROSSWORD

ACROSS

1 Rhythmic monologue to music (3)
8 System of shops opening only in the morning one day a week (5,7)
9 Railway coach (3)
11 Yellowish-brown (5)
12 Gland secretion (7)
14 Scratch (at) (4)
15 French brandy (6)
18 Waster (6)
20 Pay attention to (4)
23 Blue-flowered garden plant (7)
25 Prepare a financial account (5)
27 Gases in the atmosphere (3)
28 Tide level (3-5,4)
29 Disease-prone tree (3)

DOWN

1 Resolve the differences between (9)
2 Extra benefit (4)
3 Large naval force (6)
4 One who has little faith in human sincerity or goodness (5)
5 First-class mark (5)
6 Russian monarch (4)
7 Unique occurrence (3-3)
10 Instruct (a computer) again (9)
13 Barn bird? (3)
16 Ape with very long arms (6)
17 T'ai ___, martial art (3)
19 Difficult experience (6)
21 Connect (an electrical device) with the ground (5)
22 Milking house (5)
24 Lascivious (4)
26 Extract (4)

ACROSS

1 Publisher's brush-off (9,4)
9 Energy (6)
10 Eager for money (8)
11 Political protest march (4)
12 Receiver of stolen goods (5)
13 Aromatic herb (4)
14 Set (3)
15 18th-century gambling card game (3)
16 Become worn at the edges (4)
18 Restive (5)
20 Grassy area (4)
22 Female relation (8)
24 Postpone (6)
25 Aid to progress (8,5)

DOWN

2 Omit (a syllable) (5)
3 Study of the environment (7)
4 Coal distillate (3)
5 Any vital part of the body (5)
6 Nicely rounded (7)
7 Mischievous child (3)
8 Warm and cosy (4)
12 Hinged lid (4-3)
13 Diluting agent (7)
17 Horse of mixed colour (4)
19 Small dog (5)
21 Knitted (5)
23 Obtain, acquire (3)
24 Drop in the middle (3)

ACROSS

1 Association (7)
7 Provide (for) (5)
8 Central (3)
9 Energy, style (4)
10 Smack (4)
12 Independence (8)
14 Whale-killer (9)
15 Snowball (8)
18 Removable orb? (5,3)
21 From the barrel (of beer) (2,7)
23 Get lost! (5,3)
25 Unit of matter (4)
26 Termites (4)
28 Butt (3)
29 Wild infectious fear (5)
30 Father, Son and Holy Ghost (7)

DOWN

2 Great painter of former times (3,6)
3 Populous place between village and city in size (4)
4 Praising (13)
5 Extra-sensory perception between two minds (9)
6 Change to suit the circumstances (5)
11 Mohair (6)
13 More parched (5)
16 Person who spreads or enjoys gossip (13)
17 Shining (5)
19 Asian medicine man (6)
20 Holdall for a sleeping bag (5,4)
22 Plant seed eaten as a snack (9)
24 Leaves a car (5)
27 Gyrate (4)

First block in some squares in a symmetrical pattern to make a crossword. Next number the squares crossword-fashion, allowing for words ACROSS and DOWN. Finally, put the correct numbers against the jumbled clues below.

S	A	G	A	N	C	A	E	S	A	R
L	I	M	B	O	O	K	A	C	R	E
I	N	T	O	S	S	P	I	R	I	T
P	I	H	U	E	F	L	E	A	D	U
L	O	A	T	H	R	A	C	T	O	R
P	A	L	E	E	A	T	S	C	A	N
L	E	G	A	L	I	E	C	H	O	B
U	S	E	A	L	L	Y	R	A	I	L
N	A	R	R	O	W	L	E	D	G	E
G	A	I	T	W	A	R	E	R	I	A
E	R	A	S	E	R	S	K	I	C	K

ACROSS

— (They) exist
— Constricted
— Consume
— Deliver a blow with the foot
— Emotional state
— Hoot with derision
— Keen on
— Legitimate
— Long detailed story
— Pledge
— Reverberate
— Rim
— Rubber
— Stage-player
— Type of salad

DOWN

— African republic
— Come back
— Fluid escape
— Hi
— In the area or vicinity
— Inadvertent mistake
— Item of crockery
— Period of conflict
— Relieve an itch
— Steep drop
— Stream of water smaller than a river
— Type of lettuce

383 *CROSSWORD*

ACROSS

1 Cylinder around which thread is wound (5)
4 TV programme with contestants (4,4)
11 Good poker hand (4,5)
12 Musician present at many Scottish events (5)
13 Minor irritation (4)
14 Roof beam (6)
16 Stuff chewed by a cow (3)
18 Electrically charged particle (3)
19 With parents closely related (6)
22 Test of public opinion (4)
24 Unit of gas measurement (5)
26 Vast (9)
27 Timid (8)
28 Warm by rubbing (5)

DOWN

2 Bird with an enormous bill (7)
3 Darts player's starting point (4)
5 Deflect (5)
6 Ace (6)
7 Move on one leg (3)
8 Top-notch, globally (5-5)
9 Umpire or referee, eg (10)
10 Chrysalis (4)
15 On account of (3)
16 Simmer down (4,3)
17 More indistinct (6)
20 Meat eaten at breakfast (5)
21 Be resentful of (4)
23 Roguish (4)
25 Take into the mouth, chew and swallow (3)

All the letters needed for the answers in each row and column are given – cross-referencing coupled with anagram skills will ensure the correct solution. To get started, locate the rarer letters first.

ACROSS

1 AEPSSSTW
2 AELOORST
3 ADDEERS
4 AACDEMTY
5 ACEST
6 AGINPSTV
7 AEENTVY
8 EENORTUY
9 ADENSSSY

DOWN

1 AAPRSTWY
2 AACEENOR
3 ADNOSSTU
4 ACDST
5 ADEEISSTV
6 DENNT
7 EEEGLSST
8 AEEMOPSY
9 AERSTVYY

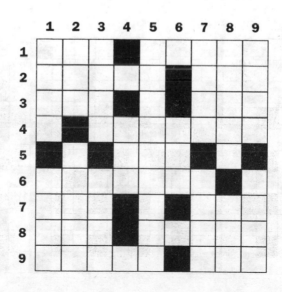

ACROSS

4 Nut variety (5)
9 Hot to the taste (7)
10 Be alive (5)
11 Sprint, hurry (3)
12 Straight away (3)
13 Grass grain (3)
14 Appearing (7)
15 Device allowing pedestrians to go over a road (7,8)
19 Apparition (7)
20 Organised conflict (3)
21 Contagious disease (3)
22 Constricting snake (3)
23 Concreted area between house and garden (5)
24 Turning on an axis (7)
25 Suffering deprivation (5)

DOWN

1 Begin business for the day (4,2)
2 Gush (4)
3 Disparagement (11)
4 Heap on which a corpse is ceremonially burned (4)
5 Official with power to expurgate films etc (6)
6 As a matter of course (11)
7 Bathing costume (6)
8 Male deer (4)
16 Add-on shed (4-2)
17 Deft (6)
18 Dirt (6)
19 Bursts suddenly (4)
20 On your guard (4)
21 Silver paper (4)

ACROSS

4 Tail movement (3)
8 Eastern beverage (5,3)
9 Fairness (6)
10 Oblique (6)
11 Vertically hinged window (8)
13 Tiresome thing (4)
15 Object, protest (5)
16 Floating structure (4)
18 On an unsaddled horse (8)
20 Ready for use (2,4)
22 Carriage with a folding top (6)
23 Lifestyle involving wearing no clothes (8)
24 Small breed of dog (3)

DOWN

1 Salt dispenser (6)
2 Freezing precipitation (4)
3 Version of poker (4)
4 Manufacture and repairing of timepieces (11)
5 Water spout (6)
6 Masque actor (6)
7 Render senseless with a blow (4)
12 Sound expressing mild disapproval (3)
13 Pat gently (3)
14 Too hungry? (6)
15 Come to a halt (4,2)
17 Conclude (6)
19 Partially open (4)
20 Small amount (4)
21 Deer (4)

387 *CROSSWORD*

ACROSS

1 Cloth put on the floor when decorating (4,5)
9 Rust (7)
10 Be obliged to repay (3)
11 Race again (5)
12 Too quick? (5)
14 Indian savoury cake, often of onions (5)
16 Corn for grinding (5)
18 Slow-growing tree with tight-grained wood (3)
19 Upper limb (3)
21 Arrive eventually (3,2)
22 House made of ice (5)
23 Mask (5)
25 Departure (5)
26 Rear of a ship (3)
27 South American pig (7)
28 Procession for a visit by a head of state (9)

DOWN

1 Visit (4,2)
2 Alternate (3-3)
3 Street running parallel to a main route (7,4)
4 Fuming (7)
5 Twenty hundredweight (3)
6 Conservative (5-6)
7 Apple seeds (4)
8 Moist (4)
13 Neophyte (4)
15 Man of the moment (4)
17 Indent with a mark (7)
19 Llama-like animal (6)
20 Produce a blotchy effect (6)
23 Cloak (4)
24 Immoral or evil behaviour (4)
25 PE hall (3)

The black squares have to be filled in as well as the words. For a start, four black squares and four numbers have been inserted. The black squares form a symmetrical pattern.

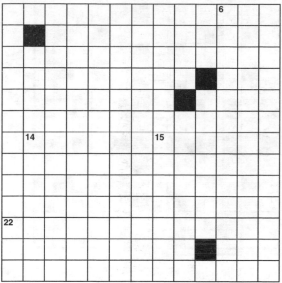

ACROSS

- **1** Person who looks after kids
- **9** Clerk, officer worker etc
- **10** Handbill
- **12** Protective covering for a shoe
- **14** Clear jelly of stock and gelatine
- **15** Corrode
- **19** Swear
- **20** Imaginary monster
- **22** Destruction of germs
- **24** (Of a rule) possible to make sure people obey it

DOWN

- **2** Make a sound like a bee
- **3** Small metal prong that holds a wheel in place
- **4** Control
- **5** Standard, par
- **6** Substance emanating during a seance
- **7** Overjoyed
- **8** Reality
- **11** Rule (a country) inefficiently
- **13** Sugar variety
- **16** Small white flower that grows on lawns
- **17** Imaginary belt in the heavens
- **18** Pointless
- **21** Writing instrument
- **23** Ailing

389 *DILEMMA*

Two straightforward crosswords – but their clues have been mixed up. You have to decide which clue belongs to which pattern, but two words have been entered to give you a start.

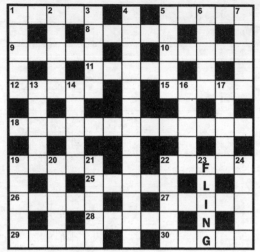

ACROSS

1 Arm joint	1 Sweetener
5 Alloy of copper and zinc	5 Very good
8 Concur	8 Oak-tree seed
9 Cake topping	9 Once more
10 Tracking device	10 Start
11 Bid	11 Slide
12 Removed	12 Drainage channel
15 Pulsate	15 South African antelope
18 Regular payment from a bank account (**8,5**)	18 Dance arranger
19 Heavenly messenger	19 Liberated
22 Bravery award	22 Submit to
25 Surplus to requirements	25 Film star
26 Coral island	26 Wild rose
27 Pungent vegetable	27 Set phrase
28 Brightly coloured	28 Moan of pain
29 Topic	29 In that place
30 Bird of prey	30 Perfume

DOWN

1 Burn with liquid
2 Enormous mythical being
3 Four-wheeled vehicle
4 Fire
5 Flat hat
6 Italian food
7 Clean with a brush
13 Bury
14 Kayak
16 Failure in duty
17 Musical entertainment
19 Banquet
20 Dirt
21 Big
22 Female servants
23 Throw, hurl
24 Boundary

1 Proclamation
2 Eye movement
3 US stock-farm
4 Quarrelsome
5 Sleeper's noise
6 Venomous snake
7 Evaluated
13 Pale
14 Spooky
16 Multitude
17 Female relation
19 Senior monk
20 Run away to marry
21 Dig
22 Male honey-bee
23 Propel a vehicle
24 Wash in clean water

390 ARROWORD

The arrows show the direction in which the answer to each clue should be placed.

___ Rabbit, JC Harris character ▼		Covered (with) ▼		Short musical start? ▼		Unlikely comedy ▼	
▶							
Modern name for Ceylon (3,5)		She-sheep! ▼		Sicilian volcano ▼		Strengthen ▼	
▶							
Chopin's first name	Rolls up		Franchot ___, 1930s actor ▶				
Sherilyn ___, Twin Peaks star ▶	▼				Ticking over		Worcester's river
▶		Arrogance, pomposity ▶		▼			▼
Passenger-carrying vehicle		Born Free lioness	Horse's pace	Jack ___, surly comedian ▶			
___ Eagles, Daryl Hannah film ▶		▼	▼			Erika ___, notorious streaker	
▶				Anger ▶		▼	
La ___ Bonita, Madonna hit	Italian title for a man ▶						
Wine container ▶				Inside info ▶			

452|

ACROSS

6 Hastily written (9)

7 Seed of the oak (5)

8 Pale, sickly (3)

9 Effortlessness (4)

10 Girl's name or part of the eye (4)

12 Very large South American snake (8)

15 Dowdy (8)

17 Unblock (9)

18 Dictatorial person (8)

20 Walk or march wearily and with effort (8)

23 Abhor (4)

24 Trace of a wound (4)

27 Perish (3)

28 Squeeze (out) (5)

29 Poster (4-5)

DOWN

1 Long-bodied vehicle (6,3)

2 Shafts (6)

3 Steak (1-4)

4 Bloomed (8)

5 Peculiarity (7)

11 Impart (ideas) (11)

13 Fruit like a small peach (7)

14 Close (4)

16 Frozen cataract (7)

17 Part of a telephone (4)

19 Gross amount (9)

21 In a surreptitious fashion (2,3,3)

22 Gloomy (7)

25 High point (6)

26 Doubly (5)

392 *CROSSWORD*

ACROSS

4 Pickpocket, colloquially (3)
8 Kidnap, spirit away (8)
9 Shoot better than (6)
10 Coarse, red-faced (6)
11 Cruel or violent act (8)
13 Sort, kind (4)
15 Number of years celebrated by a golden wedding (5)
16 Electrical resistance units (4)
18 Entrancing (8)
20 Gambling house (6)
22 Ride quickly across water (3-3)
23 Hollow or scoop out (8)
24 Male relation (3)

DOWN

1 Slightly cold (6)
2 Frozen crystals of rain (4)
3 People in general (4)
4 Alienated (11)
5 Inexpertly (6)
6 Plaster ornamentation (6)
7 Kick (a football) (4)
12 Word of consent (3)
13 Male domestic cat (3)
14 Tangle up (6)
15 Passionate (6)
17 Short time (6)
19 Smooth, level (4)
20 Male lobster (4)
21 Conserve (4)

ACROSS

4 Civilian clothing (5)
9 Allay, placate (7)
10 Baby's absorbent towel (5)
11 Feel unwell (3)
12 Overindulgent (3)
13 Electrically charged atom (3)
14 Spotted big cat (7)
15 Endure misfortune stoically (4,2,2,3,4)
19 Run-of-the-mill (7)
20 Part of the foot (3)
21 Plastic coat? (3)
22 Sadness, heartache (3)
23 Round of gunfire (5)
24 New soldier (7)
25 Man-made fabric (5)

DOWN

1 Pork-based cooked meat (6)
2 Culmination (4)
3 Meeting organiser (11)
4 Average (4)
5 Remove the bones from (6)
6 Confusion (in language) (11)
7 Sound of an object hitting water (6)
8 Coloured (4)
16 Noble, splendid (6)
17 Single (ticket) (3-3)
18 Subtlety (6)
19 Covering for the face (4)
20 Black and white seabird (4)
21 Injure by rough handling or clawing (4)

ACROSS

1 Impute, assign (7)

7 Total change of mind (1-4)

8 Gentleman's title (3)

9 Arrive, show up (4)

10 Pack away (4)

12 Musical group (8)

14 Remaining in the original state (9)

15 Start off (8)

18 Spinal pain (8)

21 Explorers (9)

23 Festive spruce (4,4)

25 Novice reporters (4)

26 Lecherous look (4)

28 Admit (3)

29 Place for a sleeping bird (5)

30 Embrace as a cause (7)

DOWN

2 Popular dance sound (4,5)

3 Classify (4)

4 Rapid informal information network (4,9)

5 Accelerate (7,2)

6 Boasts (5)

11 Pass on (6)

13 Joined on (5)

16 Reduction in an insurance premium (2-6,5)

17 Treat badly (5)

19 Admittance (6)

20 Cinema torch-bearer (9)

22 Shocking (9)

24 The real ___, genuine (5)

27 Musical composition for three instruments (4)

ACROSS

- **8** Incompetence (10)
- **9** Double-reed woodwind instrument (4)
- **10** Lamb chop (6)
- **11** All existing matter and space (8)
- **12** Ambush (4)
- **14** Not quite good enough (6,4)
- **16** Sacrilege (11)
- **20** Lagging (of pipes) (10)
- **22** Twisted loop (4)
- **23** Full of twistings and windings (8)
- **25** Site of the 1948 summer Olympic Games (6)
- **27** Ancient South American (4)
- **28** Student's written or practical projects (10)

DOWN

- **1** Act of asking for information (7)
- **2** Iridescent precious stone (4)
- **3** Revulsion (8)
- **4** Mystical adviser (4)
- **5** Skin wound (6)
- **6** Multi-storied building (5,5)
- **7** Be composed (of) (7)
- **13** Occurring before marriage (10)
- **15** Small breed of dog (5)
- **17** Lacking melody (8)
- **18** Ruin (7)
- **19** At home (7)
- **21** Immediately, straight away (2,4)
- **24** Nutritious liquid (4)
- **26** Recent information (4)

ACROSS

8 Intermediate insect stage (4)
9 Chief, foremost (3-7)
10 Street thief (6)
11 Small carved ornament (8)
12 Forceful persuasion (8)
14 Generally (6)
15 Malicious allusion (11)
19 Merely (6)
21 Lovely (8)
22 Joke-telling entertainer (8)
24 Watersport vehicle (3,3)
25 Across the country (10)
26 Red planet (4)

DOWN

1 Hen-pecked (3-4)
2 Parasite (6-2)
3 Goad for a horse (4)
4 Hedonistically (4-11)
5 Holier-than-thou (4)
6 Natural (6)
7 Foolishly (7)
13 Frostily (5)
14 Melted ice (5)
16 Extra work (8)
17 Key, important (7)
18 1940 French evacuation port (7)
20 Summary (6)
23 Hostelries (4)
24 Birds of the crow family (4)

Puzzle 1

```
 T H I N S   C A F F E I N E
G O E   O   R   O   V   V
R E N E W A B L E   R H Y M E
A   E T   E   N   E     R
V I S A   B Y W A Y S   W R Y
I   T   A     I   T   H   W
T O Y   B U L G E S   S I G H
A   A   I   A   S   S   E
T I G H T   N O T E P A P E R
E   E   E   S   A   E   E
D E L U D I N G   S M A R T
```

Puzzle 2

```
D I S H U P      D E R B Y      S H R E W D
U   T   N      S   N   R   U      I   I   O   A
S H A M A N    P A C K E R S    G I B B O N S
K   M   W   T    I   L   A   U    N         P
  S M E A R Y    C R A C K E R    O R I G A M I
    E   R   R    E   V   U   Y    N   R   R   R
  B R E E Z E      W E E P Y      H E C K L E
```

Puzzle 3

```
P R E M I U M   W A S T E
U   F   T   A X E   Q   V
F I F T E E N   E X U D E
F   O   M   Y A K   A   N
Y A R D   S   L O W   I
    T O T A L L Y   K I N
C   G   G   E   J   G
H O W   N O S E B A G
A   H O E   K   B U F F
S   E   A R C   B   N   I
S H E E R   A R R A N G E
I   Z   B A R   E   E   N
S H Y L Y   P O W E R E D
```

Puzzle 4

```
J O I N E D U P
O   N   N   N   U
B Y D E G R E E S
L   E   A   A   E
O A F   G E R M S
T   A   I   T
  Q U E N C H E S
B   L   G     T
E A T S   A G A R
T   A   L   I
T A K E S T O C K
E   I   K   A   E
R E T R E A T E D
H   E   D     O
A L S O   S P E W
L   O   E   N
F U S S P O T S
    O   E   I   P
J A P A N   T E A
O   R   P   I   S
S T A L L I O N S
H   N   A   N   O
  G O I N G S O N
```

Puzzle 5

```
G   T F C X   E   R
H E R M I T A G E   D I E
O   E   R   N   R D   V
S P A D E   I R O N A G E
T   S   A   N   X     R
  Q U A R T E T   B O S S
M   R   M     Y   U     E
A V E R   U P B E A T S
H   W   A   L   S   V
J A Z Z I L Y   L O W L Y
O   I   N   I   O   I
N U N   K I N S W O M A N
G   G   S   G   Y   S   G
```

Puzzle 6

```
  H I P H O P   H A R A S S
O   N   I   U N I   A     W
I N F I D E L   G O R I L L A
N   E   E   V   H   E   S   S
T U R K   B E L L Y   P A N T
M   I     R   I   E       E
E Y E D   D I N G O   W I M P
N   X   H   S   H   K   N   I
T S U N A M I   T A N K T O P
S   L   L   N E E   I   E
  S T R O N G   R E T U R N
```

Puzzle 7

```
E M P T I E D   W I S E R
A   R   O   O W E   A   H
S W E E T E N   A M P L Y
E   F   A   E L K   P   M
D E A F   E   L I E   I
  B R A M L E Y   D I N
C   Y   I   N   A     G
H A S   C R A V I N G
A   C O O   Y   D U C K
R   U   P A W   H   L   E
M U F T I   O V E R P A Y
E   F   E R R   A   E   E
D O S E S   D E L U D E D
```

Puzzle 8

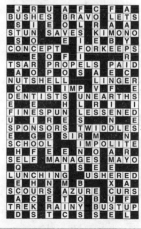

```
  J   R   U   A F C   F   A
B U S H E S   B R A V O   L E T S
  S   I   E O L   R   A   A
S T U N   S A V E S   K I M O N O
  S   O   E   I   E B   Y
C O N C E P T   F O R K E E P S
    E   O F I       I       R
T S A R   P R O P E L S   P A I D
A   O   P   O   S   A   E   C
N U T S H E L L     F   L I N G E R
  C   R   I M P   V   F     E
D E N T I S T S   U N E A R T H S
E   E     H   L   R   I     I
F I N E S P U N   L E S S E N E D
U   I   R E   S   S   N   E
S P O N S O R S   T W I D D L E S
E   G   B   S I R   M   N
S C H O O L   I M P O L I T E
H   F   E   E   N   O   A   R
S E L F   M A N A G E S   M A Y O
Q       I   S   E   E
L U N C H I N G   U S H E R E D
E   H   N     M   B   X   A
S C O U R S   A Z U R E   C U R S
A   C   E   T   O   B   U   F
T R E K   R A I N Y   B U S T U P
D   S   T   C   S   S   E   L
```

SOLUTIONS

Puzzle 9

```
 ATLARGE I
L A W O I
AMBER VIM
N L Y E A
DUES TRUG
S W D N E
COINEDIT
A N L N A
PREJUDGES
E X B I
 ASTEROID
A L D E
GLASSEYE
A P W C
ITALICISE
N N T N N
 EDUCATES
Q T H R O
UNIT BOAR
A C B U I
YAK ROBIN
S L E L G
 TEDDIES
```

Puzzle 10

Puzzle 11

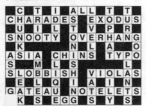

Puzzle 12

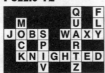

Puzzle 13

Puzzle 14

Puzzle 15

SOLUTIONS

Puzzle 16

```
S U R L I N E S S   A B O V E
N   E   U     H   S   E     I
C L O V E N   I N T E R N A L
O   E   S   F     E   R     L
S C O R E   S T Y E   Y E W S
  K     S O W E D         I
U S E R   A N O N   O M E N S
    E   G   R   T   A   C
C O M E B A C K   W O R T H Y
R   K   S   E   I   I   E
A B Y S S   D R U N K A R D S
```

Puzzle 17

```
A   F D   I S   D   A   B
M O U S E T R A P   R I S E R
O   N   S   I   E   T     I
U N D R E S S   C H A R R E D
R     R     R   U   D   I   L
S C E P T I C A L   F E N C E
  X     I   O   A   U   G   S
  F O R T U N E T E L L E R
A   R   E   V   O   N
B A C O N   E A R N E S T L Y
R   I   D   N   N   T   L
I N S P E C T   P A T E L L A
D   I   R   I   E   R   A   n
G U N G E   O P E R A T I O N
E   G   D   N   P   P   D   S
```

Puzzle 18

```
E X P E C T E D   W R A P
X   R   O   A   C   A   A
A M E N D   T W I S T E R
L   Q   E   E   R   I   T
T H U G   B R O C C O L I
    E   W   Y   U   N
S A L T E D   Z I G Z A G
I   B   H   T   E
L I F E S P A N   W A I F
V   R   I   I   H   L   A
E J E C T O R   A V O I D
R   A   E   D   L   U   E
Y O K E   C O N F U S E D
```

Puzzle 19

```
T I L E S   A G O
O   E   H   T   V
R A T I O N A L E
E   T   R   S   R
  S U B T I T L E
M   C   A   R   X
O V E N G L O V E
O   E   K   R
N A B S   F E E T
S   A   A     I
  T W O B Y T W O
S   L   B   O   N
H U S H E D U P
A   Y   T   P
V A S E   A S I A
I   E   C   U
N O V E L I S T S
G   E   E   I
C O N T A C T S
R   T   V   C   U
E L E V A T O R S
A   E   G   M   E
M A N   E A S E D
```

Puzzle 20

```
S   S R   G     F     G
C R O M W E L L   C I R C L E
A   C   A   E   S   R   H   N
B R I A N   N O T R E D A M E
I   A   D       A   W   R   V
E L L   A C O R N   A L L O A
S   S     R   D   L   O
  A C A C I A   A R L O T T
I   R   T     R   T   T   H
G E E S E   O R D E R   E G O
E   N   O   R     U   R   L
R E C E S S I O N   S K U L L
B   E   O   O   K   S   S   A
I N S I T U   R O B I N S O N
L   E       N   N   E   D
```

Puzzle 21

```
  C O   S V   E T   C C
C O N F E C T I O N E R   O W L S
  L F   A I R   T   A   O   O
J U S T   T E A C H   U N P A C K
  M H       L   U M   E   K
A N N E X E S   S P A R R O W S
    B   N   L   I       A
H O B O   S C A N N E R   C O T S
S   N   U   W   G   H   C   H
M A T E R I A L   S L O T H S
  K   N   E L F   T   P   I
S A U S A G E S   I M A G I N E D
E   W   S   R   T   S   I
C O M E D O W N   E R E C T I O N
E   A   P   E   L   E   G
D I S R U P T S   I M P E R I L S
E   W   O   S A G A   I
S C O O T S   H A R D N E S S
  H   R   E   T   A   A   T
Q U I D   S O R B E T S   R U S K
  N     A   R   O   R
S T R I V I N G   A L C O H O L
  E   N   N   E   C   W   P
B R A V E S   D R A M A   B I T S
  I   E   I   I   R A W   O   I
A N O N   S T E E R C L E A R O F
  G   T   T   S   Y   S   T   N
```

Puzzle 22

```
N E X T T O N O T H I N G
V   Y   D   L   E   I   S
K I P P E D   D I L A T I N G
  L   I     E   M     U
U S E S   H O R S E   J A B S
    T O O     T E A
Z A P S   S A V E S   C U S P
  B     T   I     U   L
G U N B O A T S   P I Z Z A S
  T   O   G   T   A   Z   N
    C A V E P A I N T I N G S
```

Puzzle 23

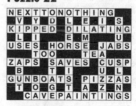

```
  A   T E   W W E   W
E M B A L M   A R R A N G E D
  B   N   I   G   I   D   E
R I D D A N C E   T R O O P S
  V   E   R   E   D
W A R M O N G E R   W E A R Y
  L   T   D   A   R   A
W E I R D L Y   A D A M A N T
  N   I   Y   R   D   D
A T O N E   T I T R A T I O N
  G   W   V   E   A   M
T E R R O R   A S S A S S I N
  V   O   O   L   S   S   S
R E T A I N E R   E L E V E N
  R   D   G   Y   E   L   D
```

The five-letter word is: **WATER**

461

SOLUTIONS

Puzzle 24

Puzzle 25

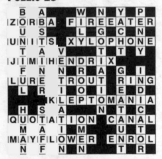

Puzzle 26

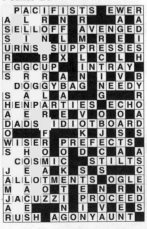

Puzzle 27

Puzzle 28

Puzzle 29

Puzzle 30

Puzzle 31

Puzzle 32

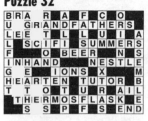

Puzzle 33

Puzzle 34

Puzzle 35

Puzzle 36

The missing letter is: W

Puzzle 37

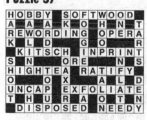

Puzzle 38

SOLUTIONS

Puzzle 39

Puzzle 40

Puzzle 41

Puzzle 42

Puzzle 43

Puzzle 44

Puzzle 45

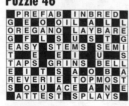

The five-letter word is: CLOSE

Puzzle 46

Puzzle 47

Puzzle 48

Puzzle 49

Puzzle 50

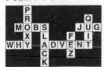

Puzzle 51

Puzzle 52

Puzzle 53

Puzzle 54

Puzzle 55

SOLUTIONS

Puzzle 56

```
B U N G A L O W   T R E A T Y
R   L   E   H   H   T   E
E G O I S M   E L E P H A N T
E   S   O   R   S   O   A
I N S T A N C E   A B S E N T
T   E   A   A   U   T
    O R C H E S T R A T E
    E   A   U   H
    A D M I R A L S H I P
S     R   R   R   D
D E C A M P   B A N I S T E R
A   R   I   I   I   T
B R I E F E S T   G U I T A R
C   N   C   E   H   E   I
P H R A S E   R E T I R I N G
```

Puzzle 57

```
O   I   C   D
M A N D O L I N
E   C   P   S   R
G N U   P E E V E
A   B   I   M   E
M A T C H B O X
H   T   E   A   A
E X I T   P R O M
L   O   S   K   I
P I N C H   I N N
S     R   N   E
  S A V I N G S
P   W   M     A
R U E   P A C T S
O   I   S   O   C
D A N E   O N T O
U   S   M   S   T
C A P S U L E S
I   I   S   C   G
N E R V E   R U N
G   I   U   A   A
  A N I M A T E S
  G   S   E   H
```

Puzzle 58

```
Q   S   K     T   Y   I
A U S T R I A   H E R O I N E
A   R   L   L   A   G   F
P R E Y   O M A R S H A R I F
R   C   G   N   E     E
Z E P H Y R   C O T S W O L D
L   N   A   A     E   D
  J I M M Y S A V I L E
U   N   T   E   L   R
E N G E N D E R   X F I L E S
L   A   I   A   N   P
F A I N T H E A R T   G A T E
D   O   L   N   I   T   I
B E A T N I K   M O N O C L E
N   E   A     N   N   E
```

Puzzle 59

```
S   H   U   E N D E D   O   D
C H U R N E D   O   I T C H Y
R   N   C   A R C   S   L   E
I R K   E L M   I N C R O W D
P   R   L   H   C
T I G H T R O P E W A L K E R
  H   A   B     R     O
F L O R I S T   M U G   B O B
O   U   N   A G O   I   O   U
U N L I T   I   S I N G L E S
L   S   Y O N K S   G   D   T
```

Puzzle 60

```
  S   P   D   B   M   M
  C R I M I N A L I S E D
  R   E   T   R   S   S
F O U R T H   B O T C H
U       E       I
I N F E R R E D   K I D S
G   M   E   A   E   I
K E L P   D E F T N E S S
    O       F       P
  B A W D Y   O C C U L T
  A   E   E D   A   A
  I N C R E A S I N G L Y
  E   S   R   L   E   S
```

Puzzle 61

```
  H   O   A   M   U   C   F   R
C O N F E S S I O N A L   L O O P
  O   F   I   O N   D   O   A   U
O V A L   A T O N E   V A U N T S
  E   I       R   R   E   N   E
B R I C K I E   M A R I T I M E
    E   N   H   I       A
S K I N   F E I G N E D   F I R S
H   C   E   B   E   E   U   C
C A R E F R E E   B I R T H S
K   N   R O B   A   T   L
D I E D D O W N   R E S T H O M E
R   I   A   O   E   E   N
E L E P H A N T   O B S E R V E D
D   L   R   I   M   T   I
G O T O T O W N   S T A Y O V E R
E   M   U   G U T   U   N
S C R A P S   I N T I M A T E
H   C   E   N   C   O   E   R
S E X Y   S P E A K U P   T O Y S
R   I   S   S   H   I
P I N C H I N G   G Y R A T E S
S   L   M   H   A   L   N
S H R I M P   B E N D S   F L I P
I   M   O   G O O   W   G
K N O B   D O U B L E W H A M M Y
G   S   E   R   E   S   Y   A
```

Puzzle 62

```
C H A I N   Q
E   C   L O U D
M A K E D O   I
V   P   W I C K
D E T A I L   K
H   C   E   E
L O O K O V E R
E   B   E   P
V I S U A L I S E
I   E   L   N S
T A R   S U C K S
A   V   O   R I
T R I E R   E L M
I   N   A   A I
O R G A N I S T S
N   L   E   T
  C O L L U D E S
O   T   N   X
D   H A L V E D
O G L E   A   C
E   R U C K U S
T R U E   E   T
S   A S T E R
```

466|

Puzzle 63

L		I		I		L		L	T		N	T
I	N	C	E	N	S	E		I	S	R	A	E	L	I

The five-letter word is: UNTIL

Puzzle 64

Puzzle 65

Puzzle 66

Puzzle 67

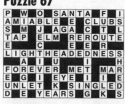

Puzzle 68

Puzzle 69

Puzzle 70

The missing letter is: N

Puzzle 71

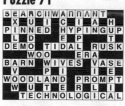

Puzzle 72

SOLUTIONS

Puzzle 73

Puzzle 74

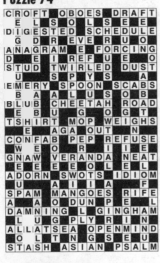

Puzzle 75

Puzzle 76

Puzzle 77

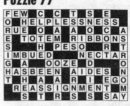

Puzzle 78

Puzzle 79

468

Puzzle 80

```
A H T   P   T
BOOKWORMS
D L I E H
USING SKI
C E S I R
TORS EDIT
O   O E S
RESOUNDS
S H T     C
DOUBTFUL A
  R U I   A
GETTINGON
A E L M
PARODIES
S   I N A
FRENETIC
L E G   I
AWLS SCUD
W I A L D
LUG PRIOR
E I R N O
SHOWINGUP
S N L S S
```

Puzzle 81

```
B O G P S F V
HAVERSACK LEA
A E I P   E L
JERKS ITERATE
I T T S R   T
  QUALITY YULE
A R E     N D
ZONE REFEREE
I K L T V X
MADONNA WHERE
U O O I O N
TOO CONTRALTO
H M K E K Y N
```

Puzzle 82

```
SCRAG LEFTWING
O E L E A I U A
BACKEDOFF MINES
S O A   F P   H
GUINEA INSPIRE
S N   WIN   R S
PETUNIA GODSON
I   Y K   W N A
CHARM EMBLAZONS
Y R P N U R U K
EMPHASIS FETES
```

Puzzle 83

```
  D P A T
HERE NEON
P R O R
SUBMARINE
T       A
HYMN KILT
  E     A
CROSSWORD
E T A D
FALL LIES
L E L R
```

Puzzle 84

```
VEERS PAR
O N C R E
WATERBIRD
S H U V L
  SURPRISE
S S L   T
PRECEDENT
A S G E
TOFF PEAR
S U B   D
  ANGELICA
U G E N Y
NAILFILE
F S A F
LIPS TYPO
A O H U
TAPDANCER
T U I L
ENLARGES
R A G R
INTERNING
N E I C L
GAS PESKY
```

Puzzle 85

```
      QUARTZ
    B P   Y
FLOCKS  W  H E M
    X   JIVE
        N   M
        G
```

```
S       A
CHEAPLY
A F   L E
REF OIL
A I M L
BUGABOO
Y       W
```

Puzzle 86

```
SPOTS STOODOUT
W R U K E P A R
INESSENCE PUKKA
R P K I T O N
EXAM ITCHES ARC
H Y A U E N E
ADS SEWERS MOLL
I T A I S R I
ROTOR KNOCKBACK
E I A E T I K E
DECRYING AMISS
```

Puzzle 87

```
LADDISHNESS
U I E A O H U
SEDUCTIVENESS
H R L L E U
EXCEEDED SPUR
R A P D P F P
AFFIX BROOK
E E T D E L U
JUTS PROVIDES
E E M I E A
CIRCUMVENTING
T I L E T R E
GATECRASHER
```

Puzzle 88

```
SWATS BLOBS ABUSE
H A I A A U U W
RECKONED REPENTED
R E T YOB HK A
DEVOURS R ROBBERY
O F U FAG L E
CHEF TRILLED DUBS
I H L O S A
AGGRO CLUBS SMACK
H A O I A S A K
STAY VANILLA FOOD
E O E R T U
MANNER MEW EXALTS
A DYE EEL U
TENNER NOD LODGES
M A A R I O N
ABUT FANBELT GUTS
A T T O F E M I
PRAYS CRAFT FANCY
G A D I A E
CORM BRIDGED LODE
O A COY M Y
SOURING U BIGGAME
N T D ORE R U
PARANOIA GLEAMING
I L N T G S E E
BRASH CHOSE ASIDE
```

SOLUTIONS

Puzzle 89

Puzzle 90

Puzzle 91

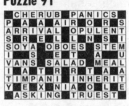

Puzzle 92

The five-letter word is: STOKE

Puzzle 93

Puzzle 94

Puzzle 95

Puzzle 96

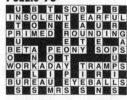

Puzzle 97

Puzzle 98

```
O N C O U R S E
H O N   L   S
D I P P E D O U T
E H   A   P   O
A D O   R I P U P
R   L   N   E
  A D D E N D U M
B O D       O
O A F S   S W O T
T     P   A   O
T A L L O R D E R
L   I   I   E S
E A V E S D R O P
F   E   E   O
E A S Y   B L U R
E   L   I   T
D I S T O R T S
    N O   I   L
F L O C K   G O O
A W   I   I   U
D O M I N I O N S
S E T   U   E
  E N D O R S E S
```

Puzzle 99

```
T   P       I
W A L K E R S
I   U   M   O
T O R   P A L
C   A   L   A
H E L P O U T
Y   Y   Y E
```

```
A G E D
R   U   P
M O A N E R
W   G   E
U N E A S E
P   O   T
  N E O N
```

```
R       B
S I N K E R
V   N   U
C A N A S T A
L   C   I
R A K I S H
Y       H
```

Puzzle 100

```
W   S S   F   W A
H A T C H   O P I U M
E   A   O   R   N U
T O M B O L A   G E L
    E       G   E
S Y N O D   E M M E T
P   E       E
H I T   V A G R A N T
E   E O   L   S   O
R E A C T   A G L O W
E   K E   D   Y   N
```

Puzzle 101

```
C A T A C O M B S   S M E A R
  C   U   D   A   F   O   P
S T A T E D   N U R T U R E S
  U   O   S   K   I   S
C A U S E   A R M S   E C H O
  R       C L O A K       E
D Y E D   H E L D   U S E R S
  O   A   L   S   K   E
G L A D I O L I   I D I O T S
  A   G   S   N   L   N   I
S W A Y S   A G N O S T I C S
```

Puzzle 102

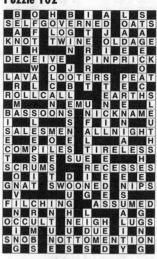

```
  B   O H B I A   L S
S E L F G O V E R N E D   O A T S
  A   F   L O G T   J A   A A
K N O T   T W I N E   O L D A G E
  I   H     N   R I   E E
D E C E I V E   P I N P R I C K
      W   O J   R R         O
L A V A   L O O T E R S   P E A T
  R   L C B     T T E   C
R O L L C A L L     E A R T H S
  M     E   N EMU N   E     L
B A S S O O N S   N I C K N A M E
I     L     S   F I   N     U
S A L E S M E N   A L L N I G H T
E   E   O   E   L       A   H
C O M P I L E S   T I R E L E S S
T     S   E   SUE   E       H
S C R U M S     R E C E S S E S
O   I   ST   D   I   E   E
G N A T   S W O O N E D   N I P S
V       U   G       E   S
F I L C H I N G     A S S U M E D
  N   R   NHL     L         A G
O C C U L T   N E I G H   L U G S
I   M   U   U   DUE   I   N
S N O B   N O T T O M E N T I O N
G   S   E   S   S   D   Y   G
```

Puzzle 103

```
D U C A L   P R O J E C T
E   O   O   O   B   L   W
C O M P L E X   V A L U E
O   P   L       I       E
C R O S S E S   A R M E D
T   S       W   T   I   S
  O U T S P O K E N L Y
S   R   A   R       I   E
T R E N D   D E B A T E S
R       D   U   A       S
A L G A E   B O N A N Z A
F   N   S   U   C   T   Y
E Q U A T E S   H A S P S
```

Puzzle 104

```
  F R Y   Q
  L       U
D E V O T I N G
  X   H   Z
J     M
B A C K S
W
```

The missing letter is: P

```
P L A C E B O
A   O   A
L E C T E R N
  T   O
W H I T I N G
O   E   O
A S H A M E D
```

SOLUTIONS

Puzzle 105

```
A G K A A
COLONISTS
C I O C T
ELBOW E G O
S L S N U
SAYS EDEN
I B E D
OFFLOADS
N L O P
TORTURER
U L E E
HANGINGUP
O C C A
OVERKILL
K I I B
BOUNDARY
P L G N
AIDE MENU
R F S U M
ILL THROB
A A U E E
HOMEMAKER
S E P A S
```

Puzzle 106

```
DREGS THEORY
J E R P Y A O
AGGRAVATE KEY
Z A P N N T O
ZILCH CHAIRS
Y I A E
FLICKKNIVES
O E N W
QUIVER SAMBA
N D I O I O F
USE XYLOPHONE
M S E L I S R
BITING EDGES
```

Puzzle 109

```
U X P TEMPO G S
PURSUES A DWELT
H A N AIR D M A
ICY CUR KISSING
L T E A N
LABOURINTENSIVE
R A D D M
STARTLE HOE PUB
I Z I AWE N A O
FEIGN L WADDLES
T L GASES S S S
```

Puzzle 110

```
BIG SIR KINKY    A P
E U K I W L I    BABYGRO
DANCING HILLOCK  S O R S
O D I C K K      CONTENT
INJURED SKYBLUE  O E B A
N U O L E U P    ONESTEGG
GAG WAY PRATE    D E
```

Puzzle 107

```
RAINDROPS CRAB
A W I O O E O
SWATTED LEGALLY
S R S E I A O I
UNDO HOWSTRICKS
M U S H G A H
EXPAND INLETS
S R L S N I E I
SIDELONG NOSES
A M A N G O
PEARSHAPED IDOL
P C H T V H E A
RAYS SAFETYBELT
O C N P M E
VIDEO FITTEDIN
E U M A S D N E
ASPECT BULGES
D T I H S P C
RECONVENED ALSO
Y O T R T M I R
RAVIOLI OVEREAT
U E N U L I S
NORM AGITATING
```

Puzzle 108

```
WASHBAG DEVISED
A C L EMU I E U
AS ERUPT GIVEN G
TAP F A I DUO
E T FONDLED I I
SLIP U D M SNUG
CULT O BRAG
P K DINER L A
RISK I Y OURS P
E HANDMEDOWNS P
SKI G ASH
A NAVELGAZING A
GUYS R O YELL
E C ALLIN M T
FOBS I KIPS
BOOT E M E HULK
O I ASCENDS C O
OIL L S K COS
Z IDIOM GRIME H
E N B RUE N E
REGAINS MATADOR
```

Puzzle 111

```
ESTUARY
M M S A S
INANE COP
L R R E A
LATE CROW
I A S E N
POLITELY
E E E A T
DECORATOR
E E I A
IDEOLOGY
B O N S
LANDMASS
A E A C
SLAUGHTER
E N P O U
ADDICTED
E D E H E
MAUL BEEN
B S S B E
EAT COOPS
D E A N S
ADORNED
```

Puzzle 112

```
I B B B E D D
ENDEARMENT RARE
S T E E U A U
ITHACA RUDIMENT
A D A A K
ENID BABYSITTER
T E L L I N
BLUNDERBUSS
B I E E E R
DOWNGRADED DRAB
L E A L P
ESPALIER IBERIA
H T D A N E
ROLE EASTENDERS
I S R P N Y S
```

The five-letter word is: BRIDE

472

Puzzle 113

```
S E A R C H P A R T I E S
L   A   A   L O   E   S
B I N N E D   P I P E L I N E
T   S   H   P       U
M E M O   G R A I L   D A B S
      M O O       E W E
K I P S   U P P E D   A P S E
R       L   A   D       E
C O N T R A R Y   W E E D E D
N   W   S   I   O   N   D
  T O T H E N A K E D E Y E
```

Puzzle 114

```
  O V E R S T O C K E D
C   E   E   A   O   X   W
H E N   C H I H U A H U A
I   O   O   L   P   A   Y
R U M O U R E D   B L E W
O   R   D   R   E       A
P A P I S M   F E E D E R
O   A   E   C   L       D
D I V A   M A C A R O O N
I   L   F   V   P   R   E
S M O U L D E R S   G A S
T   V   E   L   E   A   S
  P A R A G L I D I N G
```

Puzzle 115

```
S H A K E S P E A R E       B
E   U   L   I   N   L   V   R
B A D M I N T O N   I C E N I
    E   Z   T   J O R   T
H E N M A N   P O R T R A I T
M       B       I   L   E
S O C C E R   W E S L E Y A N
    H   T   D   S   A   N
B L E N H E I M   T U R N E R
A   Q       S   R       H
B L U E B I R D   C I R C U S
B   E   A   A   S   E   A
A R R A N   E X C A L I B U R
G   S   K   L   O   E   Y
E       S A I N T G E O R G E
```

Puzzle 116

```
P R I S M   P U P
E   N   O   L   R
P A T R O N A G E
S   R   R   T   S
  P U R I F I E S
A   D   N   T   R
F U E L G A U G E
O       S   D   L
O A S T   W E R E
T   U   F       A
  I N F L A T E S
B   U   Y   O   E
A P P O I N T S
C       N   E   B
K I S S   T S A R
S   U   H       A
T I P T O E I N G
A   P   M   N   S
B O O K E N D S
B   R   B   U   U
I N T E R A C T S
N   E   E   E   E
G O D   W A S P S
```

Puzzle 117

```
  C   W   C   D
B A T H   H A I L
  N   A   A   S
H A R M O N I C A
  R           G
T Y R E   E A R N
  N           E
P A R S O N A G E
  C   I   E   A
C R A G   W O R D
  E   N   S   D
```

Puzzle 118

```
J O T   S   B E   A   A
U   H O M E L E S S N E S S
S E A   O   U   S T   C B
T   T A K E R   A U S T E R E
R   E   B U Y S   N   D
I N F E S T   E A R T H S
G O   E B B S   L   P
H A R R I E R   Q U A L M
T M   M   A U   S   I R E
  S A F A R I J A C K E T A
  T M   N D   A   T A D
```

Puzzle 119

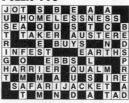

```
      J     T
Q U E N C H   R
      M       R
Z A P   G L O W
    V       B
F I X     S K Y
    D
```

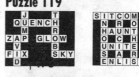

```
S I T C O M
N   R   O
H A U N T
O   C   H
U N I T E
S   A   R
E N L I S T
```

Puzzle 120

```
  H A V E I T C H Y F E E T
S   M   F A   E   A N   U
O N O F F E R   R E D U C E S
C   U   E   E   S   O   E
C U R D C H E E S E   E M I K
E   T   X Y   F   P   S
R E C R U I T S   F L Y A T
  O   A R   S   O Y S   S
C O M P L I A N T   O N S E T
O   P     S   A D     E
N E U T E R   F I L L E D U P
T   T   N H   D   I   E   O
O V E R V I E W   S T R A I N
U   I   M   M   C   I
R I P E R   S C A P E G O A T
S   E   O T   N   M   N
  S P A N S   S U P P O S E D
W   P   S S   A   L   O
I C E S   F U L L B O D I E D
L   R   B D   Y   N
L E O T A R D   S T I P P L E
S   N   S E   U   N   U
  H I G H A N D M I G H T Y
```

Puzzle 121

```
S   U P   S
M O N O R A I L
A   I   E   L O
R A N   F I V E S
T   V   E   E T
  S O R C E R E R
B   L   T   L L
L O V E   Z I N C
A   E   R   N H
B U D G E   I C E
S       V   N S
  T H R O N G S
A   I   L   U
F A G   T A P E S
A   H   S   R U
S O F T   P E E R
T   I   T   E P
B E D R O O M S
U   E   E   P S
C O L I C   T O O
K   I   A   I A
  S T O P O V E R
    Y   S   E S
```

Puzzle 122

```
    N   R     P
  E R A S E   L
B   J U M B O
F R Y   E M I N
  A   S T A L K
A S H       K
  K   H E R O N
S A L I V A   E
      T E N S E
R A I L R O A D
  G   E T U D E
O M A R   T E D
```

SOLUTIONS

Puzzle 123

```
A W S C   W B   B
STOMACH ARENA A
T O C   A L A B
ELDER PERJURY
R W E   U     I
  MINDLESSNESS
M N     A   N H
INDECOROUSLY
D   R     N A B
WELFARE PURGE
E A V   A L G R
EXILE SQUEEZY
K D N T G R L
```

Puzzle 124

```
  I R R   E S   S S
IINSOLE APPETITE
  C C   I S A O R
ITANK NUTCRACKER
  M E   S E K E
IHEARTTHROB INTO
  R   A N L   N
MACHETE PUNGENT
    A E S E   I
TAXI DELIBERATE
D R     E O E R
IADOLESCENT SHOT
  I E L   P T I G
IICESKATE LISTEN
  T S M R E T N
```

Puzzle 125

```
LICIT PASSIONS
I O I I T M O P
NUMBERTWO PAWNS
K M I R E A
  QUENCH ILLWILL
F T EYE N M
ICEDTEA SEQUIN
L R L U R F
MECCA ENDEAVOUR
S A M R I F N A
  PROPOSED FISHY
```

Puzzle 126

```
PHEASANT ITSELF
E L C E N T O
LANCET ASTEROID
T H O C E A T
RESEARCH RAPIER
R M E P R
  GINGERBREAD
  S R E B
  STRAIGHTEST
D N A T I
SORTED LETHARGY
M I L A I N
DIAGNOSE CENSOR
N E S O I E
SOURCE NOTARIES
```

Puzzle 127

```
  G B   A M T E
XRAYS INSURANCE
  E Z   N L R L
KEBAB YESTERDAY
N N Q   I Y T
ZESTFULNESS
Y I   I O T F L
DEAN CANTO OPAL
  D E K E R O W
      SWITZERLAND
W H   I   Y H M
VIDEOTAPE RAZOR
D N T U R W
JOHNKEATS UDDER
W A D T Y R
```

Puzzle 128

```
RINGS   D
N O WOES
BLOTCH S
I B IRKS
IMPART J
B C T O
BOOKCLUB
E C E O
EXCURSION
R U E N T
CUP DITTO
E A D E A
LANCE NIL
L T N T O
ASSASSINS
R W O E
EXAMINER
C I N N
L TEEOFF
MAXI R O
I NETTLE
FROG L D
S HARSH
```

Puzzle 129

```
MOUSE TWERP STIFF
C A S A A U R I
SERVICED PENDANTS
A A A EAT W W I
SNAGGLE V FILLING
E E I VIA N E A
AWED NEEDLED DOGS
I G S B S O
AGENT STAIN SPOTS
G Y E A N S U O
GLAM SOLDOUT KIPS
E P C I R K O
ASTHMA WEE ENACTS
O PEA BRA O
HOOPLA DAB MOROSE
P I D D E U T
HEWN EMPOWER MOAN
N U S A H S B S
ADOPT BRAIN PATHS
A A I N A E
HYPE BRAGGED DADO
O A I HUE J E W
BARRELS S BONFIRE
R M I WHY U A I
CREAMTEA ONREMAND
O R Y N M N S
AWOKE STOPS ADDER
```

474|

Puzzle 130

```
 A D D O N   G O L D D I S C
O   E   C   A   V   I   L   O
S A F E H O U S E   V I L L A
T   L   E   T   R   I       S
E W E S   B O L T E D   T O T
N   C   A       O   E   O   G
S I T   S L I G H T   G U R U
I       W   N   U   S   C   A
B O N C E   O F F T H E A I R
L   O   L   N   F   O   N   D
Y O D E L L E D   S T A S H
```

Puzzle 131

```
M   L   M   R   R   A   A   M
A V A R I C E   U N N E R V E
R   M   S   A   B   K   B   A
A L B U M   L I B R A R I A N
C       A       E   R   T   I
A D U L T E R E R   A P R O N
S   N   C   E   T       A   G
  M A Y H E M   R A R I T Y
R   T       O   E   E   O   L
U T T E R   R E E N F O R C E
N   A   E   T       O       P
A R C H A N G E L   R U L E R
W   H   S   A   O   M   E   O
A G E L O N G   U S E L E S S
Y   D   N   E   T   R   K   Y
```

The five-letter word is: MURAL

Puzzle 132

```
C O N S O R T S
A   A   V   O   S
B Y T H E B O O K
L   U   R   L   I
E A R   T A K E N
S   A   I       I
  C L I M A T I C
B   L   E       H
O N Y X   G L E E
O       S   E   R
T R I C K S T E R
L   N   I   G   Y
I N T H E S O U P
C   E   S       I
K I R K   E P I C
E       L   U   K
R E A L I S T S
  C   B   A   E
P A C E R   C O X
U   L   E   R   I
F R A C T I O N S
F   I   T   S   T
  E M B O S S E S
```

Puzzle 133

```
H   E   B   W   A   S
A W F U L   A N G E L
L   F   O   R   A   O
F L A T T E R   R A P
    C       E       P
C R E S T   N E R V Y
Y       A       E
G E M   M U S T A N G
N   E   P   E   P   A
E R A S E   W H E E L
T   D   R   N   R   L
```

Puzzle 134

```
R I V A L S   P R O M I S E D
E   O   O   L E E   U   T   O
P I T   F A U N A   G O O E Y
E   E   T   L   D   S   C   E
L I D S   F L A Y S   A K I N
L       I       S   M   W   S
E D G I N G   A P H I D S
D   R   S   M   D       I   D
  R I D I C U L E   P A S T A
S   N   G   E       S   S   M
T I N W H I S T L E   A S K S
Y   E   T   L O O   S   L   E
M O D E   F I R S T O F A L L
I       T       S   A   Y   S
E M P T Y   O V E R P A I D
D   H   R   B   S   B   N   S
  S E V E R S   F O R G O T
H   N   S   E   S   X       A
U P O N   B R O W S   U S E R
M   M   T   V   I   O   C   T
B E E C H   A F F I X   I L L
U   N   O   N E T   E   F   E
G R A T U I T Y   S N A I L S
```

Puzzle 135

```
  R E D C A P   G R O U S E
C   G   O   R Y E   A   H   F
L E G I B L E   T O R N A D O
O   E   S   S   T   S   L   R
S I D E   P U T O N   G L A M
E       L       P   G       U
D U N K   S P I E S   O R A L
O   A   V       O   T   C   A
W O R K E R S   H E L D O U T
N   K   T   E V E   E   K   E
  M Y W O R D   R E F U S E
```

Puzzle 136

```
    W   F
    H   L   J   K
S Y C A M O R E
Q       X   B   P
U               T
Z I N G
D
```

```
T B O N E       H
A       I   H
S C A L L O P
K       R
C U N N I N G
  P   I   E
    S P A D E
```

The missing letter is V

Puzzle 137

```
  S A V E D U P
J   N   A   M   A
E X A M S   B A D
L   L   T   I   A
L O G S   B L A G
Y   E   P   I   E
B E S M I R C H
A   I   F   A   U
B A C K F I L L S
Y       L   C   A
  L I F E L O N G
M   N       R   E
E X P O U N D S
R   O   N       A
C H I M I N G I N
Y   N   S   E   I
  A T B O T T O M
S   O   N   A   A
L I F T   S C U T
O   F   A   R   I
B O A   B L O W N
S   C   L   S   G
  A T H E I S T
```

SOLUTIONS

Puzzle 138

```
M  P  C  D     S  K  P
CAREER  ESTONIAN
R  P  E  S     O  O  L
ITRAP  ABSOLUTELY
I  E  M  E  I        E
NARRATOR  DEARTH
G  M  E     T        T
SEMINAR  STATURE
N     O  O     E     E
MATTER  PARSNIPS
M     A  P     T  D  O
MONTECARLO  ACRE
R  W  K     E  I  N  T
CARELESS  SUCKER
L     E  T  S  E  E  R
```

Puzzle 139

```
A  A  Q        T     T  F
DISTURB  AMAZE
V  S  I     I  X     V
AVERT  COLLIDE
N  M     A  G        R
COB  WORKABLE
E  L  A  B  T  A  S
   FEARSOME  MAY
S     H  N     I     N
PERSONA  BANJO
A  E  R  T  E  A     N
SEARS  EXACTLY
M  D  E     K  E     M
```

Puzzle 140

```
ICELANDIC  CASTE
T  Y  N  I  A  O  K  N
AHERN  COMPUTING
L  O  U  A  E  G  L  L
IMPALING  CHILLI
A  E     I  D     S
NUNEATON  FRENCH
E  N     H  O  O
GERMAN  SCEPTRES
L  S     A     W  T
EIGHTY  ETCETERA
A  R  A  O  A  R  G  S
SUEZCANAL  IRISH
O  E  I  U  A  C  A  E
NOKIA  SUNTANNED
```

Puzzle 141

```
B  S  K  COD  B  S
HYACINTH  ERUPTS
G  A  O  I  N  S  O
BORROW  NOTAHOPE
N     W  E  E  N  N
REAL  WEALD  DIED
E     I  O  G        G
FOLKSONG  FORAGE
N  E     I  O  A  N
MUSLIN  NEWSROOM
S  Y  GAG  L  E  G
```

Puzzle 142

```
CAVALRY  SCUM
H  T  C  I  I  U  I
OPT  CONUNDRUM
L  I  U  G  T  D  E
LOCUM  SPELLS
E     U     R  E  A
REGALE  TRADES
S  R  A     O     S
KOWTOW  GAFFE
S  O  I  H  A  L  R
COMPONENT  OUT
O  E  N  R  E  W  S
TIDE  LEASING
```

Puzzle 143

```
G  C  S  S  D  D  B  G
RUNOUT  PRICE  AWRY
N  P  A  O  P  A  N  A
UGLY  BOUGH  REGIME
H  E     T  T  E  U  O
COLDEST  HORNPIPE
I  U  H  O        H
SMUT  BROWNIE  COOS
E  O  Z  R  G  N  O  N
SCARPERS  DANCER
C     R  EGG  M  T
BACKDOOR  EGOTRIPS
U  E  I  N  S  A  I
FOREHAND  TOTALLED
F  P  I  I  L  T  U
ELECTRON  EMPLOYEE
R  O  L  GAG  R  V
SCOUSE  ISOLATES
E  N  S  R  A  D  E  N
FRET  SCORNED  ROTS
T     U  T  E  O
PIFFLING  ADAPTED
F  L  N  H  T     L  A
BYLAWS  EXITS  ARTS
I  B  U  N  P  I  N  I
SNUB  REEKS  CLEANS
G  Y  E  D  Y  K  S  G
```

Puzzle 144

```
C  A  S     I  U
HATSTANDS
E  O  A  T     E
COMET  HOD
K  I  E  E     C
LICK  AREA
I     S  E     R
STAMPEDE
T  M  I     H
BARNACLE
S  N     Y  M
MESSINGUP
A  E  N  N
PEDIGREE
S  O  T  I
INQUESTS
F  O  T     L
ARTS  ASIA
I  A  S  L  N
ROT  CRIED
D  A  R  N  E
OILTANKER
S  L  M  S  S
```

Puzzle 145

```
C              DEPUTY          F  D
CARVERY        I  O  I        PETRIFY
J  I  E        ENIGMA         D  E  E
TORNADO        N  E           WOMANLY
L  Y  U        STROKE         R  M  O
FETLOCK        E  F  Y        CALUMNY
   E           TRIFLE            P  Y
```

Puzzle 146

```
T B S URGES S B
RELATES A INCUR
I O I EGG D A A
VOW PER GLEAMED
I U L E P
ANEWLEASEOFLIFE
N A R F X
FAINTER LIE COP
A G I AXE C O O
CAMEO N SETTLES
E A NOTES S D E
```

Puzzle 147

```
F H C D T G X
INOCULATE LIE
Z N R P X E R
ZOOMS PLACEBO
Y L O L S X
QUARTER MERE
K L Y A L S
NOUN SWAGGER
A B A R C Y
VOUCHER OUTRE
E N A M U R M
RED JETENGINE
Y O I H D C N
```

Puzzle 148

```
COMEOFFIT TALC
U G Y A M D A
SALIENT PALAVER
I E S H A O O E
NODS COPRODUCER
G G M T G A S
UNWRAP IDIOTS
P H N C N E O
PINGPONG GUSTY
O R W L S S S
BYREASONOF ABET
S E Y U P G I E
CADS FREELOADER
U A N F D S
REFER RHETORIC
E A T E D R N A
SCRIMP HINGES
S E S R P T S
UNFEASIBLE OGRE
R A N S O B L R
FUCHSIA VIOLENT
E T L E O A S
DOSE ASCRIBING
```

Puzzle 149

```
BEERMAT FOCUSED
U I A ERA O T U
RIGHTON CENTRED
Y H C TOT S A S
ETCH W IMPS
B S BOWLERS L G
LOO O I B T INN
A MIXED BASIN A
BEEN O E NEWS
S SHOWEDOFF H
TRIO E AUTO
T DWELLINGS S
BASE O M EARN
O USING AMISS O
NUN N O G N TUB
E S DUSTERS E S
ACME O TORS
O R N AMP A I W
WREATHS AMNESIA
E E E KEN E K R
DENUDES TREASON
```

Puzzle 150

```
TUBES ADS
O O P V I
WATERMAIN
S A A L G
SNOWFALL
E I L N E
JOCKEYCAP
E D H A
CAME BEAR
T I Q E
UNBUTTON
G C I E T
OPENNESS
F S T N
OPUS HYPE
R N R W
TASTELESS
H E C S Y
ENCHANTS
K U N A E
IRRITATED
L E E E G
LAD DISHY
```

Puzzle 151

```
C D N M
TRIO OPEN
E S R A
DETERMINE
P A
HYMN LOCK
U A
DRUGSTORE
I G A P
IDLE NEED
E T K T
```

Puzzle 152

```
S B M K D C M
MACARONI ANIMAL
L B L W T T C
BANANA ICECREAM
M S L I R
MIXERS LAMBCHOP
Y EDAM O
CHEERS G SPRING
O MEAT O
EGGTIMER REDUCE
S O N A A
CHESTNUT ISLAND
E S O O N A N
BAKERS ABERDEEN
D D H D R Y D
```

Puzzle 153

```
L H
SELFSAME E
A AIL A
SPARKLER
E RHETT
ODD GAY
FOOL
JOEL R M
P ERICA
JAMAICAN
L SNAPS
USA KLEE
```

SOLUTIONS

Puzzle 154

```
S U C B
HANDRAIL
O R A L T
WEE VILER
S S A O I
MOUTHFUL
F L S R O
LIVE ZING
O E I G I
WIDEN HOE
S S D T S
ATWORST
T I U T
EYE BUDDY
M U T E P
PIPE ACME
T I S K S
FANATICS
A K A H F
TUNER AGO
E O L I L
STAIRROD
S T S S
```

Puzzle 155

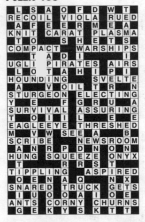

```
L S A O F D W T
RECOIL VIOLA RUED
A F E E R M E A
KNIT CARAT PLASMA
T O S H E T S
COMPACT WARSHIPS
T A D I I
UGLI PIRATES AIRS
L O T A H I P I
HOUNDING SVELTE
A V O I L T R N
STURGEON ELECTING
Y E F G R U
SURVIVAL ASSURING
T O I L L E
EAGLEEYE THRESHED
M V W SEE A B
SCRIBE NEWSROOM
A N R P D N O N
HUNG SQUEEZE ONYX
T E R R S T
TIPPLING ASPIRED
O E N A Q N X
SNARED TRUCK GETS
I U O O A I O E
ANTS CORNY CHURNS
G E K Y S K T T
```

Puzzle 156

```
DECENTRALISED
X Q O C N A S
SCOUSE OFFERING
E A R R O
BLAB TANGO ORBS
LOO NIP
HAZE ORBIT URGE
L M A L L
SOURPUSS TREMOR
E O C E O N O
ATTHESAMETIME
```

Puzzle 157

```
V
CHEFS
P R X Q
ZLOTY MUD
S K A
JIB W
ING
```

```
BACKROW
A O U I
SAX BIN
R H D
FOG CAB
U I H A
LONGING
```

Puzzle 158

```
SPIED F
R L WALK
BIKINI A
M T SOSO
JULIET H
L S E E
MASTERED
A P I D
ICESKATER
N C E R A
CUT STORM
O A T M A
ULCER BAT
R L E O I
SEEDLINGS
E E E T
REVERSES
A I E Y
D LADLED
HIFI D B
A SHERRY
ETCH E O
E DRAWS
```

Puzzle 159

```
M S F B I A D P
ENTERTAIN NAIVE
T U A W Q T V A
RADICAL USELESS
I A I R R A
CHRISTMAS ORGAN
E O E I O E T
OVERSTATEMENT
S O E C O C
TULIP HARDINESS
E U E S M I
EXTRACT REPLACE
P I T A A L S
LOOSE CONFIDENT
E N D K D R S A
```

Puzzle 160

```
CROSSEXAMINES
P A C N M O N E
RETIRED ATTACKS
I E E Z A I S
CODSWALLOP AREA
E B E N U C Y
SURFACES SMELT
U L W T B E P
JUMPLEADS RISER
U P Y A E E
MOLEST DRILLING
B E A G S L N N
ONDEMAND NAUSEA
J P O S T N
EQUAL MANGETOUT
T N E E O S R
ADORE SUNCREAM
H E S S T A U
OURS CHISELLING
P W P A A R
ICEPICK PETHATE
T A N E I O T D
BROKENHEARTED
```

478

Puzzle 161

```
V I E   F   B   A   S   E
I   G O R M L E S S N E S S
D O G   U   U   I   A   S   L
E   S N I F F   A P P E A S E
O     T   F I N E   Y   N
T H R U S T     N U R S E D
A   E     O A K S   N       A
P A S S I O N   H A R E M   N
E E   T   N   E   E   I C E
  I N A C T U A L F A C T   A
    T   H   L   L   D   E R R
```

Puzzle 162

```
S   C   F   M   I   A   B
M O R A L L Y   M A N N A
A   U   O   T   A   T   G
L I N E R   H U G G I N G
L   C   E       E       A
  W H I T E W A S H I N G
C   E     A     N   E
R E D I S T R I B U T E
U   E         O   R   S
S L A N T E D   W H E E L
H   W   T   U   E   P   O
E M A I L   P A R R I E S
S   Y   E   E   S   D   H
```

Puzzle 163

```
A   C   K   A   U   T   J
N Y L O N   M A N H O L E
T   E   E   U   B   G   S
H O A X E R S   I N A P T
E   N     E   A   E
M A S S E U S E S   E R R
    E   N     E   M
I T S   S N O W D R I F T
N   L   U       S   O
S E P I A   S Q U A S H Y
E   E   V   T   R   I   I
T R A P E Z E   G R O W N
S   K   D   D   E   N   G
```

Puzzle 164

```
  L   E   L   L   K   U   F
F I E S T A   E T H E R E A L
N   P   B   S   A   B   R
U S U R I O U S   K L A X O N
E   I   U   O   I   N
K E T T E R I N G   F I X E D
D   D   S   U   T   G
L O C K J A W   U N D E R G O
I   I   Y   F   D   B
K L U T E   F I N E T U N E D
  E   L   E   R   P   A
F L A M B E   F U S S P O T S
O   A   A   D   O   I   E
E S P R E S S O   L U S T R E
  E   K   T   M   D   H   S
```

The five-letter word is: FLUKE

Puzzle 165

```
S H E E P D I P
N   N   U   C   D
I N T E N S E L Y
F   O   I   O   E
F L U   S A V E D
S   R   H   E
  C A R E E R E D
B   G   D       E
E W E S   A L E C
S       W   A   O
T A K E A F T E R
B   I   K   H   A
I N C L E M E N T
T   K   S       I
T O S S   A M M O
E       E   E   N
R A C I N E S S
  O   D   S   F
B I N G O   A I L
O   T   R   B   A
S N O W S H O E S
H   U   E   U   K
  P R E D A T E S
```

Puzzle 166

```
  J   C       N   D   V   T
Q A T A R   F E R O C I O U S
  C   N       O   C   S   D
G O O D S   I N T U I T I O N
  B   I   W   M   A   R
K I N D H E A R T E D
T   A   L   I   N   M   U
Z E S T   L I G H T   O W N S
S   E   W   H   A   U   D
      P I C T U R E S Q U E
E   Y   S       Y   E   L
X E N O P H O B E   A T L A S
R   U   E   E       R   T
H I S T O R I A N   S A L E S
E   H   S   M       P   S
```

Puzzle 167

```
        V       C
P A R A L L E L
  T   L E I     A
D O M I N O E S
  M   D A N E S
A S P   E L Y
      A I L S
A C M E   B   F
L   S A L M A
M O T O R A I L
Y   P A I N S
U S E   B R I E
```

Puzzle 168

```
C   S   A     R I F F
R O U S I N G   G O   S
U   R   M   I   A N O R A K
C O T   P A L   O   E   A
I   A   O   I   R E L A T E
F O X T R O T   E   E   E
Y   T   Y           G O R Y
```

```
  D       D
W I N G E R
  G   R   E
K N E E C A P
  I   E   M
F A N O U T
Y       P
```

SOLUTIONS

Puzzle 169

Puzzle 170

Puzzle 171 Puzzle 172

Puzzle 173

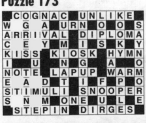

Puzzle 174

Puzzle 175

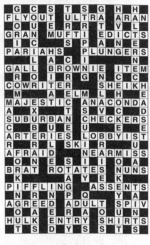

Puzzle 176

Puzzle 177

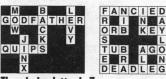

```
B A N D A G E . R E S I D E
U . O . B . X . I I . E . A
S E I N E . O R G A N I S E D
S . S . T . N . H C . T . H
T R E A T M E N T . E E R I E
O . O . . O . R . R O . . R
P O W E R . A R C H E T Y P E
. A . . . T . H . . . E . .
I N T E R V E N E . P U R S E
N . E . A . . A M . R . . N
F O R U M . H E I R E S S E S
U . P . B . A . S . C . O U
S P O T L I G H T . I D L E R
E . L . E U . R . S I . E .
. C O A R S E . Y I E L D E D
```

Puzzle 178

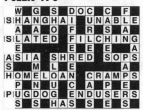

```
. W G S . D O C . C F
S H A N G H A I . U N A B L E
. A A . O F . R . S A
S L A T E D . F I L C H I N G
. E . . . E E . E . A
A S I A . S H R E D . S O P S
S . M . L . E . . A
H O M E L O A N . C R A M P S
P . N . U . C A P E
P U G D O G . E N D U S E R S
. S S H A S . S E S
```

Puzzle 179

```
. P H A G E . Q U A R T Z
Y Y . R . J T . I . . O
I N E L E G A N T . C A N
E . N . E . C E O . . E
L E A R N . K A R A T E
D . . E . K . T
. W E A R A N D T E A R
. M . . I . A . . A
M A S S I F . V I X E N
F N A . I E . Y . G
O V A . B A N K R O L L S
L . T . R . G N E T
D E E P E R . N A O M I
```

Puzzle 180

```
. S P L O D G E
H E . D . R G
A I R E D . A G O
V . M . S P . O
E V I L . S P I N
A . T G L . . S
B U T T O N I T
A . E . B N S
S I D E L I G H T
H . I . H O
. M O W N D O W N
U U . O . Y
S E T B A C K S
H O E . . E
E N F O R C I N G
R T . I N G
. S H E A T H E S
B E L . A H
L I F E . F R E E
A R . U N L
B O A . S P E L L
S M E . S S
. D E P R E S S
```

Puzzle 181

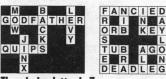

```
. M . B . L          F A N C I E D
G O D F A T H E R     R . I . N . A
W . C . V . Y         O R B . K E Y
. J . K               S . . . . . L
Q U I P S             T U B . A G O
. N . X               E . R . L . N
                      D E A D L E G
```

The missing letter is Z

Puzzle 182

```
. F I N D F A U L T W I T H
P D A D . I I . H . . . A
U N L O C K S . B O N K E R S
R . E . H . E . K . O . H
S I D E S A D D L E . A C M E
E . H . I . S . P . C . S
R E C O U R S E . L A Y U P
. L . N . C A N . L . P
A C I D D R O P S . O U T E R
C . P . . S . C R . . I
T A P I N G . S O Y A B E A N
I . E . I D . T . M X C
V E R A N D A S . D A P H N E
I . E . U . F . . I L
T R O O P . B A R R O W B O Y
Y . N . I . S . O . F . I
H Y M N S . I L L F A T E D
S O . S . S I C . . . E
M A U D . S P E C I A L I S T
A . R . T . A . M D E
S O O T H E R . F E E L E R S
H . W O E . E R . A T
U N P U T D O W N A B L E
```

Puzzle 183

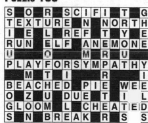

```
S O R . S C I F I . T G
T E X T U R E . N . N O R T H
I E . L . R E F . T Y E
R U N . E L F . A N E M O N E
U . . O . . M . R U
P L A Y F O R S Y M P A T H Y
. M . T I . . R . . I
B E A C H E D . P I E . W E E
O Z U . D U E . T I L
G L O O M . L . C H E A T E D
S N . B R E A K . R S S
```

Puzzle 184

```
. A F O
S C R I M P E D
. A . R U E A
A C E . D R A T
. I . D A R E
M A R D I . A
. O . E B B S
G L E N D A U
. O . L A S
R O M U L U S
D E F Y . A D E
. T A R D I S
```

SOLUTIONS

Puzzle 185

D	E	F	I	A	N	C	E			
E		U		R		O		S		
B	E	M	Y	G	U	E	S	T		
I		I		U		X		A		
T	O	G		A	X	I	N	G		
S		A	B	B	S					
	A	T	H	L	E	T	I	C		
S		E		E		O		O		
C	O	D	E		O	V	A	L		
A		A		V		I		D		
R	U	L	I	N	G	O	U	T		
P		A		E		L		U		
E	A	S	Y	C	H	A	I	R		
R		S		K		K		K		
I	R	O	N		O	G	R	E		
N			T		E		Y			
G	R	A	D	U	A	T	E			
		I		N		A		A		
S	C	R	A	G		C	U	B		
O		P		S		R		U		
S	O	L	U	T	I	O	N	S		
O		A		E		S		E		
G	Y	M	N	A	S	T	S			

Puzzle 186

W	E	B		S	O	B
A		U		K		I
D	A	N	C	I	N	G
D			O			O
I	N	B	U	I	L	T
N		U		L		E
G	E	T		K	I	D

	M	O	C	H	A
W		U		U	
A	I	R	T	I	M	E
N		N		M	
S	T	I	C	K	U	P
E		O	S		
D	R	A	P	E	

S				C
M	O	R	O	C	C	O
A		O		H		R
R	E	T	H	I	N	K
T		O		L		A
E	A	R	P	L	U	G
N				E	

Puzzle 187

D	I	S	T	U	R	B		C	L	I	F	F
R		T		G		A	D	O		N		R
A	C	R	Y	L	I	C		L	A	D	L	E
K		A		Y		K	I	D		I		E
E	X	I	T		F		L	A	G		Z	
		T	O	T	A	L	L	Y		O	W	E
J		W		I		A				R		
A	S	S		C	R	A	V	I	N	G		
N		E	M	U		E		D	R	A	B	
I	Q		R	I	P		C		U		O	
T	R	U	S	T		I	N	H	U	M	A	N
O		E		L	I	E		I		P		E
R	E	L	A	Y		D	E	C	A	Y	E	D

Puzzle 188

G	R	O	U	P	P	R	A	C	T	I	C	E
E		N		U		M		Y		U		B
H	I	C	C	U	P		P	E	P	P	E	R	E	D
G		L		L		I		L		A		
O	N	T	O		J	E	E	P	S		F	U	R	S
		G	N	U			T	O	O		
O	H	M	S		N	U	M	B	S		R	A	T	S
A		A		G		A		S		O		
W	R	I	G	G	L	E	S		W	R	A	P	U	P
T		O	E		O		O		L		T	
	N	O	N	S	E	N	S	E	V	E	R	S	E

Puzzle 189

	I	N	V	I	N	O	V	E	R	I	T	A	S
	M		E		N		R		N		C		L
T	A	P	P	E	T		I	S	A	B	E	L	L	A
	C		A		E		G		M		L		E
S	K	O	L		R	E	A	D	E		A	N	N	E
E			E		E		M		L		N	
P	R	O	B	O	S	C	I	S		A	D	L	A	I
E		E		T		A		I		I	
F	L	U	T	E		S	M	A	R	T	C	A	R	D
	H		A		Y		K		T	
A	B	E	L		R	U	M	B	A		V	L	A	D
L		E		N		U		N		E		I
Y	A	S	H	M	A	K	S		S	T	R	O	D	E
	I		E		U		I		A		D		S
C	R	E	M	E	D	E	C	A	S	S	I	S

Puzzle 190

P	A	V	E	S		P	O	P
O		A		E		A		L
O	R	C	H	E	S	T	R	A
P		C		S		R		N
	V	I	R	T	U	O	S	O
A		N		A		L		F
G	U	E	R	R	I	L	L	A
G			S		E		T	
R	I	F	T		E	D	I	T
O		I		Q			A	
	I	N	P	U	B	L	I	C
C		E		I		O		K
O	N	R	E	C	O	R	D	
N			K		R		P	
S	U	C	H		T	Y	P	O
E		A	F		I		L	
R	E	B	E	L	L	I	N	G
V		I		A		D		S
A	G	N	O	S	T	I	C	
T		C		H		O		T
I	R	R	I	G	A	T	E	S
S		E		U		I		A
M	O	W		N	I	C	E	R

Puzzle 191

V	I	C	V	V	A	C		A	C
V	I	E	T	N	A	M	E	S	E		L	E	A	F
G		E		P		R		T		T
C	O	M	M	I	T		L	I	M	E	R	I	C	K
U			U		A		I		U		A
A	R	I	A		I	N	V	I	N	C	I	B	L	E
S		L		N		O		S		L
	V	E	R	S	A	T	I	L	I	T	Y
V		X		E		U		I		I
V	O	C	A	L	C	O	R	D	S		C	E	N	T
Y		N		H		C		S		S
L	A	N	D	F	I	L	L		I	N	C	I	T	E
G		R		L		U		O		O		E
L	E	V	I		L	I	T	H	U	A	N	I	A	N
R	A	Y	E	S			S		K		D

The five-letter word is: CAVIL

Puzzle 192

B	O	S	O	M		B	E	H	A	V	I	N	G
O		W		O		R		U		O		I		P
B	O	O	K	S	T	A	L	L		W	I	P	E	S
S		T		E		K		E				A
S	T	A	Y	U	P		I	L	L	W	I	L	L
S		E		I	N	N			N			N	M
W	E	D	D	I	N	G		G	E	T	O	F	F
A			D		G			E		L	A
T	A	W	N	Y		I	N	T	H	E	M	A	I	N
S		O	L	E		I		T		T		T
	C	O	A	L	E	S	C	E		H	E	E	L	S

Puzzle 193

H	O	R	S	E	M	A	N		B	O	F	F	I	N
R		I		E		O		A		O		N
D	I	S	M	A	L		S	O	L	E	C	I	S	M
G		P		O		T		L		A		I
A	I	R	L	I	N	E	R		E	N	L	I	S	T
N		E		U		R		T
	S	T	R	E	A	M	L	I	N	E	D
		O		N			N		G
	I	N	S	C	R	U	T	A	B	L	E
O		H		N			A		B
S	C	A	M	P	I		C	O	L	A	N	D	E	R
T		E		L		L		T		W
D	A	T	A	B	A	S	E		A	N	I	M	A	L
N		N		D		A		M		N		R
G	E	I	S	H	A		N	E	A	T	E	N	E	D

Puzzle 194

P		P				S		S		B	C
U	S	H	E	R		O	P	T	O	M	E	T	R	Y
E		D		A		P		T		U
S	U	P	E	R	B		R	E	H	E	A	R	S	E
D		S		R		R		I		H
F	O	R	T	U	I	T	O	U	S	L	Y
N		R		D		W		T		O		F
S	Y	R	I	N	G	E		R	I	T	U	A	L	S
	M		A		E		C		N		Y
	L		N	A	T	I	O	N	A	L	G	R	I	D
	L		H		T		B		N
M	I	S	S	P	E	N	T		E	U	L	O	G	Y
M		I		G		A		O		F
A	B	U	N	D	A	N	C	E		R	O	B	O	T
O		K		P		T		D		X

482|

Puzzle 195
ACROSS: 1 Stark 4 Crossbow 11 Neon light 12 Flora 13 Epic 14 Devout 16 Cot 18 One 19 Wipers 22 Oral 24 Input 26 Guest book 27 Goatherd 28 Spite
DOWN: 2 Two-time 3 Roll 5 Retro 6 Safety 7 Boo 8 Wraithlike 9 Unbecoming 10 Ogle 15 Vie 16 Carport 17 Swatch 20 Pager 21 Reek 23 Step 25 Pea

Puzzle 196
ACROSS: 1 Astride 7 Noted 8 Sax 9 Wail 10 Mars 12 Overrate 14 Shopfront 15 Forensic 18 Blocking 21 Unexposed 23 Free fall 25 Open 26 Ogre 28 Bid 29 Carve 30 Eyesore
DOWN: 2 Set fire to 3 Ride 4 Distant cousin 5 Snow goose 6 Exist 11 Trifle 13 Stock 16 Ozone-friendly 17 About 19 Kipper 20 Adulterer 22 Swaggerer 24 Combs 27 Acts

Puzzle 197
ACROSS: 1 Response 6 Abasement 7 Lop 8 Cocky 9 Premolar 12 Onyx 13 Gala 16 Pot-pourri 18 Easter egg 19 Iced 20 Bang 23 Narrator 26 Gumbo 27 Elk 28 Fire alarm 29 Heraldry
DOWN: 1 Really 2 Stag party 3 Overcome 4 Stencil 5 Stay 10 Reading age 11 Complexion 14 Agree 15 Bones 17 Taste 21 Aforesaid 22 Panorama 24 Remorse 25 Skimpy 26 Gift

Puzzle 198
ACROSS: 1 Lions 4 Aid 6 Ballistic 7 Capsicum 9 Pepperoni 10 Keys 12 Fens 14 Bump into 17 Edginess 19 Ibex 21 Pyre 23 Interplay 25 Alarmist 27 Ingenious 28 Nod 29 Later
DOWN: 1 Lobe 2 Oil lamp 3 Spinster 4 Artichoke 5 Decommission 8 Spike 11 Young 13 Up-end 15 Nosey 16 Debilitation 18 Beryl 20 Estranged 22 Criminal 24 Lose out 26 Tsar

Puzzle 199

Puzzle 200
ACROSS: 5 Slithery 7 Eat 8 Lycra 9 Printout 11 Iron 12 Stun 14 Faddy 15 Ewe 16 Adulate 20 Rob 21 Surly 23 Avow 24 Emir 26 Scheming 28 Dance 29 Six 30 Rubicund
DOWN: 1 Islet 2 Sisterhood 3 Whaling 4 Trick or treat 6 East-Ender 10 Jiffy 13 Cyclist 17 Debt of honour 18 Cream soda 19 Hydro 22 Romanesque 25 Imperil 27 Exude

Puzzle 201
ACROSS: 1 Salad cream 6 Iced 9 Moralistic 10 Amos 12 Over and above 15 Tolerable 17 Borer 18 Titan 19 Title role 20 Took the floor 24 Loop 25 Accessible 26 Wish 27 Appearance
DOWN: 1 Sumo 2 Lark 3 Delivery note 4 Riser 5 Alignment 7 Common room 8 Dishearten 11 Rabble-rouser 13 Statute law 14 Gluttonous 16 Buttercup 21 Liege 22 Oban 23 Hebe

Puzzle 202
ACROSS: 1 Opacity 7 Outer 8 Lip 9 Cool 10 Snow 12 Scottish 14 Forefront 15 Eclectic 18 Good turn 21 Thereupon 23 Autocrat 25 Mite 26 Kiln 28 Chi 29 Dwell 30 Agility
DOWN: 2 Patio door 3 Card 4 Talent spotter 5 Vouchsafe 6 Spawn 11 Stifle 13 Stack 16 Close-run thing 17 Agate 19 Tremor 20 Instantly 22 Pertinent 24 Smock 27 Idol

SOLUTIONS

Puzzle 203
ACROSS: 7 Neptune 8 Jupiter
10 Planet 11 Asteroid 12 Lunar
14 Magnitude 18 Fuel 20 Pluto
21 Star 22 Spaceship 24 Comet
27 Aeronaut 30 Meteor
32 Capsule 33 Sunspot
DOWN: 1 Tell 2 Stanza 3 Unite
4 Just 5 Vibrates 6 Yeti 9 Data
13 Usurp 15 Neon 16 Drake
17 Opus 19 Lacrosse 23 Iota
25 Obtuse 26 Imbue 28 Edam
29 Ally 31 Oboe

Puzzle 204
ACROSS: 1 Close down 6 Stag
10 Gushing 11 Trestle 13 Item
14 Untroubled 16 Septic 18 In-tray
21 Contrary 22 Omega 24 Propulsion
26 Well 29 Need 30 Devilishly
32 Court 34 Windsock 36 Stiles
37 Chilli 40 Impatience 41 Claw
44 Piccolo 45 Irately 46 Call
47 Stagehand
DOWN: 2 Lisle 3 Sail 4 Dugong 5 Water
lily 7 Titillate 8 Greedy 9 Against
12 Equation 15 Wistful 17 Propose
19 Lassie 20 Baileys 23 Spinach
25 Orient 27 Ethical 28 Kitschy
31 Stiletto 33 Untypical 34 Washed
out 35 Airways 38 Biopic 39 Acting
42 Lie-in 43 Hash

Puzzle 205
ACROSS: 1 Duster 4 Priest 7 Ream
9 Nit 10 Lion 11 Tern 12 Abet 13 Ear
14 Tablet 17 Dangle 20 Gander
23 Reader 26 Ale 27 Part 28 Poem
30 Noel 31 Tea 32 West 33 Relive
34 Trance
DOWN: 1 Direct 2 Seat 3 Rennet
4 Petard 5 Edit 6 Tenure 8 Meal
10 Lean 15 Bun 16 Ewe 18 Ape
19 God 20 Garner 21 Deal 22 Rattle
23 Repast 24 Anew
25 Rustle 27 Peal 29 Mean

Puzzle 206
ACROSS: 4 Sod 8 Thank you 9 Outing
10 Growth 11 Tutelage 13 Tyre
15 Bound 16 Dope 18 Bedstead
20 Divers 22 Gateau 23 Nearside
24 Pug
DOWN: 1 Chirpy 2 Gnaw 3 Myth 4 Suet
pudding 5 Dotted 6 Stolid 7 Snug
12 Eye 13 Tub 14 Easter 15 Brew-up
17 Parody 19 Exam 20 Deal 21 Vest

Puzzle 207
ACROSS: 1 Incessant 9 Assured 10 Pin
11 Inapt 12 Inept 14 Groom 16 Easel
18 Net 19 Sap 21 Dirge 22 Alike
23 Gloom 25 Capri 26 Rum 27 Patella
28 Redundant
DOWN: 1 Impugn 2 Cannot 3 Skimmed
milk 4 Amateur 5 Tat 6 Oscillation
7 True 8 Edit 13 Peak 15 Real
17 Stepped 19 Sierra 20 Pelmet
23 Gape 24 Oath 25 Car

Puzzle 208
ACROSS: 1 Mikado 5 Recipe 9 Fee
11 Face-off 12 Petunia 13 Earl
15 Screw 16 Poem 17 Lute 19 Aphid
20 Bawl 24 Fielder 25 Halyard 26 Toe
27 Steely 28 Decode
DOWN: 2 Incur 3 Aloe 4 Office
party 5 Replenished 6 Cite 7 Panto
8 Afterlife 10 Marmalade 14 Lie
16 Pub 18 Theft 21 Award 22 Edge
23 Alec

Puzzle 209
ACROSS: 6 Barrow-boy 7 Trash 8 Rut
9 Neat 10 Riff 12 Customer 15 Muscle
in 17 Mare's nest 18 Addendum
20 Hogshead 23 Owls 24 Glib 27 Pal
28 Civil 29 Cockfight
DOWN: 1 Obstinacy 2 Armada 3 Moths
4 Abortive 5 Mystify 11 Conciseness
13 Slurred 14 Gnat 16 Execute
17 Moat 19 Edibility 21 Oil slick
22 Coppice 25 Lovage 26 Scoff

Puzzle 210

D	I	S	H	O	N	E	S	T	
L	I	D	O		F		W	O	O	D
E	V	E	N		F		E	R	N	E
T	E	A		C	A	D		T	E	N
H		W	A	L	E	S				I
A	L	T	A	R		C	L	I	N	G
R		D	E	L	A	Y				R
G	E	M		T	O	Y		S	P	A
I	M	A	M		W		S	P	A	T
C	I	T	E		E		K	A	N	E
	R	E	W	A	R	D	I	N	G	

Puzzle 211

ACROSS: 4 Throw 9 Ammeter 10 Hyena
11 Arm 12 Man 13 May 14 Imprint
15 Careless driving 19 Habitue 20 Hog
21 Moo 22 Ago 23 Patio 24 Lionise
25 Needy
DOWN: 1 Tarmac 2 Omen 3 Stimulation
4 Tray 5 Remind 6 Whipping boy
7 Gemini 8 Halt 16 Rebate 17 Sleaze
18 Grower 19 Hope 20 Holy 21 Maim

Puzzle 212

C	A	N		B	A	G	E	L
E	X	I	L	E		A	D	O
D	E	N		A		L	I	P
E		E	M	U	L	A	T	E
	H		A	T	E		S	
T	E	R	R	I	E	R		V
I	R	E		F		E	Y	E
C	O	D		U	N	I	O	N
K	N	O	L	L		N	U	T

Puzzle 213

ACROSS: 1 Floating voter 10 Overtly
11 Related 12 Sleepiness 14 Snap
16 Regulate 18 Judas 21 Soft touch
22 Chewy 23 Rarity 25 Gold disc
28 Esteemed 29 Eleven 31 Other
33 Slow march 35 Ideal 36 Neurosis
40 Roam 41 Amalgamate 44 Big band
45 Whinger 46 Paddle steamer
DOWN: 2 Liege 3 Autopilot 4 Icy
5 Garish 6 Oily 7 Extenuate 8 Dowser
9 Adopt 13 Not out 15 Suicidal
17 Go for it 19 Chaos 20 Hyacinth
21 Surveyor 24 Tie-break 26 Inverts
27 Verse 30 Do well 32 Hydrangea
34 Margarita 37 Spears 38 Probe
39 Smudge 42 Argue 43 Hand 45 Wit

Puzzle 214

ACROSS; 6 Family quarrel 8 Inborn
9 Estrange 10 Sal 11 Esteem
12 Cassette 15 Ache 17 Sistine
19 Oarsmen 22 Dent 24 Agitated
27 Relate 28 Ido 29 Contempt
30 Casino 31 Transport café
DOWN: 1 Immodest 2 Clansman
3 Squelch 4 Cactus 5 Create
6 Finishing-post 7 Light sentence
13 Aeon 14 Sir 16 Cede 18 Ida
20 Atrocity 21 Salesman 23 Edition
25 Titian 26 Tamest

Puzzle 215

ACROSS: 1 Hubbub 5 Biceps 9 Aga
11 Seismic 12 Rotunda 13 Boys
15 Splay 16 Tour 17 Down 19 McCoy
20 Chic 24 Termini 25 Skinned 26 Nil
27 Throng 28 Yeomen
DOWN: 2 Unity 3 Bump 4 Backpacking
5 Barbarously 6 City 7 Pinto 8 Use-by
date 10 Patricide 14 Sin 16 Tic
18 Worth 21 Hinge 22 Lido 23 Giro

Puzzle 216

ACROSS: 1 Ski 8 Decisiveness 9 Owl
11 Exile 12 Diocese 14 Seer 15 Corona
18 Evince 20 Spew 23 Burnish
25 Arras 27 Opt 28 Interstellar 29 Ear
DOWN: 1 Stock cube 2 Idle 3 Action
4 Ashes 5 Evade 6 On to 7 Astern
10 Hereafter 13 Ire 16 Raring 17 Ass
19 Virile 21 Phase 22 Waxed 24 Idea
26 Sore

Puzzle 217

C	A	R	D	I	F	F		S	C	O	T
A		L		E		A		G		L		A
B	U	B	O	N	I	C		A	L	A	R	M
I		U		U		T		M		U		E
D	A	M	O	N		O	V	E	R	D	O	
I		C		R		R		S		I		C
N	I	A	C	I	N		S	M	O	O	T	H
G		M		A		D		A				E
	T	I	P	T	O	E		N	I	C	K	S
S		A		I		B		S		O		T
T	A	B	O	O		U	N	H	I	N	G	E
O		L		N		N		I		G		R
W	A	Y	S		S	K	I	P	T	O	N	

SOLUTIONS

Puzzle 218

ACROSS: 1 Dot 8 High-handedly 9 Sea
11 Think 12 Clutter 14 Yoke 15 Azalea
18 Gothic 20 Ibis 23 Gorilla 25 Endow
27 Ilk 28 Draughtboard 29 End
DOWN: 1 Discharge 2 That 3 Ignite
4 Shaky 5 Snick 6 Menu 7 Glitch
10 Pre-cooked 13 Leg 16 Aurora
17 Ail 19 Old man 21 Bathe 22 Set by
24 Loud 26 Wide

Puzzle 219

ACROSS: 1 River 4 Laser
7 Issue 9 Grief 10 Vital 11 Loose
12 There 15 Lunar 18 Bed
20 Safari 21 Indoor 22 Tap
24 Shots 27 Truth 30 Tiger
31 Arena 32 Album 33 Multi
34 Sharp 35 Linen
DOWN: 1 Right 2 Voice 3 Rifle
4 Level 5 Satin 6 Ruler 8 Score
13 Heath 14 Roast 16 Under
17 About 18 Bit 19 Dip 23 Angel
24 Seats 25 Opera 26 Stamp
27 Trail 28 Urban 29 Human

Puzzle 220

Puzzle 221

ACROSS: 1 Schmaltz 6 Small beer
7 Mat 8 Irony 9 Rush hour 12 Rink
13 Twig 16 Talk radio 18 Catatonia
19 Inns 20 Boll 23 Eyeliner 26 Ochre
27 Ban 28 Celebrant 29 Unneeded
DOWN: 1 Sesame 2 Heartburn
3 All-night 4 Tremolo 5 Fray
10 Regionally 11 Protective 14 Widen
15 Trots 17 Let on 21 Overboard
22 Likeable 24 Echelon 25 United
26 Once

Puzzle 222

ACROSS: 9 Gusher 10 Banks 11 Ours
12 Clot 13 Manse 14 Homing
15 Primate 17 Anarchic 19 Flag
21 Overact 23 Foal 24 Fructose
25 Eclair 27 Art 29 Seedless
31 Rhomboid 32 Pampered
34 Culpable 35 Opponent 36 Dividend
39 Ear 40 Estate 42 Industry 45 Flay
46 Torrent 47 Ache 48 Athletic
51 Renewal 54 Guinea 55 Crepe
57 Earl 58 Ghee 59 Moths 60 Cranny
DOWN: 1 Curler 2 White magic 3 Grim
4 T-bone 5 Antenatal 6 Asthma
7 Cosmic 8 Frangipani 16 Twosome
18 Release date 20 Large 22 Trefoil
23 Full board 26 Redhead 28 Truck
driver 29 Suppose 30 Diplomacy
33 Re-elect 37 Vedette 38 North
41 Self-taught 43 Siamese cat
44 Precocity 49 Landed 50 Trauma
52 Arrant 53 Cease 56 Each

Puzzle 223

ACROSS: 4 Won 8 Shanghai 9 Italic
10 Skiing 11 Electric 13 Wrap
15 Foamy 16 Rows 18 Knee-deep
20 Mantis 22 Poetic 23 Near miss
24 Hag
DOWN: 1 Choker 2 Anti 3 Chug
4 Wire-tapping 5 Nicety 6 Taster 7 Mini
12 Cos 13 Wok 14 Pretty 15 French
17 Whimsy 19 Nook 20 Moan
21 Numb

Puzzle 224

ACROSS: 1 Crash-land 9 Agitate 10 Oar
11 Unify 12 Pygmy 14 Shush 16 Expel
18 Yam 19 Ark 21 Idyll 22 Acute
23 Crown 25 Bhaji 26 Urn 27 Foresee
28 Emergency
DOWN: 1 Choosy 2 Atrium
3 Haughtiness 4 Agilely 5 Day
6 Displeasing 7 Gang 8 Dewy 13 Mart
15 Hair 17 Palmate 19 Autumn
20 Keenly 23 Cafe 24 Ours 25 Bee

SOLUTIONS

Puzzle 225

ACROSS: 4 Embed 9 Abashed 10 Enact
11 Egg 12 Ink 13 Men 14 Leisure
15 Spoilt for choice 19 Artisan 20 Owe
21 Pip 22 Gap 23 Smell 24 Allegro
25 Yodel
DOWN: 1 Caries 2 Walk 3 Shamelessly
4 Eden 5 Bugler 6 Delightedly 7 Lazuli
8 Stye 16 Outlet 17 Fanged 18 Employ
19 Also 20 Opal 21 Page

Puzzle 226

ACROSS: 6 Laminated 7 Ovate
8 Cap 9 Army 10 Bake 12 Labourer
15 Complete 17 Messiness
18 Vanguard 20 World war 23 Obey
24 Jaws 27 Bus 28 Spoof 29 Stationer
DOWN: 1 Allowable 2 Embalm 3 Annex
4 Stockade 5 Adopted 11 Bumptiously
13 Blouson 14 Lens 16 Eyebrow
17 Move 19 Crossfire 21 Overseas
22 Bombast 25 Abound 26 Aspic

Puzzle 227

ACROSS: 1 Out 8 Highly strung
9 Sue 11 Mango 12 Atelier 14 Fine
15 Normal 18 Erotic 20 Else
23 Basmati 25 Latch 27 Art
28 Draught-proof 29 Tor
DOWN: 1 On stand-by 2 Them
3 Agenda 4 Aloof 5 Asian 6 Free
7 Anoint 10 Cricketer 13 Tee 16 Rosary
17 Let 19 Ration 21 Lithe 22 Elope
24 Abut 26 Haft

Puzzle 228

ACROSS: 1 Thirteenth 6 Half
10 Repel 11 Chauffeur 12 Site 13 Stun
14 Shake 16 Insect 17 Befriend
19 Eyesight 22 Inform 25 Blurb
26 Rain 27 Sign 29 Spacesuit
30 Okapi 31 Need 32 Refreshing
DOWN: 1 Turnstile 2 Impetus 3 Tile
4 Excite 5 Trainee 7 Average 8 Farce
9 Offspring 15 Scribbled 17 Bet
18 Demanding 20 Emulate 21 Hirsute
23 Origami 24 Filter 25 Bison 28 Boss
THE HEART OF A GOOF

Puzzle 229

ACROSS: 1 Email 5 Food 6 Plasma
7 Itch 8 At will 9 Lacerate
12 Muscleman 15 Ape 16 Baste
17 Tenet 18 Emu 19 Net profit
21 Manacled 24 Look-in 25 Poll
26 Even up 27 Mind 28 Pyrex
DOWN: 2 Militia 3 Inspire 4 Porcine
5 Fail-safe 9 Lambasting 10 Cashew
nut 11 Unrequited 13 Lobster
14 Masterful 20 Panelled 21 Melodic
22 Closely 23 Epicure

Puzzle 230

ACROSS: 1 Mining 4 Author 7 Garage
9 Soft 11 Ago 12 Left 13 Curves
15 Elbow 17 Dear 18 Edge 20 Tough
23 Unions 25 Mass 27 Sir 28 Here
29 Legend 31 Kitten 32 Depths
DOWN: 1 Magic 2 Nor 3 Grease
4 Absorb 5 Hate 6 Routine 8 Advertise
10 Flowering 14 Use 16 Log
17 Denmark 19 Gin 21 Unseen
22 Hurled 24 Sides 26 Shut 30 Eat

Puzzle 231

ACROSS: 9 Incident room 11 Abut
12 See 13 Limp 14 Stain 15 Ragman
16 Petrify 18 Calfskin 20 Maxi
22 Serious 24 Apex 25 Moonrise
26 Excess 28 Tor 30 Bad patch
32 Eligible 33 Cast iron 35 Hysteria
36 Lemonade 37 Telltale 40 Rip
41 Devout 43 Optimist 46 Felt
47 Relieve 48 Toot 49 Stiletto
52 Bye-byes 55 Dragee 56 Aired
59 Laid 60 Age 61 Stem
62 Decongestion
DOWN: 1 Unlike 2 Dispersion 3 Mess
4 Steal 5 Connector 6 Amoral
7 Haggis 8 Queasiness 10 Net
17 Fascist 19 Freethinker 21 Aroma
23 Species 24 Architect 27 Seepage
29 Red-hot poker 30 Buckled 31 Put
to rout 34 Roaster 38 Lathery
39 Lasso 42 Electorate 44 Mutability
45 Allowance 50 Legume 51 Tweedy
53 Editor 54 Crank 57 Egg 58 Deed

SOLUTIONS

Puzzle 232

ACROSS: 1 Spit 6 Sack 8 Brush 9 User 10 Ogre 11 Trace 13 Rose 15 Adept 18 Mite 19 Elan 21 Drape 24 Need 25 Eager 28 Stew 29 Fade 30 Easel 31 Gnar 32 Tier
DOWN: 2 Pistol 3 Tor 4 Abut 5 Tuna 6 Shoe 7 Corset 12 Rap 14 Earn 16 End 17 Tea 18 Mien 20 Listen 22 Roe 23 Meddle 25 Ewer 26 Gust 27 Rely 29 Fat

Puzzle 233

ACROSS: 1 Spitting image 9 Wrap up 10 Banknote 11 Talc 12 Alder 13 Ohms 14 Arc 15 Air 16 Hall 18 Canal 20 Iota 22 Unafraid 24 Chalky 25 Summer holiday
DOWN: 2 Parka 3 Topical 4 Imp 5 Go bad 6 Mineral 7 Gun 8 Stem 12 Acclaim 13 Origami 17 Anna 19 Nadir 21 Tikka 23 Flu 24 Coo

Puzzle 234

ACROSS: 1 Spire 4 Son-in-law 11 Petulance 12 Frost 13 Imam 14 Boater 16 Per 18 Lee 19 Wicked 22 Gall 24 Valet 26 Burnished 27 Low-lying 28 Swede
DOWN: 2 Pet name 3 Rill 5 Overt 6 Infirm 7 Loo 8 Water slide 9 Split-level 10 Undo 15 Auk 16 Poached 17 Swotty 20 Cabin 21 Ears 23 View 25 Law

Puzzle 235

```
D E F A C E   S T A T I C
I   R   R   S   E   R   A
S E A L A N T   M O I S T
H   N   M   A   P   L   E
  S K I P   G R E Y L A G
C   L   Y   R       O
R O Y A L S   C A N C E R
E   O   S       R   Y
A R M L O C K   P A I L
T   E   K   A   R   N   F
I G L O O   T R E K K E R
O   O   U   E   S   L   E
N I N E T Y   A S C E N T
```

Puzzle 236

ACROSS: 1 Valid 4 Cud 6 Ectoplasm 7 Bogeyman 9 Ginger nut 10 Nape 12 Area 14 Junk mail 17 Evenness 19 Oast 21 Snag 23 Goose-step 25 Sessions 27 At a stroke 28 Tie 29 Ensue
DOWN: 1 Veer 2 Let-down 3 Depleted 4 Coalminer 5 Demonstrably 8 Agony 11 Plume 13 Skunk 15 Arson 16 Decongestant 18 Agape 20 Snow-scape 22 Belittle 24 Tenuous 26 Mere

Puzzle 237

```
S E T   T O P   I M P
O O   A   E   N   A
W I N D C H E A T E R
    S   T A P   E
T W I G   M   B R I E
U   L E I S U R E   R
B I L L   T   A S I A
I   I   T E A   T
B U T T E R F L I E S
I   I   A   A   N   A
B U S   M A R   G A G
```

Puzzle 238

ACROSS: 5 Villainy 7 Nag 8 Mocha 9 Wild duck 11 Oche 12 Punt 14 Dry up 15 Own 16 Adverse 20 Elf 21 Testy 23 Edam 24 Scan 26 Triangle 28 Venue 29 Rib 30 Proposer
DOWN: 1 Ovine 2 Sluggishly 3 Man-made 4 Unscrupulous 6 Marketing 10 Woods 13 Aplenty 17 Deflationary 18 Receptive 19 Dying 22 Secularism 25 Unkempt 27 Abort

Puzzle 239

ACROSS: 8 Mead 9 Tonic 10 Lager 12 Wine 13 Port 14 Cordial 16 Bitter 18 Coke 19 Mild 21 Flip 23 Punch 24 Oolong 25 Nectar 27 Booze 28 Sake 30 Beer 31 Soda 32 Shandy 35 Seltzer 37 Fizz 38 Hock 41 Stout 42 Hogan 43 Asti
DOWN: 1 Yeti 2 Advent 3 Stupor 4 Inert 5 Ace 6 Band 7 Befallen 11 Borehole 15 Boyhood 17 Ill 19 Miles 20 Anybody 22 Peter 23 Perished 26 Elements 29 Kid 32 Sizing 33 Ash-can 34 Ridge 36 Taut 39 Cite 40 Shy

Puzzle 240

ACROSS: 9 Antagonistic 11 Hart
12 Fen 13 Hard 14 Twirl 15 Rotund
16 Decamps 18 Narcotic 20 Aped
22 Amasses 24 Grew 25 Brunette
26 Advise 28 Rye 30 Resounds
32 Navy blue 33 Falsetto 35 On strike
36 Exorcist 37 Poachers 40 Sea
41 Tuxedo 43 Sections 46 Uses
47 Settees 48 Must 49 Stamp out
52 Editing 55 Flouts 56 Theft
59 Rugs 60 Car 61 Once 62 Direct
action
DOWN: 1 Unmade 2 Handmaiden
3 Loft 4 Minim 5 Stalinist 6 Scorer
7 Ghetto 8 Crankiness 10 New
17 Phaeton 19 Water sports 21 Purse
23 Starves 24 Give birth 27 Elevens
29 Encompassed 30 Reflect
31 Observers 34 Tailors 38 Accused
39 Rants 42 Unsettling 44 Immaturity
45 Statutory 50 Mouser 51 Onside
53 No-good 54 Recce 57 Fat 58 Tram

Puzzle 241

ACROSS: 1 Stroganoff 6 Smut 9 Visitor
10 Regalia 12 Fits and starts
14 Roll-on 15 Schemata 17 Umbrella
19 Bistro 22 Pitched battle 24 Astarte
25 Tenable 26 Toby 27 Engagement
DOWN: 1 Save 2 Restful 3 Get it
together 4 Norman 5 Foredeck
7 Malaria 8 Translator 11 Go the
distance 13 Triumphant 16 Bludgeon
18 Bathtub 20 Tremble 21 Martha
23 Heat

Puzzle 242

ACROSS: 1 Postman's knock 9 Snappy
10 Bluebell 11 Trio 12 Altar 13 Come
14 Son 15 Ash 16 Swat 18 Trawl
20 Ease 22 Entwined 24 Pastis
25 Trim your sails
DOWN: 2 Owner 3 Topmost 4 Any
5 Sabot 6 Neutral 7 Cob 8 Clam
12 Antonym 13 Chelsea 17 Wane
19 Audio 21 Still 23 War 24 Par

Puzzle 243

ACROSS: 1 Edict 5 Gain 6 Uptake
7 Tote 8 Mouser 9 Catch-all
12 Scrapyard 15 Ion 16 Irate 17 Drunk
18 Yet 19 Stage door 21 Man-eater
24 Starry 25 Glut 26 Enough 27 Boor
28 Aside
DOWN: 2 Diploma 3 Classic
4 Pigtail 5 Get ready 9 Cosmic dust
10 Tarantula 11 Adventurer 13 Prickle
14 At any cost 20 Gangster 21 Million
22 Amazons 23 Enraged

Puzzle 244

Puzzle 245

ACROSS: 1 Aglow 4 Fall over
11 Fantasise 12 Blast 13 Iris
14 Loaded 16 Pro 18 Ice 19 Warmly
22 Stir 24 Trait 26 Bewitched
27 Ditching 28 Spado
DOWN: 2 Genuine 3 Oval 5 Ahead
6 Libido 7 Via 8 Retrograde 9 Affiliated
10 Kilo 15 Aim 16 Pitched 17 Switch
20 Robin 21 Lawn 23 Stop 25 Aft

Puzzle 246

ACROSS: 7 Sandwich 8 Goat 9 Disc
10 Army 11 Ill 13 Teeth 14 Perfect
16 Calorie 18 Bench 21 Ivy 22 Mill
23 Nail 25 Acid 26 Economic
DOWN: 1 Native 2 Education 3 Final
4 Chamber 5 Egg 6 Garlic 12 Afternoon
15 Citizen 17 Advice 19 Crisis 20 Blood
24 Odd

SOLUTIONS

Puzzle 247

Puzzle 248

ACROSS: 4 Sag 8 Properly 9 Errant
10 Tsetse 11 Counting 13 Snub
15 Bored 16 Orgy 18 Marksman
20 Joyous 22 Cornea 23 Under-age
24 Yes
DOWN: 1 Prison 2 Spit 3 Tree
4 Synchronous 5 Gerund 6 Grotto
7 Anon 12 Guy 13 Sam 14 Baking
15 Bombay 17 Grudge 19 Atom
20 Jade 21 Yarn

Puzzle 249

ACROSS: 9 Quirks 10 Wails 11 Hale
12 Fend 13 Refit 14 Insets 15 Success
17 Although 19 Semi 21 Council
23 Coal 24 Stencils 25 Bemuse
27 Tit 29 Bandanna 31 Episodic
32 Unhinged 34 Restarts 35 Back
door 36 Targeted 39 Duo 40 Rabble
42 Revolves 45 Huge 46 Seesaws
47 Buys 48 Streamer 51 Used car
54 Grouts 55 Gauge 57 Nook 58 Putt
59 Eater 60 Shunts
DOWN: 1 Bureau 2 Prediction
3 Tsar 4 Swift 5 Mint sauce 6 T-shirt
7 Physio 8 Plate glass 16 Section
18 Substandard 20 Extra 22 Lobbies
23 Come of age 26 Excused
28 Territorial 29 Blubber 30 Drinkable
33 Grovels 37 Revises 38 Every
41 Adulterous 43 Libidinous
44 Segregate 49 Exults 50 Masses
52 Aborts 53 Purrs 56 Ease

Puzzle 250

ACROSS: 1 H-bomb 4 Rid 6 Date stamp
7 Jabberer 9 Pseudonym 10 Nick
12 Tern 14 Semolina 17 Exorcism
19 Mode 21 Semi 23 Rancorous
25 Sweet pea 27 In-service 28 Nit
29 Dream
DOWN: 1 Hide 2 Outrage 3 Busybody
4 Rearrange 5 Departmental
8 Spiny 11 Credo 13 Conch 15 Issue
16 Reimpression 18 Kiosk 20 Dinner
set 22 Tortured 24 One-time 26 Deem

Puzzle 251

ACROSS: 5 Symmetry 7 Oak 8 Caper
9 Check out 11 Roue 12 Moth
14 Weeks 15 Ill 16 Ability 20 Mar
21 Early 23 Echo 24 Spin 26 Leathery
28 Susan 29 Tar 30 Millpond
DOWN: 1 Ascot 2 Smokehouse
3 Peacock 4 Cryptologist 6 Erstwhile
10 Crows 13 Psalter 17 Birthday suit
18 Embellish 19 Lying 22 Reparation
25 Shingle 27 Crude

Puzzle 252

Puzzle 253

ACROSS: 1 Befitting 9 Own goal 10 Ebb
11 Tweed 12 Balmy 14 Shall 16 Ember
18 Ten 19 Boa 21 Angus 22 Acorn
23 Joust 25 Okapi 26 Sum 27 Twinned
28 Essential
DOWN: 1 Breast 2 Fabian 3 Titillating
4 Iceberg 5 God 6 Inebriation 7 Fowl
8 Cloy 13 Moor 15 Hero 17 Bus pass
19 Bonsai 20 Animal 23 Jets 24 Unit
25 Ode

Puzzle 254

Puzzle 255

ACROSS: 7 Coronet 8 Emerald
10 Bauble 11 Diamante 12 Cameo
14 Seed-pearl 18 Drop 20 Beryl
21 Sard 22 Jewellery 24 Tiara
27 Heliodor 30 Diadem 32 Diamond
33 Jacinth
DOWN: 1 Toga 2 Cobble 3 Sewer
4 *Emma* 5 Dreamers 6 Flat 9 Idle
13 Agree 15 Doll 16 Rarer 17 Abel
19 Premiums 23 Rory 25 Italic
26 Ideal 28 Edit 29 Dent 31 Eats

Puzzle 256

ACROSS: 4 Pears 9 Emanate 10 Plane
11 Spa 12 Sot 13 Kit 14 Conquer
15 Impenetrability 19 Whitsun 20 Pig
21 Bra 22 Duo 23 Dingo 24 Snorkel
25 Porch
DOWN: 1 Jet ski 2 Hart 3 Talking shop
4 Pest 5 Acacia 6 Spinning top 7 Saluki
8 Fear 16 Pliant 17 Tinder 18 Yearly
19 Wade 20 Posh 21 Bike

Puzzle 257

ACROSS: 7 Helmet 8 Unique 9 Ham
10 Bust 11 Taut 12 Sly 14 Byron
17 Earth 19 Impel 20 Royal 22 Fable
24 Beg 26 Ajar 28 Robe 29 Urn
30 Acumen 31 Radius
DOWN: 1 Beauty 2 Emit 3 Ethos
4 Jumpy 5 Jilt 6 August 13 Lapse
15 Ray 16 Nil 17 Elf 18 Rub 21 Object
23 Labour 24 Blunt 25 Genre
27 Rump 28 Rude

Puzzle 258

ACROSS: 1 Downwards 6 Acre 10 Tick
off 11 Clearer 13 Lard 14 Triple jump
16 Embark 18 In-tray 21 Fountain
22 Inert 24 Inadequate 26 Clog 29 Site
30 Tiger prawn 32 Vista 34 Underpin
36 Fathom 37 Stigma 40 Millstream
41 Jaws 44 Sell out 45 Sensory
46 Dado 47 Adulatory
DOWN: 2 Occur 3 Noon 4 Affirm
5 Deception 7 Circulate 8 Enrapt
9 Stalker 12 Electric 15 Bronzed
17 Buoyant 19 Lazuli 20 Staging
23 Missive 25 Tweedy 27 Leaning
28 Operate 31 Machismo 33 Stable
lad 34 Unmerited 35 Cat's-eye
38 Amused 39 Causal 42 Amour
43 Gnat

Puzzle 259

ACROSS: 7 Debris 8 Adhere 9 Lap 10
Dive 11 Mane 12 Tar 14 Snore 17 Infer
19 Rabid 20 Cobra 22 Enrol 24 Arm
26 Idle 28 Hate 29 Par 30 Lamina 31
Condor
DOWN: 1 Design 2 Free 3 Islet 4 Caper
5 Sham 6 Trance 13 Amber 15 Orb 16
Era 17 Ide 18 For 21 Ordeal 23 Option
24 Appal 25 March 27 Evil 28 Hint

Puzzle 260

ACROSS: 1 Bellow 5 Genius 9 Awe
11 Friends 12 Reactor 13 Loth
15 Await 16 Maze 17 Vile 19 Final
20 Wear 24 Untwist 25 Ill-bred 26 Ego
27 Locked 28 Neaten
DOWN: 2 Evict 3 Lane 4 Wasp-waisted
5 Germination 6 Near 7 Ultra
8 Effluvium 10 Free trade 14 Hoe
16 Mew 18 Let go 21 Eyrie 22 Pink
23 Plea

Puzzle 261

ACROSS: 1 And 8 Unprincipled
9 Lot 11 Youth 12 Almoner 14 Tuna
15 Usurer 18 Garlic 20 Oaks
23 Beloved 25 Chimp 27 Ore
28 Hagiographer 29 Key

SOLUTIONS

DOWN: 1 All thumbs 2 Duty 3 Spruce
4 Might 5 Ocean 6 Spam 7 Fennel
10 Precisely 13 Lag 16 Unload 17 Roe
19 Alight 21 Adage 22 Scram 24 Void
26 Pork

Puzzle 262

Puzzle 263

ACROSS: 1 Sitting tenant 9 Client
10 Lameness 11 Swim 12 Apron
13 Soya 14 Awl 15 Axe 16 Fool
18 Motel 20 Lack 22 Listen in
24 Booing 25 Concentration
DOWN: 2 In-law 3 Thermal 4 Nut 5 Tiler
6 Nominal 7 Nan 8 Esky 12 Almanac
13 Sell out 17 Omit 19 Tenon 21 Canto
23 Two 24 Bar

Puzzle 264

```
A   S T A P L E R   M
D R U D   E R A S E
D   S T E W A R D   W
E R A   N A P   A T E
R N D   X   P R O D
    V   R O W E R   W
V E R Y   O   E P E E
O R E   P R O   A L L
T   M I L K M A N   A
E R I C A   A L E R T
R   T E N D R I L   E
```

Puzzle 265

ACROSS: 6 Ship canal 7 Mug up 8 Oaf
9 Eddy 10 Pike 12 Reticule 15 Roof
rack 17 Prominent 18 Pedantic
20 Disloyal 23 Arty 24 Scow 27 Cog
28 Hunch 29 Sharpener

DOWN: 1 Asymmetry 2 Singed 3 Scope
4 Unsocial 5 Bluffer 11 Eco-friendly
13 Twofold 14 Skit 16 Amenity 17 Pipe
19 Flow chart 21 Integral 22 Carcase
25 Caning 26 Chips

Puzzle 266

```
G A S   C I G A R
I G L O O   A G A
B O A   N   L O P
E   P I Q U A N T
  S   O U R   Y
E M I N E N T   V
P A D   R   R Y E
I L L   O N I O N
C L E A R   O U T
```

Puzzle 267

ACROSS: 1 Private income 10 Liturgy
11 Fatally 12 Smokestack 14 Omen
16 Anterior 18 Coots 21 Catalogue
22 Large 23 Splash 25 Surprise
28 Air force 29 Beaker 31 Lupin
33 Rainstorm 35 Gnash 36 Compress
40 Lung 41 Cavalryman 44 Maudlin
45 Crowbar 46 Satsuma orange
DOWN: 2 Ratio 3 Vertebral 4 Toy
5 Infect 6 City 7 Milometer 8 Alaska
9 Dying 13 Trough 15 Collapse
17 Titular 19 Venus 20 Cerebrum
21 Casually 24 Slowness 26 Irksome
27 Scary 30 Mimosa 32 Peninsula
34 Supernova 37 Sentry 38 Plume
39 Magnum 42 Mr Big 43 Plus 45 Coo

Puzzle 268

ACROSS: 1 Agility 7 Embed 8 Ego
9 Tote 10 Clap 12 Elegance 14 Find
fault 15 Isolated 18 Glass eye
21 Intrinsic 23 Indicate 25 Pops
26 Bent 28 Chi 29 Perks 30 Let down
DOWN: 2 Go-between 3 Lady 4 The old
country 5 Beetle off 6 Corps 11 Manful
13 Study 16 Starting price 17 Again
19 Spirit 20 Scientist 22 Scarecrow
24 Space 27 Spud

Puzzle 269

ACROSS: 1 Placebo 7 Remit 8 Gel
9 Airs 10 Ward 12 Hose-reel 14 Foot
fault 15 Sculptor 18 Heliport
21 Sceptical 23 Strictly 25 Wine 26 Hill
28 Orb 29 Green 30 Express
DOWN: 2 Lambrusco 3 Cute
4 Big-game hunter 5 Preachify 6 Glide
11 Artful 13 Stork 16 Collecting box
17 Ghost 19 Patois 20 Play along
22 Cattiness 24 Swoop 27 Agar

Puzzle 270

ACROSS: 4 Her 8 Draughty 9 Evenly
10 Eschew 11 Roasting 13 Dyed
15 Lucid 16 Waft 18 Newcomer
20 Lustre 22 Silica 23 Outweigh
24 Run
DOWN: 1 Crispy 2 Lush 3 Thaw
4 Hydrocarbon 5 Regard 6 Bestow
7 Flan 12 Gut 13 Dun 14 Deceit
15 Lumbar 17 Forage 19 Emit 20 Lots
21 Seed

Puzzle 271

Puzzle 272

ACROSS: 1 Absorb 5 Shadow 9 Aisle
10 Recess 11 Easter 12 Hotel 14 Sari
17 Nit 18 Mist 20 Theme 22 Pinch
23 Parasol 24 Caper 26 Padre 29 Idol
30 Bit 32 Need 33 Recap 35 Concur
36 Lament 37 Lemon 38 Eyelet
39 Nectar

DOWN: 1 Arrest 2 Secure 3 Rash
4 Bison 5 Sleet 6 Heal 7 Detain
8 Warmth 13 Titanic 15 Ahead
16 Impel 18 Milan 19 Score 21 Ear
22 Pop 24 Circle 25 Pounce 27 Deceit
28 Editor 30 Beret 31 Talon 33 Rule
34 Pane
ACROSS: 1 Basket 5 Artist 9 Phase
10 Impair 11 Samson 12 Cover
14 Hole 17 Wit 18 Acme 20 Trend
22 Altar 23 Replace 24 Demon
26 Error 29 Oral 30 Pip 32 Tuna
33 Banal 35 Banger 36 Timbre
37 Stack 38 Enmity 39 Heresy
DOWN: 1 Bright 2 Supple 3 Epic
4 Throw 5 Asset 6 Rear 7 Insect
8 Tender 13 Villain 15 Order 16 Enrol
18 Alert 19 Mason 21 Den 22 Ace
24 Double 25 Magnum 27 Rubble
28 Rarely 30 Party 31 Patch 33 Best
34 Like

Puzzle 273

ACROSS: 1 Countess 6 Privilege 7 Lap
8 Booth 9 Educator 12 Lode 13 Data
16 Radicchio 18 Influenza 19 Tory
20 Sell 23 Copybook 26 Hippo 27 Apt
28 Well-being 29 Hardened
DOWN: 1 Cupola 2 Unimpeded
3 Tailback 4 Seek out 5 Mesh
10 Reasonably 11 Altruistic 14 Ashen
15 Scout 17 Defer 21 Evocation
22 Absorbed 24 Papilla 25 Staged
26 Hawk

Puzzle 274

ACROSS: 1 Agent 4 Atom bomb
11 Fungicide 12 Rifle 13 Loin
14 Jaunty 16 Irk 18 Con 19 Expend
22 Beta 24 Inlet 26 Throwback
27 Niggling 28 Snake
DOWN: 2 Gentian 3 Nail 5 Tie
in 6 Martyr 7 Off 8 Break ranks
9 Affliction 10 Visa 15 Use 16 Ice pack
17 Dental 20 Put on 21 Norm 23 Swan
25 Log

SOLUTIONS

Puzzle 275

ACROSS: 9 Humour 10 Epics 11 Abut
12 Step 13 Mince 14 Embody
15 Crucial 17 Armature 19 Taxi
21 Tricorn 23 Tied 24 Long face
25 Harass 27 Tap 29 Ancestor
31 Employee 32 Majestic 34 Air rifle
35 Eyepiece 36 Twenties 39 Day
40 Sonata 42 Spaceman 45 Hazy
46 Lookout 47 Acts 48 Keel over
51 Typeset 54 Scorer 55 Edify 57 Bite
58 Anon 59 Entry 60 Waters
DOWN: 1 Cutter 2 Hop-picking
3 Cram 4 Jenny 5 Liberator 6 Esteem
7 Rabbit 8 Rudderless 16 Attract
18 Sidetracked 20 Acorn 22 No-hoper
23 Terrorist 26 Seekers 28 Penalty
spot 29 Aimless 30 Exemplary
33 Toenail 37 Exactly 38 Exalt
41 Opalescent 43 Exacerbate
44 Courgette 49 Larynx 50 Vortex
52 Entire 53 Vinyl 56 Yawn

Puzzle 276

ACROSS: 1 Flighty 7 Natal 8 Kin 9 Even
10 Used 12 Sob story 14 Figure
out 15 Unhoused 18 Mind's eye
21 Speechify 23 Asbestos 25 Have
26 Dram 28 Fir 29 Alert 30 Zealots
DOWN: 2 Litterbug 3 Gild 4 Take
seriously 5 Intensify 6 Snide 11 Stereo
13 Study 16 Nonsense verse 17 Amass
19 Sicken 20 Gypsy moth 22 Interject
24 Chafe 27 Pall

Puzzle 277

ACROSS: 1 Fishwife 6 Continent 7 Leo
8 Elder 9 Informed 12 Note 13 Opus
16 Imbroglio 18 Analgesia 19 Idly
20 Flit 23 Eyeshade 26 Brain 27 Sir
28 Capillary 29 Defender
DOWN: 1 Fickle 2 Sun bonnet
3 White-hot 4 Fiefdom 5 Star
10 Disloyalty 11 Indicative 14 Poles
15 Doggy 17 Brawl 21 Lady's maid
22 Chenille 24 Example 25 Prayer
26 Beck

Puzzle 278

ACROSS: 4 Pap 8 Stay over 9 Adonis
10 Append 11 December 13 Faze
15 Bumpy 16 Sage 18 Taxation
20 Tabard 22 Red-eye 23 Third age
24 Die
DOWN: 1 Utopia 2 Type 3 Avid
4 Predominate 5 Patchy 6 Cosmos
7 Pile 12 Rue 13 Fat 14 Elated
15 Boiled 17 Garage 19 Apex 20 Toil
21 Body

Puzzle 279

ACROSS: 1 Deify 5 Hook 6 Tomato
7 Main 8 Jingle 9 Pectoral
12 Brainwash 15 Low 16 Stain
17 Demur 18 Hum 19 Singleton
21 Maniacal 24 Author 25 Flak
26 Egg-nog 27 Sour 28 Angst
DOWN: 2 Emotive 3 Fraught 4 Conical
5 Home brew 9 Pebble-dash
10 Charwoman 11 Phenomenal
13 Nostril 14 Apathetic 20 Gunmaker
21 Mailbox 22 Antigen 23 Amorous

Puzzle 280

ACROSS: 5 Pilchard 7 Raw 8 Mecca
9 Sometime 11 Inky 12 Chin 14 Perks
15 Err 16 Address 20 Ram 21 Corps
23 Vote 24 Byte 26 Severely 28 Optic
29 Elm 30 Yodeller
DOWN: 1 Spare 2 Slow cooker
3 Chimney 4 Brackishness 6 Pageantry
10 Zippy 13 Ostrich 17 Demotivation
18 Provision 19 Isles 22 Royal jelly
25 Cracker 27 Emery

Puzzle 281

ACROSS: 8 Baseline 9 Envied 10 Clot
11 Photograph 12 Comparable 14 Hits
15 Amnesty 16 Stature 20 Isle
22 Windowpane 23 Battle-axes
24 Love 25 Planet 26 Contrite
DOWN: 1 Ballroom 2 Felt 3 Dispirit
4 Redoubt 5 Before 6 Over the top
7 Despot 13 Presenting 17 Thousand
18 Renovate 19 Inexact 21 Stable
22 Wreath 24 Lard

SOLUTIONS

Puzzle 282
ACROSS: 4 Cop 8 Strimmer 9 Ironic
10 Ageist 11 Peppered 13 Mane
15 Scion 16 Rasp 18 Paranoia
20 Margin 22 Revere 23 Look over
24 Lay
DOWN: 1 Stigma 2 Kiwi 3 Smut
4 Cryptically 5 Pippin 6 Voyeur 7 File
12 Dip 13 Map 14 Eraser 15 Shovel
17 Skiver 19 Amen 20 Moon 21 Rook

Puzzle 283
ACROSS: 1 Hacksaw 5 *Macbeth*
9 Bluff 10 Roc 11 Adapt 12 Tabasco
15 Oatmeal 18 Cab 19 Precook
21 Earthen 23 Ideally 25 Bad debt
26 Awe 27 Helmets 30 Correct
34 Gamut 35 Moo 36 Bathe
37 Earmark 38 Synonym
DOWN: 1 Habit 2 Crumb 3 Safes
4 Warlock 5 Microbe 6 Chart 7 Elate
8 Hotel 13 Abridge 14 Acclaim
16 Matador 17 Acerbic 20 Oil 22 Aga
24 Yashmak 25 Beckons 27 Hague
28 Lemur 29 Extra 31 Robin 32 Eaten
33 Therm

Puzzle 284
ACROSS: 9 Pudding basin 11 Airy
12 Nub 13 Snip 14 Sneer 15 Give
up 16 Faraway 18 Nearside 20 Sari
22 As a rule 24 Goes 25 Downbeat
26 Ill-use 28 But 30 Taxpayer
32 Emerging 33 Infringe 35 Retainer
36 Largesse 37 Suspense 40 Rut
41 Tirade 43 Roasting 46 Rich 47 Get
back 48 Iced 49 Junk mail 52 Trident
55 Strait 56 Snuff 59 Alga 60 See
61 Ludo 62 Obliteration
DOWN: 1 Guinea 2 Adaptation 3 Inns
4 Abbey 5 Astronaut 6 Enigma
7 Canvas 8 Groundless 10 Gun
17 Academy 19 Fast breeder
21 Aroma 23 Evident 24 Gelignite
27 Engorge 29 Terrestrial 30 Triplet
31 Paragraph 34 Nest egg 38 Stalker
39 Sense 42 Iniquitous 44 Third
party 45 Stylishly 50 Klaxon 51 Action
53 No-good 54 Fusty 57 Fee 58 Fern

Puzzle 285
ACROSS: 7 Antler 8 Obsess 9 Era
10 Felt 11 Ever 12 Nod 14 Attic
17 Abode 19 Alert 20 Manor 22 Extra
24 Gnu 26 Smut 28 Late 29 Art
30 Binder 31 Impure
DOWN: 1 Infest 2 Flit 3 Green 4 Board
5 Isle 6 Ascend 13 Ocean 15 Tan
16 Car 17 Ate 18 Opt 21 Armpit
23 Retort 24 Glare 25 Untie 27 Tide
28 Lope

Puzzle 286
ACROSS: 1 Rewarding 9 Elusive 10 Coy
11 Claim 12 Arabs 14 Swarm 16 Infer
18 Say 19 Sop 21 Erect 22 Orate
23 Stoat 25 Bleat 26 Asp 27 Lozenge
28 Disk drive
DOWN: 1 Recess 2 Waylay
3 Race meeting 4 Imagine 5 Gem
6 Sugar-coated 7 Diva 8 Mews
13 Boot 15 Want 17 Fitness 19 Safari
20 People 23 Sale 24 Ooze 25 Bed

Puzzle 287
ACROSS: 1 Hosepipe 6 Small beer
7 Log 8 Ready 9 Promoter 12 Pore
13 Step 16 Confusing 18 Panatella
19 Onyx 20 Talc 23 Elevator 26 Capes
27 Ewe 28 Rearguard 29 One-sided
DOWN: 1 Hustle 2 Swaggerer
3 Pilgrims 4 Precast 5 X-ray
10 Repugnance 11 Space probe
14 Trial 15 Quilts 17 Nanny
21 Aforesaid 22 Marsh gas 24 Explain
25 Beaded 26 Care

Puzzle 288

SOLUTIONS

Puzzle 289

ACROSS: 1 Totem 4 Cut 6 Barracuda
7 Tall ship 9 Sinusitis 10 Urge 12 Germ
14 Guardian 17 Overcast 19 Rusk
21 Stew 23 Manhattan 25 Raincoat
27 Inside out 28 Lid 29 Go mad
DOWN: 1 Toby 2 Terrain 3 Meatless
4 Couchette 5 Trappist monk 8 Use up
11 Gouge 13 Brace 15 Inset 16 Court
martial 18 Swans 20 Sun-kissed
22 Watchdog 24 Tea room 26 Stud

Puzzle 290

S	T	E	P		S		R	A	N	D
A		L	E	A	T	H	E	R		U
V	I	S	A		Y		V	I	N	E
E	L	E	C	T		A	U	D	I	T
	L		E	A	G	L	E		G	
B	E	T		L		T		W	E	E
	G		L	O	C	A	L		R	
S	A	T	I	N		R	I	G	I	D
P	L	U	M		S		B	R	A	Y
A		R	I	V	I	E	R	A		K
M	I	N	T		X		A	B	L	E

Puzzle 291

ACROSS: 1 Unmerited 9 Utilise 10 Mac
11 Voice 12 Essay 14 Skirl 16 Macro
18 Ken 19 Mad 21 Airer 22 Azure
23 Allot 25 Ruche 26 Sit 27 Tapioca
28 Profanity
DOWN: 1 Unmask 2 Muck in
3 Revaluation 4 Trimmer 5 Due 6 Video
camera 7 Pips 8 Deny 13 Ajar 15 Keel
17 Curacao 19 Muesli 20 Deftly
23 Ants 24 Lope 25 Rap

Puzzle 292

F	O	R		P	U	P	I	L
O	D	O	U	R		O	N	E
N	E	T		E		P	U	S
T		A	N	S	W	E	R	S
	C		A	C	E		E	
M	O	N	G	R	E	L		F
A	P	E		I		O	I	L
U	S	E		B	R	A	C	E
L	E	D	G	E		N	E	W

Puzzle 293

ACROSS: 9 Floors 10 Curvy 11 Vine
12 Area 13 Stung 14 Lowers
15 Unwinds 17 Accolade 19 Kiwi
21 Railcar 23 Pace 24 Slogging
25 Potash 27 Err 29 Provider
31 Edifying 32 Laughter 34 Entrance
35 Cast-iron 36 Borehole 39 Tie
40 Tsetse 42 Rapeseed 45 Bind
46 Orbital 47 Dank 48 Pullover
51 Ushered 54 Spiral 55 Silts 57 Fits
58 Knee 59 Moved 60 Back up
DOWN: 1 Florin 2 Royal icing 3 Asks
4 Scout 5 Pregnancy 6 Cyclic 7 Avowal
8 Introduces 16 Dirtied 18 Fingerprint
20 Idler 22 Repaint 23 Petty cash
26 Hygiene 28 Reverberate 29 Polecat
30 Vegetated 33 Torpedo 37 Ripples
38 Lie-in 41 Ski-jumping 43 Side effect
44 Obtrusive 49 Larder 50 Volume
52 Eat out 53 Plods 56 Sobs

Puzzle 294

ACROSS: 1 Whippet 9 Alexandra
10 Overtax 11 Firewater 12 Snigger
13 Eat 14 Affable 16 Estonia
20 Unchain 24 Hirsute 25 Ego
26 Lunatic 27 Wassailed 28 Anagram
29 Sceptical 30 Leather
DOWN: 2 Having fun 3 Paragraph
4 Tax-free 5 Secrete 6 Ragwort
7 Edition 8 Paprika 15 Lei 17 Ski
18 Onslaught 19 Intricate 20 Untwist
21 Chester 22 Atlanta 23 Neglect
24 Holdall

Puzzle 295

ACROSS: 4 Polar 9 Another 10 Elate
11 Ant 12 Add 13 Soy 14 Edifice
15 Middle of the road 19 Finesse
20 Set 21 All 22 Rip 23 Motto
24 Avocado 25 Payer
DOWN: 1 Salaam 2 Fold 3 Whistle-stop
4 Pray 5 Latent 6 Redirection 7 Casino
8 Mete 16 Donate 17 Overly 18 Dollop
19 Fame 20 Spar 21 Arab

Puzzle 296

ACROSS: 1 Cherub 5 Grange 9 Ace
11 Marbles 12 Spatula 13 Leek
15 Basis 16 Lyre 17 Tend 19 Sinus
20 Dams 24 Martini 25 Abandon
26 Cat 27 Chance 28 Enrapt
DOWN: 2 Horde 3 Rule 4 Basmati
rice 5 Gesticulate 6 Away 7 Gauzy
8 Small-time 10 Caressing 14 Kid
16 Lad 18 North 21 Add up 22 Lion
23 Pair

Puzzle 297

ACROSS: 1 Cow 8 Homelessness
9 Rye 11 Trunk 12 Emperor 14 Euro
15 Nutmeg 18 Wallet 20 Aunt
23 Fatness 25 Opium 27 Ivy 28 Flying
saucer 29 Eve
DOWN: 1 Cordon off 2 Whet 3 Impute
4 Fluke 5 Usher 6 Snip 7 Astral
10 Prototype 13 Mow 16 Tattle 17 Gas
19 Apiece 21 Usage 22 Topaz 24 Evil
26 Mire

Puzzle 298

ACROSS: 5 Partwork 7 Rat 8 Sissy
9 Primrose 11 Hail 12 Aria 14 Guess
15 Tug 16 Afflict 20 See 21 Turks
23 Rude 24 Spur 26 Dead-heat
28 Lasso 29 Act 30 Singular
DOWN: 1 Spark 2 Fraternise
3 Twosome 4 Aristocratic 6 Tyre gauge
10 Thigh 13 Isolate 17 Freudian slip
18 Astraddle 19 Usury 22 Repeatable
25 Through 27 Start

Puzzle 299

ACROSS: 1 Roger 3 Baldwin 6 Brett 8
Bradley 9 Colin 11 Liam 13 Tom 15
Cameron 17 Eva 18 Neil 19 Peter 22
Gilbert 24 Helen 25 Bernard 26 Henry
DOWN: 1 Robertson 2 Grey 3 Bob 4
Lear 5 Willis 7 Thomas 10 Irene 12
McCartney 14 Joseph 16 Miller 20
Vera 21 Alan 23 Ted

Puzzle 300

Puzzle 301

ACROSS: 1 Cry-baby 7 Ricks 8 Rim
9 Grey 10 Mark 12 Pleading 14 Wire
brush 15 Accented 18 Perspire
21 Keep at bay 23 Estimate 25 Heir
26 Herb 28 Fop 29 Creel 30 Promise
DOWN: 2 Racketeer 3 Base
4 Bargain-hunter 5 Frogspawn
6 Smoke 11 Edible 13 Shade
16 Carpet slipper 17 Spiky 19 Placid
20 Hyperbole 22 Blameless 24 Shift
27 Scum

Puzzle 302

ACROSS: 9 Sharp-tongued 11 Tuck
12 Owe 13 Zinc 14 Plain 15 Uppity
16 Receipt 18 Averages 20 Stub
22 Shining 24 Paid 25 Contrite
26 Avenge 28 Cog 30 Thickset
32 One-liner 33 Downpour
35 Treating 36 Lifeboat 37 Grandees
40 Eve 41 Stoats 43 Tolerate
46 Bury 47 Sockets 48 Dart
49 Inaction 52 Psychic 55 Emboss
56 Moors 59 Rile 60 Met 61 Snap
62 Disaffection
DOWN: 1 Choice 2 Cricket bat
3 Stop 4 Sneak 5 Guinea pig
6 Adduce 7 Utopia 8 Scattering
10 Owl 17 Pasties 19 Directorate
21 Tooth 23 Glad eye 24 Predicted
27 Enrages 29 Got together
30 Toddles 31 Centenary 34 Oboists
38 Atlases 39 Eater 42 Tournament
44 Redecorate 45 Economist
50 Chomps 51 Inside 53 Igloos
54 Comfy 57 Ref 58 Stew

SOLUTIONS

Puzzle 303

ACROSS: 6 Slush fund 7 Erupt
8 Tom 9 Ever 10 Barn 12 Teenager
15 Disprove 17 Profiteer 18 Overhear
20 Shoehorn 23 Okra 24 Solo 27 Rot
28 Besom 29 Pig-headed
DOWN: 1 Usherette 2 Future 3 Chute
4 Suitcase 5 Oddment 11 Lamplighter
13 Epitome 14 Dear 16 Oregano
17 Pool 19 Incommode 21 Heritage
22 Corrupt 25 Onside 26 Abbey

Puzzle 304

ACROSS: 1 Dandruff 6 Sage-green
7 Get 8 Oasis 9 Maharaja 12 Axel
13 Eyed 16 Gift token 18 Scintilla
19 Ache 20 Acre 23 Emphatic 26 Fly in
27 Boy 28 Full blast 29 Appendix
DOWN: 1 Dosage 2 Negotiate
3 Regional 4 Freesia 5 Onus 10 Aid
and abet 11 Large-scale 14 Yokel
15 State 17 Faith 21 Clipboard
22 Damnable 24 Payslip 25 Syntax
26 Fife

Puzzle 305

Puzzle 306

ACROSS: 1 Flat of the hand 9 Tripod
10 Volition 11 Maxi 12 Diced 13 Duke
14 Dye 15 Age 16 Hone 18 Mummy
20 Cock 22 Heptagon 24 Fodder
25 Condescending
DOWN: 2 Larva 3 Topside 4 Fad
5 Havoc 6 Holiday 7 Not 8 Monk
12 Demigod 13 Decided 17 Over
19 Minds 21 Clean 23 Too 24 Foe

Puzzle 307

ACROSS: 1 Agile 4 Demerara
11 Fantasist 12 Clear 13 Earn 14 Stay
up 16 Peg 18 Tip 19 Wimple 22 Coma
24 Shaft 26 Storeroom 27 Elephant
28 Colts
DOWN: 2 Gin trap 3 Load 5 Entry
6 Except 7 Are 8 Aerogramme
9 Aftertaste 10 Hilt 15 Amp 16 Provost
17 Twitch 20 Mason 21 Loom
23 Memo 25 Ale

Puzzle 308

ACROSS: 4 Oil 8 Foolscap 9 Atomic
10 Ignore 11 Occupier 13 Wake
15 Actor 16 Edgy 18 Donation 20 Put
out 22 Reveal 23 Theology 24 Dry
DOWN: 1 Loggia 2 Alto 3 Acme
4 Opportunity 5 Lancer 6 Corpse
7 Wile 12 Ray 13 Wed 14 Enamel
15 Afield 17 Grungy 19 Oven 20 Poet
21 Toll

Puzzle 309

ACROSS: 1 Strand 5 Asgard 9 Audit
10 Allege 11 Dublin 12 Tender
15 Oddest 17 Yet 18 Dairy 19 See
20 Aim 22 Hover 24 Cad 26 Beacon
27 Regale 28 Oblong 30 Yogurt
31 Dover 32 Detest 33 Smelly
DOWN: 1 Scanty 2 Relent 3 Nagged
4 Due 5 Aid 6 Sturdy 7 Allies 8 Denote
13 Eerie 14 Radon 15 Order 16 Sepal
20 Abroad 21 Mallet 22 Hounds
23 Reform 24 Casual 25 Deftly 29 Got
30 Yes
ACROSS: 1 Record 5 Scheme 9 Argue
10 Colony 11 Elapse 12 Editor
15 Pigeon 17 Tie 18 Magic 19 Dig
20 Age 22 Since 24 Deb 26 Bolted
27 Hair-do 28 Untrue 30 Air-gun
31 Range 32 Tidier 33 Orange
DOWN: 1 Racket 2 Collie 3 Random
4 Dry 5 Sue 6 Celtic 7 Espied 8 Eyeing
13 Dingo 14 Rapid 15 Pitch 16 Oiled
20 Abduct 21 Elated 22 Secure
23 Easier 24 Dragon 25 Bounce
29 Ear 30 Ago

SOLUTIONS

Puzzle 310

ACROSS: 9 Ill-treatment 11 Ever 12 Tut 13 Ming 14 Skirt 15 Piston 16 Concise 18 Ringside 20 Saga 22 Unhinge 24 Arch 25 Bottle up 26 Ogress 28 Sop 30 Redolent 32 Omission 33 Death row 35 Kangaroo 36 Engender 37 Top-heavy 40 Dim 41 Throne 43 Occupier 46 Clue 47 Sincere 48 Oaks 49 Preserve 52 Astound 55 Lively 56 Sinus 59 Tide 60 Are 61 Peke 62 Love interest
DOWN: 1 Albino 2 Stagecraft 3 Jets 4 Attic 5 Hectoring 6 Step in 7 Versus 8 Below decks 10 Auk 17 Squeeze 19 Shop steward 21 Alone 23 Erosion 24 Aerospace 27 Sensory 29 Pocket money 30 Red meat 31 On the dole 34 Redress 38 Packers 39 V-neck 42 Hellraiser 44 Promontory 45 Intensive 50 Seeker 51 Royals 53 Nudism 54 Snail 57 Urn 58 Sett

Puzzle 311

ACROSS:7 Cinema 8 Lessen 9 Doe 10 Atom 11 Earl 12 Tin 14 Onset 17 Ochre 19 Ulcer 20 Slang 22 Baste 24 Arc 26 Spar 28 Fist 29 Bra 30 Enable 31 Secret
DOWN: 1 Listen 2 Ream 3 Cadet 4 Glean 5 Isle 6 Dearer 13 Incur 15 Spa 16 Tug 17 Orb 18 Hao 21 Lupine 23 Tassel 24 Amber 25 Chase 27 Ruby 28 Face

Puzzle 312

ACROSS: 1 Upsetting 9 Utopian 10 Jam 11 Therm 12 Carry 14 Stall 16 Awash 18 Tun 19 Pot 21 Atlas 22 Llama 23 Facet 25 Churn 26 Odd 27 Amphora 28 Butterfly
DOWN: 1 Unjust 2 Sampan 3 Titillation 4 Icefall 5 Gum 6 Nonchalance 7 Liar 8 Only 13 Room 15 Tuba 17 Assault 19 Pay-off 20 Tawdry 23 Feat 24 Cope 25 Cab

Puzzle 313

ACROSS: 4 Decor 9 Abalone 10 Emote 11 Can 12 Rod 13 Yak 14 Emulate 15 Confrontational 19 Caustic 20 Pat 21 Bag 22 Tea 23 Grain 24 Cholera 25 Gorge
DOWN: 1 Fabric 2 Wand 3 Copywriting 4 Deck 5 Cinema 6 Repudiation 7 Domain 8 Peke 16 Nougat 17 Nectar 18 Logjam 19 Cage 20 Pace 21 Beet

Puzzle 314

ACROSS: 1 Nuncio 5 Age-old 9 Van 11 Tactile 12 Trapper 13 Lips 15 Space 16 Plus 17 Mown 19 Lynch 20 Prow 24 Terrace 25 Open day 26 Nun 27 Set out 28 Earner
DOWN: 2 Uncap 3 Coin 4 Overpayment 5 Anticyclone 6 Elan 7 Lapel 8 Stalemate 10 Crossways 14 Sun 16 Pep 18 Worse 21 Ridge 22 Halo 23 Bear

Puzzle 315

ACROSS: 1 Amiss 5 Neon 6 Presto 7 Vast 8 Scrape 9 Mounting 12 Seduction 15 Eel 16 Tacit 17 Enter 18 Rig 19 Ridge tent 21 Sinister 24 Enable 25 Welt 26 Abrupt 27 Gill 28 Tweet
DOWN: 2 Morocco 3 Sustain 4 Rousing 5 Novelist 9 Musketeers 10 Undulated 11 Instigator 13 Coterie 14 Incorrect 20 Gunmetal 21 Sloe gin 22 Sparrow 23 Ellipse

Puzzle 316

S	A	M	B	A		L	E	A	N	T
A		O		L	E	E		D		H
W	O	R	S	T		S	H	O	R	E
E		S	P	O	N	S	O	R		M
D	E	E	R		O		S	E	R	E
	W		I	D	I	O	T		U	
D	E	A	N		S		I	T	E	M
E		S	T	E	E	P	L	Y		O
B	O	S	S	Y		L	E	P	E	R
U		E		E	G	O		E		A
T	O	T	E	D		T	O	D	A	Y

SOLUTIONS

Puzzle 317

ACROSS: 1 Cache 4 Cue 6 Ironed out 7 Stricken 9 Punchbowl 10 Camp 12 Skim 14 Function 17 Executor 19 Romp 21 Hymn 23 Firethorn 25 Snake oil 27 Inspiring 28 Gin 29 Greed
DOWN: 1 Clip 2 Crouton 3 Eyesight 4 Clockwork 5 Entanglement 8 Spicy 11 Mauve 13 Scour 15 Ivory 16 Pearl fishing 18 Inane 20 Mortal sin 22 Steering 24 Orifice 26 Aged

Puzzle 318

N	E	W	█	I	D	E	A	S
O	N	I	O	N	█	A	G	E
O	D	D	█	H	█	S	E	A
N	█	E	L	E	M	E	N	T
█	F	█	A	R	E	█	T	█
D	R	A	W	I	N	G	█	P
O	U	R	█	T	█	A	T	E
T	I	E	█	E	N	T	E	R
S	T	A	N	D	█	E	A	T

Puzzle 319

ACROSS: 1 Wholesome 6 Edit 10 Pillion 11 Rosehip 13 Noel 14 Put an end to 16 Lassie 18 In-tray 21 Mutually 22 Emery 24 Safety cage 26 Twin 29 Used 30 Adroitness 32 Ensue 34 Unafraid 36 Belted 37 Jargon 40 Wellspring 41 Echo 44 Veranda 45 Variety 46 Lump 47 Adulation
DOWN: 2 Halve 3 Laid 4 Sinful 5 Mortality 7 Dehydrate 8 Tip-top 9 Spangly 12 Sweet pea 15 Situate 17 Souffle 19 Sliced 20 Gymnast 23 Assumed 25 Global 27 Weeping 28 Eternal 31 Jettison 33 Steel drum 34 Underhand 35 Antonym 38 Swivel 39 Snivel 42 Credo 43 Fret

Puzzle 320

ACROSS: 7 Biplane 8 Shuttle 10 Glider 11 Airplane 12 Camel 14 Dirigible 18 Puma 20 Victa 21 Nord 22 Aeroplane 24 Piper 27 Spitfire 30 Badger 32 Javelin 33 Monarch
DOWN: 1 Pill 2 Sledge 3 Inert 4 Char 5 Stallion 6 Glen 9 Taxi 13 Acute 15 Iran 16 Large 17 Oval 19 Apostles 23 Need 25 Indian 26 Abbot 28 Pray 29 Iris 31 Each

Puzzle 321

ACROSS: 1 Mop 8 Obstreperous 9 Rep 11 Elude 12 Cobbler 14 Duel 15 Pewter 18 Dampen 20 Aver 23 Arrange 25 Ovary 27 Ate 28 Photographer 29 Din
DOWN: 1 Marsupial 2 Pope 3 Assume 4 Fried 5 Spice 6 Grab 7 Curl up 10 Truncheon 13 Old 16 Worthy 17 Rag 19 Apathy 21 Verge 22 Royal 24 Nett 26 Yard

Puzzle 322

ACROSS: 1 Dentist's drill 9 Tidily 10 Republic 11 Veto 12 Dowse 13 Inch 14 Gnu 15 Tan 16 Waxy 18 Lodge 20 Same 22 Complain 24 Wiring 25 Tender-hearted
DOWN: 2 Elide 3 Trilogy 4 Sky 5 Strew 6 Replete 7 Lob 8 Zinc 12 Dullard 13 Insurer 17 Agog 19 Diner 21 Mange 23 Pie 24 Woe

Puzzle 323

ACROSS: 7 Retain 8 Insure 9 Dig 10 Hawaii 11 Desk 12 Ant 14 Zebra 17 Sorry 19 China 20 Agent 22 Ditch 24 Bet 26 Poem 28 Honour 30 Ale 31 Spills 32 Recess
DOWN: 1 Debate 2 Data 3 India 4 Light 5 Used 6 Eraser 13 Noise 15 Bee 16 Act 17 Sad 18 Rat 21 Groups 23 Clumsy 24 Blast 25 There 27 Mild 29 Nice

Puzzle 324

ACROSS: 1 Actress 7 Laird 8 Fir 9 Neat 10 Stew 12 Altitude 14 Rice paper 15 Assassin 18 Priority 21 Rat poison 23 Under-age 25 Robe 26 Edit 28 Via 29 Corgi 30 Adjourn
DOWN: 2 Climactic 3 Rode 4 Safety deposit 5 Glengarry 6 Crows 11 Utopia 13 Crone 16 Skirting-board 17 Spare 19 Rioter 20 Uncertain 22 Slanderer 24 Brave 27 Echo

Puzzle 325

ACROSS: 7 Mushroom 8 Cart 9 Liar 10 Crew 11 Egg 13 Place 14 Company 16 Freezer 18 Agent 21 Fly 22 Swan 23 Ears 25 Gear 26 Election
DOWN: 1 Burial 2 Character 3 Coach 4 Emperor 5 Ice 6 Dragon 12 Spaghetti 15 Between 17 Roller 19 Narrow 20 Under 24 Arm

Puzzle 326

Puzzle 327

ACROSS: 1 Acetate 7 Purge 8 Urn 9 Rift 10 Idol 12 Premiere 14 Undoubted 15 Home rule 18 Water-ski 21 Episcopal 23 Meteoric 25 Oche 26 Bird 28 Own 29 Chest 30 Secrete
DOWN: 2 Cornfield 3 Tied 4 Thunderstruck 5 Spark plug 6 Angle 11 Minute 13 Adder 16 Outside chance 17 Sweet 19 Racket 20 Elucidate 22 Pertinent 24 Log on 27 Acer

Puzzle 328

ACROSS: 9 Carrot 10 Crepe 11 Ally 12 Bias 13 Moult 14 Do time 15 Bar code 17 Tumbling 19 Idle 21 Bravado 23 Ruin 24 Walk tall 25 Eccles 27 Elm 29 Day-to-day 31 Abstruse 32 Ambrosia 34 One-sided 35 Imbecile 36 Last gasp 39 Rue 40 Tenors 42 Accredit 45 Fore 46 Rehouse 47 Talk 48 Observer 51 Aerated 54 States 55 Niece 57 Tory 58 Gnat 59 Risky 60 Coolly
DOWN: 1 Marina 2 Cross-check 3 Atom 4 Scour 5 Death trap 6 Seldom 7 Cartel 8 Clementine 16 Dab hand 18 Barley water 20 Drama 22 Oversee 23 Recurring 26 Speed up 28 Major league 29 Diarist 30 Threesome 33 Scissor 37 Secrete 38 Skirl 41 Exorbitant 43 Extraction 44 Shortness 49 Entity 50 Vestry 52 Eerily 53 Beryl 56 Each

Puzzle 329

ACROSS: 5 Hard core 7 Off 8 Niche 9 Drum roll 11 Lobe 12 Stab 14 Weeks 15 Ebb 16 Charity 20 Aga 21 Easel 23 Kite 24 Spam 26 Playbill 28 Combs 29 How 30 One-track
DOWN: 1 Chaos 2 Preferable 3 Economy 4 Trick or treat 6 Jelly baby 10 Blowy 13 Usurper 17 Heart-warming 18 Backspace 19 Blame 22 Sepulchral 25 Obesity 27 Awake

Puzzle 330

ACROSS: 1 Airtime 7 Usage 8 Mar 9 Akin 10 Know 12 Chat room 14 Break it up 15 Aperture 18 Twilight 21 Rhapsodic 23 Deceiver 25 Hank 26 Flit 28 Woo 29 Credo 30 Gestate
DOWN: 2 Inanimate 3 Teem 4 Moment of truth 5 Sugar cube 6 Crows 11 Broker 13 Speed 16 Private income 17 Stare 19 In step 20 Accretion 22 Devilment 24 Showy 27 Scut

SOLUTIONS

Puzzle 331

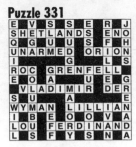

Puzzle 332

ACROSS: 4 Sin 8 Discount 9 In hand
10 Egg-nog 11 Eventing 13 Grip
15 Rowdy 16 Pact 18 Manpower
20 Morbid 22 Voyeur 23 Envisage
24 Ear
DOWN: 1 Ginger 2 Scan 3 Hung
4 Steelworker 5 Nicely 6 Shut up
7 Anon 12 Gut 13 Gem 14 Popper
15 Rewire 17 Clingy 19 Avow 20 Move
21 Rush

Puzzle 333

ACROSS: 1 Community 9 Asunder
10 Ill 11 Rev up 12 Penny 14 Forum
16 Diver 18 Sod 19 Mop 21 Torso
22 Sauna 23 Feast 25 Alibi 26 Sot
27 Synonym 28 Potential
DOWN: 1 Cliffs 2 My lord 3 Unremitting
4 Invader 5 Yap 6 Suppression 7 Eden
8 Bray 13 Neon 15 Ooze 17 Violist
19 Muesli 20 Pastel 23 Fist 24 Aunt
25 Amp

Puzzle 334

ACROSS: 8 Federate 9 Emerge 10 Able
11 Deportment 12 Art gallery 14 Spar
15 Germane 16 Nominee 20 Crow 22
Tenderness 23 Scoreboard 24 Uses 25
Fleece 26 Tangible
DOWN: 1 Seaborne 2 Sere 3 Mandolin
4 Temples 5 Nearby 6 Permission 7
Agenda 13 Game warden 17 Overdone
18 Easterly 19 Unearth 21 Recall 22
Tablet 24 Unit

Puzzle 335

ACROSS: 6 Palisades 7 Elver 8 Cur
9 Tine 10 Stab 12 Anaconda
15 Vaporise 17 Propriety 18 Muscular
20 Foul play 23 Apex 24 Acts 27 Nil
28 Durum 29 Wrong-foot
DOWN: 1 Speed trap 2 Cloven 3 Usury
4 Educated 5 Ascribe 11 Colourfully
13 Amazons 14 Very 16 Icefall
17 Pump 19 Gypsy moth 21 Overlook
22 Barn owl 25 Carboy 26 Adage

Puzzle 336

ACROSS 1 Ache 3 Borrowed
9 Parlour 10 Party 11 Administered
14 Encyclopaedia 17 Condensation
21 Olive 22 America 23 Regarded
24 When
DOWN: 1 Appeared 2 Harem 4 Oar
5 Rupee 6 Warhead 7 Days
8 Cognac 12 Swoon 13 Maintain
15 Cooking 16 Amazed 18 Drear
19 Irish 20 Hour 22 Awe

Puzzle 337

ACROSS: 9 Inarticulacy 11 Away
12 Nun 13 Mule 14 Drake 15 Otiose
16 Rejoice 18 Sunshine 20 Acid
22 Play off 24 Rote 25 Alarmist
26 Easter 28 Rod 30 Instance
32 Enduring 33 Lameness 35 Terraced
36 Reaction 37 Tenderly 40 Gnu
41 Digest 43 Tactical 46 Defy
47 Explore 48 Chew 49 Aircraft
52 Asinine 55 Vigour 56 On top
59 Rats 60 Oar 61 Flea 62 Disinfection
DOWN: 1 Unsure 2 Freeholder
3 Hind 4 Lunar 5 Make use of
6 Tycoon 7 Pariah 8 Maisonette
10 Cur 17 Caption 19 Waitressing
21 Colon 23 Fielder 24 Resurface
27 Rigidly 29 Destitution 30 Ill-bred
31 Treachery 34 Epistle 38 Nucleus
39 Leave 42 Ineligible 44 Incinerate
45 Spit-roast 50 Choral 51 Abrade
53 Notion 54 Stone 57 Oaf 58 Prey

Puzzle 338

ACROSS: 1 Anthem 4 Shamed 7 Guns 9 Awl 10 Save 11 Goad 12 Upon 13 Opt 14 Shadow 17 Easter 20 Riddle 23 Staple 26 Lei 27 Kale 28 Solo 30 Slit 31 Cat 32 Evil 33 Ranges 34 Rounds
DOWN: 1 Angels 2 Tang 3 Meadow 4 Salute 5 Mean 6 Dieter 8 Sold 10 Sobs 15 And 16 Owl 18 Ant 19 Tap 20 Rinser 21 Drat 22 Elects 23 Sister 24 Able 25 Eagles 27 Kiln 29 Oven

Puzzle 339

Puzzle 340

ACROSS: 1 Schmaltz 6 Insolvent 7 Vet 8 Prove 9 Knockout 12 Soya 13 Tofu 16 Overreach 18 Narration 19 Iced 20 Fens 23 Galactic 26 Mocha 27 Inn 28 Flow chart 29 Very well
DOWN: 1 Skivvy 2 Hesitancy 3 Allspice 4 Tremolo 5 Stye 10 Touchiness 11 Astounding 14 Okapi 15 Croak 17 Eyrie 21 Eliminate 22 Scratchy 24 Lactose 25 Instil 26 Muff

Puzzle 341

ACROSS: 4 Eland 9 Blurred 10 Axiom 11 Doe 12 Oak 13 May 14 Neglect 15 Moving staircase 19 Gorilla 20 Gnu 21 Zoo 22 Pea 23 Fount 24 Lullaby 25 Yodel
DOWN: 1 Abloom 2 Hulk 3 Criminality 4 Eddy 5 Agenda 6 Dangerously 7 Cinema 8 Smut 16 Versus 17 Shaped 18 Eponym 19 Gift 20 Gall 21 Zeal

Puzzle 342

ACROSS: 1 Toupee 5 Cry off 9 Ago 11 Chopper 12 Rag doll 13 Ours 15 Shred 16 Cant 17 Lope 19 Truss 20 Scat 24 Sarcasm 25 Old hand 26 Own 27 Isobar 28 Enmesh
DOWN: 2 Odour 3 Pipe 4 Earth tremor 5 Cornerstone 6 Yoga 7 Flora 8 Ectoplasm 10 Platitude 14 Sue 16 Cos 18 Perks 21 Crass 22 Garb 23 Edam

Puzzle 343

S		S	W	A	L	L	O	W		A
T	O	W	E	R		O	N	I	O	N
A		O	D	E		B	E	E		G
T	W	O		A	P	E		L	Y	E
E	R	N	E		E		I	D	O	L
	I		F	L	A	I	L		K	
G	N	A	T		R		K	N	E	W
E	G	G		F	L	Y		A	D	O
E		L	I	E		O	B	I		R
S	C	O	R	E		G	A	V	E	L
E		W	E	L	F	A	R	E		D

Puzzle 344

ACROSS: 1 Sea 8 Meretricious 9 Lee 11 Newel 12 Gaseous 14 Ever 15 Parcel 18 Camera 20 Item 23 Rotunda 25 Enrol 27 Art 28 Cassette deck 29 Err
DOWN: 1 Sally port 2 Amen 3 Browse 4 Stile 5 Binge 6 Miss 7 Furore 10 Escalator 13 Arc 16 Ritual 17 Lid 19 Air bed 21 Tatty 22 Meter 24 Ness 26 Lake

Puzzle 345

S	A	Y		R	A	D	A	R
W	R	O	T	E		E	R	A
I	C	Y		C		E	G	G
M		O	C	T	O	P	U	S
	P		O	A	R		E	
C	R	O	W	N	E	D		H
L	I	P		G		E	Y	E
A	C	E		L	A	B	E	L
P	E	N	C	E		T	A	P

SOLUTIONS

Puzzle 346
ACROSS: 9 Slough 10 Deems 11 Roof
12 Swam 13 Horde 14 Unwary
15 Angrily 17 Eyeshade 19 Midi
21 Wraps up 23 Pool 24 Bonehead
25 Rotten 27 Imp 29 Assesses
31 Uxorious 32 Settle on 34 Peaceful
35 Exhibits 36 Stresses 39 Sue
40 Errant 42 Levering 45 Stye
46 Dresses 47 Mail 48 Greedier
51 Asunder 54 Smears 55 Gaped
57 Teal 58 Knot 59 Extol 60 Spouts
DOWN: 1 Flew in 2 Summertime
3 Shah 4 Adore 5 Re-release
6 Assume 7 Growth 8 Torrid zone
16 Lawless 18 Laddishness
20 Irons 22 Persona 23 Pithiness
26 Nestles 28 Purposeless
29 Austere 30 Extricate 33 Evicted
37 Revises 38 Ennui 41 Retirement
43 Rumination 44 Segregate
49 Exacts 50 Instep 52 Exalts 53 Spilt
56 Dose

Puzzle 347
ACROSS: 1 Bareness 9 Elated 10 Bent
11 Evil spirit 12 Conviction 14 Ache
15 Anguish 16 Abridge 20 Hole
22 Defacement 23 Deliberate 24 Host
25 Roller 26 Reindeer
DOWN: 1 Careworn 2 Left 3 Defences
4 Aspirin 5 Lesson 6 Capitalism
7 Fetish 13 Vaudeville 17 Bacteria
18 Gangster 19 Affairs 21 Oberon
22 Dreary 24 Hide

Puzzle 348
ACROSS: 1 Off 8 Enshrinement
9 Eye 11 Drama 12 Commons
14 Deed 15 Polled 18 Do well
20 Abet 23 Lambada 25 Allah 27 Aga
28 Clearing bank 29 Ewe
DOWN: 1 Overspill 2 Feed 3 Estate
4 Broad 5 On ice 6 Imam 7 In-joke
10 Esplanade 13 Odd 16 Lamely
17 Dad 19 Oilcan 21 Basis 22 Tanga
24 Away 26 Hake

Puzzle 349
ACROSS: 1 Private income 9 Smarmy
10 Casanova 11 Taxi 12 Parka 13 Inns
14 Spa 15 Van 16 Pith 18 Samba
20 Seek 22 New broom 24 Pidgin
25 Particularity
DOWN: 2 Rumba 3 Varnish 4 Toy
5 Incur 6 Cassava 7 Man 8 Oven
12 Pass out 13 Insider 17 Ibex
19 Mimic 21 Exist 23 Bra 24 Pal

Puzzle 350

Puzzle 351
ACROSS: 1 Sieve 5 Sett 6 Lounge 7 Ally
8 Magnum 9 Retrieve 12 Admission
15 Pro 16 Eider 17 Aries 18 Leo
19 Sternness 21 Honestly 24 Walnut
25 Sign 26 Encode 27 Bold 28 Entry
DOWN: 2 Isolate 3 Vintner
4 Stylise 5 Seamless 9 Reappraise
10 Temporise 11 Enormously
13 Stetson 14 Indulgent 20 Renowned
21 Horizon 22 Silicon 23 Launder

Puzzle 352
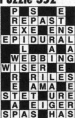

Puzzle 353

ACROSS: 7 Carriage 8 Leaf 9 Plan
10 Spin 11 Dew 13 Scape 14 Capital
16 Sparrow 18 Heavy 21 Cry 22 Step
23 Pool 25 Knee 26 Shoulder
DOWN: 1 Garlic 2 Transport 3 Cause
4 Decimal 5 Old 6 Camera
12 Pineapple 15 Contest 17 Parent
19 Violet 20 Spoon 24 Leg

Puzzle 354

ACROSS: 1 Spike 4 Make fast
11 Dalliance 12 Capri 13 Urge
14 Binder 16 Wok 18 Tun 19 Coldly
22 Grin 24 Bongo 26 Put across
27 Eggplant 28 Stiff
DOWN: 2 Polygon 3 Knit 5 Amend
6 Encore 7 Asp 8 Trickiness
9 Adjustable 10 Anti 15 Nod 16 Ward
off 17 Scroll 20 Lupin 21 Late 23 Scot
25 Nag

Puzzle 355

ACROSS: 9 Tumult 10 Click 11 Awry
12 Glut 13 Black 14 Intend 15 Encrypt
17 Regicide 19 Ogre 21 Amusing
23 Seed 24 Raincoat 25 Molest 27 Axe
29 Falconer 31 Shredder 32 Affluent
34 Adequate 35 Commuter 36 Exultant
39 Tor 40 Divide 42 Override 45 Smut
46 Equator 47 Sort 48 Snarling
51 Showing 54 Knives 55 Newel
57 Name 58 Clan 59 Riser 60 Poodle
DOWN: 1 Dunlin 2 Butter-bean
3 Stab 4 Scram 5 Milk train 6 Skiing
7 Lactic 8 Grenadiers 16 Platoon
18 Custard tart 20 Guava 22 Gum tree
23 Self-doubt 26 Torrent 28 Escape
route 29 Flaccid 30 Columnist
33 Extreme 37 Unearth 38 Nadir
41 Imminently 43 Rose window
44 Pudginess 49 Raving 50 Insure
52 Nimbly 53 Sword 56 Lips

Puzzle 356

ACROSS: 1 Rebus 4 Gum 6 Shambolic
7 Anti-hero 9 Royal Mail 10 Mats
12 Perm 14 Reinvest 17 Overdose
19 Beat 21 Plea 23 Expressly
25 Eventual 27 Oven-ready 28 Kit
29 Latex
DOWN: 1 Rosy 2 Blarney 3 Subtitle
4 Golden age 5 Microclimate
8 Frame 11 There 13 Snide 15 Easel
16 Gobbledegook 18 Satyr 20 At
present 22 Pectoral 24 Sealant
26 Lynx

Puzzle 357

ACROSS: 5 Corduroy 7 Rue 8 Dogma
9 Assorted 11 Arab 12 Know 14 Lakes
15 Ire 16 Adjudge 20 Ass 21 Ensue
23 Aloe 24 Fell 26 Airtight 28 Angus
29 Opt 30 Unhinged
DOWN: 1 Scarp 2 Greenshank
3 Outdoor 4 Long-standing
6 Landowner 10 Walls 13 Assumed
17 Discouraging 18 Catamaran
19 Wells 22 See-through 25 Pigskin
27 Study

Puzzle 358

ACROSS: 4 Sir 8 Brown rat 9 Ironic
10 Smithy 11 Fielding 13 Used
15 Hanks 16 Cubs 18 Narcotic 20 Fan
out 22 Bureau 23 Excavate 24 Bad
DOWN: 1 Primus 2 Swat 3 Dray
4 Stiff-necked 5 Rivers 6 Nordic 7 Lion
12 Gas 13 Urn 14 Docker 15 Hot tub
17 Bounty 19 Abut 20 Face 21 Nave

Puzzle 359

ACROSS: 1 Disembark 9 Iterate 10 Tab
11 Key in 12 Lobby 14 Moral 16 Sewer
18 Ebb 19 Sit 21 Games 22 Image
23 Lynch 25 Mufti 26 Pip 27 Pergola
28 Diligence
DOWN: 1 Do time 2 Suburb 3 Make
light of 4 Alyssum 5 Kin 6 Hellraising
7 Barb 8 Defy 13 Brig 15 Obey
17 Wishful 19 Sampan 20 Temple
23 Lips 24 Norm 25 Mad

SOLUTIONS

Puzzle 360
ACROSS: 4 Logic 9 Impiety 10 Owlet
11 Roe 12 Lad 13 Use 14 Tipster
15 Win by a short head 19 Venture
20 Pot 21 Woe 22 Duo 23 Metre
24 Stooges 25 Nasty
DOWN: 1 Billow 2 Spud 3 Beauty
queen 4 Lyre 5 Ghetto 6 Computation
7 Blithe 8 Stir 16 Ninety 17 Swedes
18 Dressy 19 Vamp 20 Posy 21 Wage

Puzzle 361
ACROSS: 1 Outrageous 6 Skip
10 Stash 11 Tenacious 12 Safe
13 Scar 14 Stale 16 Income
17 Retailer 19 Nuisance 22 Tedium
25 Corgi 26 Noon 27 Tern 29 Plaintiff
30 Lotus 31 Nest 32 Redecorate
DOWN: 1 Obsession 2 Traffic 3 Ache
4 Entice 5 Unnerve 7 Know-all 8 Paste
9 Ice-skater 15 Impatient 17 Rue
18 Reminisce 20 Inroads 21 Connive
23 Inertia 24 Coffee 25 Capon 28 Alto
THE LOST CONTINENT

Puzzle 362

Puzzle 363
ACROSS: 1 Joyful 5 Annual 8 User
9 Supplies 10 Throw 11 Magnify
14 Pursue 15 Signal 17 Deducts
19 Based 21 Ice-cream 23 Door
24 Absent 25 Thanks
DOWN: 2 Oasthouse 3 Furious 4 Lose
5 Applause 6 Nylon 7 Age
12 Framework 13 Seat belt
16 Grandma 18 Uncle 20 Omit 22 Cub

Puzzle 364
ACROSS: 1 Wanderers 6 Dram
10 Pale ale 11 Conquer 13 Ness
14 Supposedly 16 Laptop 18 In need
21 Hand-sewn 22 Sisal 24 Backstairs
26 Stem 29 Sire 30 Dutch treat
32 Vesta 34 Underpin 36 Thresh
37 Verger 40 Illustrate 41 Owls
44 Martini 45 Barbell 46 Yo-yo
47 Adversely
DOWN: 2 Atlas 3 Dial 4 Rhesus
5 Reception 7 Roundness 8 Martyr
9 Spindly 12 Nosiness 15 Goddess
17 Prancer 19 Deja vu 20 Climate
23 Abusive 25 Recede 27 Teeming
28 Starter 31 Water-ski 33 Scholarly
34 Unhurried 35 Gristle 38 Dismay
39 Stable 42 Wheel 43 Iris

Puzzle 365
ACROSS: 1 Propel 4 Surfed 7 Ties 9 Tar
10 Bust 11 Shut 12 Ogre 13 End
14 Turner 17 Eighth 20 Dapple
23 Skater 26 Ape 27 Sear 28 Cast
30 Teem 31 Net 32 East 33 Rotund
34 Repeal
DOWN: 1 Patent 2 Odes 3 Latter
4 Strode 5 Flue 6 Detach 8 Shun
10 Brag 15 Rap 16 Eel 18 Ink 19 Hot
20 Doctor 21 Poem 22 Earned
23 Sector 24 Apse 25 Rental 27 Seat
29 Tape

Puzzle 366
ACROSS: 1 Belt up 5 Hobble 9 Eve
11 Founder 12 Renewal 13 Cite
15 Toxin 16 Hymn 17 Undo 19 Omega
20 Pass 24 Sirloin 25 Overbid 26 Con
27 Devote 28 Embryo
DOWN: 2 Erupt 3 Tidy 4 Performance
5 Herringbone 6 Bane 7 Lowly
8 Off-course 10 Alongside 14 Ego
16 Hip 18 Dirge 21 Abbey 22 Polo
23 Kerb

Puzzle 367

ACROSS: 1 Sheet 4 Launcher
11 Funicular 12 Pitta 13 East
14 Dawdle 16 Cup 18 Vow 19 Impose
22 Alga 24 Sedan 26 Nefarious
27 Elegance 28 Boots
DOWN: 2 Handsaw 3 Etch 5 Aired
6 Nephew 7 Hat 8 Reappraise
9 Effervesce 10 Flea 15 Woo 16 Call
out 17 Zinnia 20 Panic 21 Safe 23 Brio
25 Doe

Puzzle 368

ACROSS: 1 Usury 4 Emphatic 11 Stag
party 12 Omega 13 Cake 14 Secede
16 Con 18 Odd 19 Pepper 22 Imam
24 Okapi 26 Guest book 27 Yuletide
28 Spate
DOWN: 2 Stalked 3 Rope 5 Maybe
6 Hooked 7 Tie 8 Chain-smoke
9 Psychology 10 True 15 Cap
16 Comport 17 Spoilt 20 Paged
21 Even 23 Stop 25 Awl

Puzzle 369

ACROSS: 1 Rasp 6 Fort 9 Couturier
10 Span 12 Earn 14 Tender 16 Billet
18 Extreme 20 Tiara 21 Prank 22 Ladle
23 Delft 25 Troop 27 Revenue
30 Decode 32 Aspect 35 Eros 36 Over
37 Structure 38 Pity 39 Trip
DOWN: 1 Rust 2 Scan 3 Ponder
4 Start 5 Tribe 6 Feeler 7 Oral 8 Tent
11 Perimeter 13 Reinforce 15 Exalted
17 Impetus 19 Ridge 24 Frosty
26 Report 28 Venus 29 Nasty 30 Deep
31 Cost 33 Ever 34 Trap
ACROSS: 1 Cake 6 Disc 9 Encounter
10 Aged 12 Lost 14 Tenure 16 Plenty
18 Retreat 20 Steel 21 Nepal 22 Admit
23 Beret 25 Essay 27 Dessert
30 Deride 32 Enamel 35 Unit 36 Tame
37 Conscious 38 Pier 39 Eton
DOWN: 1 Chat 2 Keen 3 Endure
4 Comet 5 Snipe 6 Delete 7 Iron
8 City 11 Gentlemen 13 Stratagem
15 Related 17 Lantern 19 Remus
24 Editor 26 Statue 28 Sense 29 Eerie
30 Dump 31 Rice 33 Mast 34 Lean

Puzzle 370

ACROSS: 1 Resistor 6 Leafiness 7 Nap
8 Trier 9 Crescent 12 Onyx 13 Maxi
16 Pot-pourri 18 Royal Mail 19 Bats
20 Wart 23 Emphasis 26 China 27 Elk
28 Work of art 29 Colander
DOWN: 1 Ruling 2 Stag party 3 Skittish
4 One-time 5 Tsar 10 Triviality
11 Comparable 14 Aorta 15 Holly
17 Tryst 21 Alice band 22 Parabola
24 Prior to 25 Skater 26 Cowl

Puzzle 371

ACROSS: 1 Befog 4 Arm 6 Dialectic
7 Scenario 9 Pepperoni 10 Love
12 Idol 14 Blinding 17 Entirely 19 Exit
21 Myth 23 Absorbing 25 Salutary
27 Autocracy 28 Fad 29 Lisle
DOWN: 1 Bode 2 Flat cap 3 Guernsey
4 Afterword 5 Microbiology 8 Spill
11 Valet 13 Snare 15 Inlay 16 General
staff 18 Thigh 20 Insulated 22 Critical
24 Inroads 26 Type

Puzzle 372

ACROSS: 5 Cohesion 7 Rat 8 Pasta
9 Reminder 11 Rain 12 Pupa 14 Mug
up 15 Tea 16 Spectre 20 Imp 21 Nasty
23 Idle 24 Aria 26 Hornpipe 28 Forte
29 Loo 30 Instruct
DOWN: 1 Score 2 Shuttering 3 Aseptic
4 Loss adjuster 6 Carry away 10 Crumb
13 Spacing 17 Popular front 18 Finish
off 19 By far 22 Scrupulous 25 Aplenty
27 Boots

Puzzle 373

ACROSS: 1 Cloud 4 Oven 6 Chin
10 See 11 Field 12 Inner 13 Cannon
14 Reserve 17 Leave 19 Gathering
22 Automatic 24 Susan 25 Foreign
27 Narrow 30 Above 32 Bacon 33 Far
34 Tree 35 Bell 36 Early
DOWN: 1 Cast 2 Opera 3 Defence
4 Overnight 5 Elder 7 Hen 8 Nurse
9 Tissue 15 Rails 16 Flea 18 After
20 Technical 21 Gone 23 Maiden
24 Strange 25 Feast 26 Noble 28 Offer
29 Grey 31 One

SOLUTIONS

Puzzle 374
ACROSS: 1 Stupefy 7 Ovate 8 Rig
9 Loss 10 Clap 12 Clear off
14 Outfitter 15 Immature 18 Mandrake
21 Classmate 23 Nauseous 25 Open
26 Fear 28 Ore 29 Wreak 30 Stand to
DOWN: 2 Tear sheet 3 Poem 4 Fork-lift
truck 5 Collector 6 Agape 11 Arnica
13 Dryer 16 Man-management
17 Smock 19 Resist 20 Keystroke
22 Atonement 24 Log on 27 Swan

Puzzle 375
ACROSS: 7 Dahlia 8 Attend 9 God
10 Skin 11 News 12 Spy 14 Error
17 Alarm 19 Equal 20 Added
22 Loops 24 Odd 26 Hard 28 Rays
29 Era 30 Shaken 31 Wiping
DOWN: 1 Darker 2 Plan 3 Wages
4 Sadly 5 Stun 6 Answer 13 Pound
15 Rid 16 Red 17 All 18 Ago
21 Deaths 23 Paying 24 Ovens
25 Draws 27 Duke 28 Rope

Puzzle 376
ACROSS: 9 Shirtwaister 11 Etch
12 Ago 13 Disc 14 Balsa 15 Aborts
16 Face-off 18 Plantain 20 Apse
22 Spinner 24 Grew 25 Glass eye
26 Obtuse 28 Rap 30 Cream tea
32 On the nod 33 Nostrils 35 Exporter
36 Unproven 37 Took heed 40 Guy
41 Essays 43 Luminous 46 Bash
47 Sprints 48 Eats 49 Unlacing
52 Asylums 55 Smiled 56 Arras
59 Cosh 60 Ode 61 Inky 62 Art
historian
DOWN: 1 Sheila 2 Cricketers 3 Swab
4 Viola 5 Strapping 6 Arcana 7 Revolt
8 Scattiness 10 Aga 17 Fastest
19 Fire-raising 21 Paler 23 Rooftop
24 Go to earth 27 Endured 29 Poverty
line 30 Conjure 31 Aftermath
34 Invests 38 Osmosis 39 Exult
42 Sea anemone 44 Needlecord
45 Braggarts 50 Alleys 51 Indian
53 Mislay 54 Groin 57 Ads 58 Sets

Puzzle 377
ACROSS: 1 Rebate 4 Errata 7 Peas
9 Pot 10 Sole 11 Rule 12 Open 13 Rap
14 Digest 17 Sermon 20 Scrape
23 Sander 26 Yap 27 Cone 28 Eats
30 Ream 31 Lea 32 Each 33 Dieted
34 Sender
Down: 1 Repaid 2 Bear 3 Expert
4 Estops 5 Anon 6 Axeman 8 Sure
10 Sear 15 Gar 16 Sap 18 Era 19 Mad
20 Sacred 21 Atom 22 Eyelid
23 Spears 24 Note 25 Rather 27 Care
29 Said

Puzzle 378
ACROSS: 1 Scalp 4 Pandemic
11 Dissolute 12 Viper 13 Omit
14 Caster 16 Chi 18 Ion 19 Aching
22 Boll 24 Infer 26 Ironed out
27 Nobility 28 Edify
DOWN: 2 Cushion 3 Loot 5 Alert
6 Divers 7 Map 8 Cordiality
9 Admonition 10 Tuba 15 Ski 16 Cool
off 17 Patrol 20 Hoist 21 Nook
23 Bend 25 Fib

Puzzle 379
ACROSS: 1 Rap 8 Early closing
9 Car 11 Khaki 12 Hormone
14 Claw 15 Cognac 18 Loafer
20 Heed 23 Lobelia 25 Audit 27 Air
28 Low-water mark 29 Elm
DOWN: 1 Reconcile 2 Perk 3 Armada
4 Cynic 5 Alpha 6 Tsar 7 One-off
10 Reprogram 13 Owl 16 Gibbon
17 Chi 19 Ordeal 21 Earth 22 Dairy
24 Lewd 26 Take

Puzzle 380
ACROSS: 1 Rejection slip 9 Vigour
10 Grasping 11 Demo 12 Fence
13 Sage 14 Gel 15 Loo 16 Fray
18 Itchy 20 Lawn 22 Daughter
24 Shelve 25 Stepping stone
DOWN: 2 Elide 3 Ecology 4 Tar 5 Organ
6 Shapely 7 Imp 8 Snug 12 Flip-top
13 Solvent 17 Roan 19 Corgi 21 Woven
23 Get 24 Sag

Puzzle 381

ACROSS: 1 Contact 7 Endow 8 Mid
9 Elan 10 Slap 12 Autonomy
14 Harpooner 15 Escalate 18 Glass
eye 21 On draught 23 Clear off
25 Atom 26 Ants 28 Keg 29 Panic
30 Trinity
DOWN: 2 Old master 3 Town
4 Complimentary 5 Telepathy 6 Adapt
11 Angora 13 Drier 16 Scandalmonger
17 Aglow 19 Shaman 20 Stuff sack
22 Groundnut 24 Parks 27 Spin

Puzzle 382

S	A	G	A		C	A	E	S	A	R
L		B	O	O		C		E
I	N	T	O		S	P	I	R	I	T
P		U		L		A		U
	O	A	T	H		A	C	T	O	R
P		L		E	A	T		C		N
L	E	G	A	L		E	C	H	O
U		E		L		R		L
N	A	R	R	O	W		E	D	G	E
G		I		A	R	E		A
E	R	A	S	E	R		K	I	C	K

Puzzle 383

ACROSS: 1 Spool 4 Game show 11 Full
house 12 Piper 13 Itch 14 Rafter
16 Cud 18 Ion 19 Inbred 22 Poll
24 Therm 26 Cavernous 27 Retiring
28 Chafe
DOWN: 2 Pelican 3 Oche 5 Avert
6 Expert 7 Hop 8 World-class
9 Officiator 10 Pupa 15 For 16 Cool off
17 Dimmer 20 Bacon 21 Envy 23 Arch
25 Eat

Puzzle 384

W	A	S		S	T	E	P	S
A	R	O	S	E		L	O	T
R	E	D		D		S	E	A
T		A	C	A	D	E	M	Y
	C		A	T	E		S
P	A	S	T	I	N	G		V
A	N	T		V		E	Y	E
Y	O	U		E	N	T	E	R
S	E	N	D	S		S	A	Y

Puzzle 385

ACROSS: 4 Pecan 9 Peppery 10 Exist
11 Run 12 Now 13 Rye 14 Seeming
15 Pelican crossing 19 Phantom
20 War 21 Flu 22 Boa 23 Patio
24 Rolling 25 Needy
DOWN: 1 Open up 2 Spew
3 Deprecation 4 Pyre 5 Censor
6 Necessarily 7 Bikini 8 Stag
16 Lean-to 17 Nimble 18 Grunge
19 Pops 20 Wary 21 Foil

Puzzle 386

ACROSS: 4 Wag 8 China tea 9 Equity
10 Skewed 11 Casement 13 Drag
15 Demur 16 Raft 18 Bareback 20 In
hand 22 Landau 23 Naturism 24 Pug
DOWN: 1 Shaker 2 Snow 3 Stud
4 Watchmaking 5 Geyser 6 Mummer
7 Stun 12 Tut 13 Dab 14 Greedy
15 Draw up 17 Finish 19 Ajar 20 Iota
21 Hart

Puzzle 387

ACROSS: 1 Dust sheet 9 Oxidise
10 Owe 11 Rerun 12 Hasty 14 Bhaji
16 Grist 18 Yew 19 Arm 21 End up
22 Igloo 23 Cover 25 Going 26 Aft
27 Peccary 28 Motorcade
DOWN: 1 Drop by 2 See-saw 3 Service
road 4 Enraged 5 Ton 6 Right-winger
7 Pips 8 Dewy 13 Tyro 15 Hero
17 Imprint 19 Alpaca 20 Mottle
23 Cape 24 Vice 25 Gym

Puzzle 388

	C	H	I	L	D	M	I	N	D	E	R	
H		U		Y		A		O		C		T
A	D	M	I	N	I	S	T	R	A	T	O	R
P		C		T		M		O		O		U
P	A	M	P	H	L	E	T		S	P	A	T
Y		I		P		R		D		L		H
	A	S	P	I	C		D	E	C	A	Y	
D		G		N		Z		M		S		I
A	V	O	W		B	O	G	E	Y	M	A	N
I		V		B		D		R				A
S	T	E	R	I	L	I	S	A	T	I	O	N
Y		R		R		A		R		L		E
	E	N	F	O	R	C	E	A	B	L	E	

SOLUTIONS

Puzzle 389
ACROSS: 1 Elbow 5 Super 8 Acorn
9 Icing 10 Onset 11 Offer 12 Taken
15 Eland 18 Choreographer 19 Angel
22 Defer 25 Actor 26 Briar 27 Onion
28 Groan 29 Theme 30 Eagle
DOWN: 1 Edict 2 Blink 3 Wagon
4 Conflagration 5 Snore 6 Pasta
7 Rated 13 Ashen 14 Eerie 16 Lapse
17 Niece 19 Abbot 20 Grime 21 Large
22 Drone 23 Fling 24 Rinse
ACROSS: 1 Sugar 5 Brass 8 Agree
9 Again 10 Radar 11 Chute 12 Ditch
15 Throb 18 Standing order 19 Freed
22 Medal 25 Extra 26 Atoll 27 Idiom
28 Vivid 29 There 30 Scent
DOWN: 1 Scald 2 Giant 3 Ranch
4 Argumentative 5 Beret 6 Adder
7 Scrub 13 Inter 14 Canoe 16 Horde
17 Opera 19 Feast 20 Elope 21 Delve
22 Maids 23 Drive 24 Limit

Puzzle 390

Puzzle 391
ACROSS: 6 Scribbled 7 Acorn
8 Wan 9 Ease 10 Iris 12 Anaconda
15 Frumpish 17 Decongest 18 Autocrat
20 Footslog 23 Hate 24 Scar 27 Die
28 Wring 29 Wall-chart
DOWN: 1 Estate car 2 Arrows
3 T-bone 4 Flowered 5 Oddness
11 Communicate 13 Apricot 14 Shut
16 Icefall 17 Dial 19 Aggregate
21 On the sly 22 Shadowy 25 Climax
26 Twice

Puzzle 392
ACROSS: 4 Dip 8 Shanghai 9 Outgun
10 Blowsy 11 Atrocity 13 Type 15 Fifty
16 Ohms 18 Mesmeric 20 Casino
22 Jet-ski 23 Excavate 24 Dad
DOWN: 1 Chilly 2 Snow 3 They
4 Disaffected 5 Poorly 6 Stucco 7 Punt
12 Yes 13 Tom 14 Enmesh 15 Fervid
17 Minute 19 Even 20 Cock 21 Save

Puzzle 393
ACROSS: 4 Mufti 9 Appease 10 Nappy
11 Ail 12 Lax 13 Ion 14 Leopard
15 Take it on the chin 19 Mundane
20 Toe 21 Mac 22 Woe 23 Salvo
24 Recruit 25 Rayon
DOWN: 1 Haslet 2 Apex 3 Facilitator
4 Mean 5 Fillet 6 Incoherence 7 Splash
8 Dyed 16 Kingly 17 One-way 18 Nicety
19 Mask 20 Tern 21 Maul

Puzzle 394
ACROSS: 1 Ascribe 7 U-turn 8 Slr
9 Come 10 Stow 12 Ensemble
14 Unchanged 15 Initiate 18 Backache
21 Searchers 23 Xmas tree 25 Cubs
26 Ogle 28 Own 29 Roost 30 Espouse
DOWN: 2 Soul music 3 Rank 4 Bush
telegraph 5 Quicken up 6 Crows
11 Impart 13 Added 16 No-claims
bonus 17 Abuse 19 Access
20 Usherette 22 Egregious 24 McCoy
27 Trio

Puzzle 395

Puzzle 396

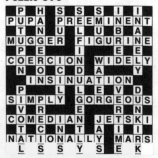